Quantitative Literacy

Quantitative Literacy

Why Numeracy Matters for Schools and Colleges

edited by

Bernard L. Madison
and
Lynn Arthur Steen

NCED

The National Council on Education and the Disciplines

Princeton, New Jersey   2003

NATIONAL COUNCIL ON EDUCATION AND THE DISCIPLINES

The goal of the National Council on Education and the Disciplines (NCED) is to advance a vision that will unify and guide efforts to strengthen K-16 education in the United States. In pursuing this aim, NCED especially focuses on the continuity and quality of learning in the later years of high school and the early years of college. From its home at The Woodrow Wilson National Fellowship Foundation, NCED draws on the energy and expertise of scholars and educators in the disciplines to address the school-college continuum. At the heart of its work is a national reexamination of the core literacies—quantitative, scientific, historical, and communicative — that are essential to the coherent, forward-looking education all students deserve.

Contents

Foreword

ROBERT ORRILL

"Quantitative literacy, in my view, means knowing how to reason and how to think, and it is all but absent from our curricula today."

Gina Kolata (1997)

Increasingly, numbers do our thinking for us. They tell us which medication to take, what policy to support, and why one course of action is better than another. These days any proposal put forward without numbers is a nonstarter. Theodore Porter does not exaggerate when he writes: "By now numbers surround us. No important aspect of life is beyond their reach" (Porter, 1997).

Numbers, of course, have long been important in the management of life, but they have never been so ubiquitous as they are now. The new circumstances arrived suddenly with the coming of computers and their application to gathering, processing, and disseminating quantitative information. This powerful tool has brought unprecedented access to quantitative data, but in so doing it also has filled the life of everyone with a bewildering array of numbers that often produce confusion rather than clarity. The possible consequences for our ability to direct our affairs are worrisome to say the least. For some observers, the flow of numbers amounts to an inundation that calls forth images of a destructive flood of biblical proportions. Looking toward the future, James Bailey warns that "today we are drowning in data, and there is unimaginably more on the way" (Bailey, 1996). Even if we manage to keep our heads above water, Lynn Steen writes, we can be sure that "the world of the twenty-first century will be a world awash in numbers" (Steen, 2001).

Gina Kolata looks at this data-drenched environment from a special vantage point. She reports on science and health issues for the *New York Times* and often hears from readers who complain that numbers presented by experts seem to mean "one thing one day and another thing the next." What are they to believe, readers ask, when a regimen first said to promote well-being is later said to undermine it? Kolata's response is that they must learn to interpret the numbers for themselves. The only remedy, she says, "is that they have to learn how to think for themselves, and that is what an education in quantitative reasoning can teach them." Such an education, she writes, "makes all the difference in the world in people's ability to understand issues of national and personal importance and helps them evaluate in a rational way arguments made by the press, the government, and their fellow citizens" (Kolata, 1997).

But, as a practical matter, Kolata counts on no such well-prepared readership in her own reporting. The attention to quantitative reasoning that she thinks so essential to sound judgment simply does not exist in the academic programs of most of our schools and colleges. Thus, even the college-educated often lack an understanding of how to make sense of numerical information. For a democracy, this is no low-stakes concern. If numbers are present everywhere in our public discourse, and many are more confused than enlightened by them, what happens to decision making in our society? If we permit this kind of innumeracy to persist, do we not thereby undermine the very ground and being of government of, by, and for the people?

Robert Orrill is the Executive Director, National Council on Education and the Disciplines (NCED), and Senior Advisor at The Woodrow Wilson National Fellowship Foundation, Princeton, New Jersey. NCED brings together university faculty and secondary school teachers to address issues of educational continuity in the later years of high school and the early years of college.

How, then, should we act to address this concern? If attention to quantitative literacy is absent from our curricula, how can we make certain that it is given the priority it deserves? These are questions that many educators in our schools and colleges are beginning to ask, but, at this point, we are still far from having programmatic answers or anything approaching a plan of action scaled to the need. This should not be surprising given that the penetration of numeracy into all aspects of life confronts us with a rapidly evolving phenomenon that we understand at best imperfectly. The need now is to make a start: to bring together the many scattered discussions that are taking place and mount a sustained national conversation about how schools and colleges can give effect to expectations for learning that better take account of the quantitative challenges of life in the twenty-first century.

To help launch this conversation, the National Council on Education and the Disciplines (NCED) sponsored a National Forum on December 1–2, 2001, aimed at promoting discussion and debate about Why Numeracy Matters for Schools and Colleges. Held at the National Academy of Sciences, the Forum was designed to bring together many different points of view — education, business, government, and philanthropy were all represented in the deliberations. International perspectives on quantitative literacy also were presented, making it clear that numeracy is a growing global concern. The most immediate outcome is the rich and abundantly informative proceedings presented in this volume, which we believe — in giving voice to a wide range of opinion — provide a benchmark discussion from which the needed national conversation can go forward.

In an introduction to the proceedings, Bernard Madison provides a comprehensive overview of the essays and commentaries collected in this volume. Here I need add only that thanks go to many who joined together in organizing the Forum and making it a success. Indeed, the event was a cooperative undertaking from first to last. Special thanks for hosting the Forum are owed to the Mathematical Sciences Education Board of the National Research Council and, for its cooperation throughout, to the Mathematical Association of America. Financial support and welcome encouragement were provided by the Pew Charitable Trusts.

A great many individuals contributed to the making of the Forum, and I am very sorry not to be able to thank them by name in these overly brief acknowledgments. But a special word must be said about Bernard Madison, who, with unfailing geniality, led every step of the way in turning the Forum from idea into reality. In all ways that count, the Forum is his handiwork. Thanks also to Lynn Steen, whose many contributions to the cause of quantitative literacy have become legendary. The Forum benefited immensely from Lynn's wise counsel throughout as well as his expert editorial work on the proceedings. Diane Foster also attended to the production of the proceedings with her uncommonly good executive sense, and Dorothy Downie watched over organizational matters with the professional skill and tact vital to all cooperative initiatives.

References

Bailey, James. 1996. *After Thought: The Computer Challenge to Human Intelligence*. New York, NY: Basic Books.

Kolata, Gina. 1997. "Understanding the News." In *Why Numbers Count: Quantitative Literacy for Tomorrow's America*. Lynn Arthur Steen (Editor), New York, NY: The College Board.

Porter, Theodore M. 1997. "The Triumph of Numbers: Civic Implications of Quantitative Literacy." In *Why Numbers Count: Quantitative Literacy for Tomorrow's America*. Lynn Arthur Steen (Editor), New York, NY: The College Board.

Steen, Lynn Arthur, ed. 2001. "The Case for Quantitative Literacy." In *Mathematics and Democracy: The Case for Quantitative Literacy*. Princeton, NJ: National Council on Education and the Disciplines.

Quantitative Literacy

PART I
BACKGROUND PAPERS

The Many Faces of Quantitative Literacy

BERNARD L. MADISON

Quantitative literacy (QL), the ability to understand and use numbers and data analyses in everyday life, is everybody's orphan (Madison 2001). Despite every person's need for QL, in the discipline-dominated K–16 education system in the United States there is neither an academic home nor an administrative promoter for this crucial competency. Needs for QL extend across the traditional American guarantees of life, liberty, and the pursuit of happiness. Health concerns increasingly are immersed in risk analysis and probabilities; government decisions and political arguments are steeped in uses and misuses of quantitative data; and consumer issues, sports, and investments frequently are reported in terms of averages, rates of change, and changes in rates of change.

To better understand quantitative literacy and the educational challenge it presents, the National Council on Education and the Disciplines (NCED) initiated a national examination of issues surrounding QL education, especially in the context of school and college studies. As a starting point, NCED published *Mathematics and Democracy: The Case for Quantitative Literacy* (Steen 2001), consisting of a case statement on numeracy in contemporary society and 12 responses. To expand the conversation about QL, NCED subsequently sponsored a national Forum, *Quantitative Literacy: Why Numeracy Matters for Schools and Colleges,* held at the National Academy of Sciences in Washington, D.C., on December 1–2, 2001. This volume represents the proceedings of this Forum and includes papers commissioned as background for the Forum, essays presented at the Forum, and selected reactions to the Forum.

Part I: Background Papers

To help interpret the implications of quantitative literacy in preparation for the national Forum, NCED commissioned several thought papers, as opposed to research treatises, on various aspects of QL. Initial drafts of these papers were read by two external reviewers prior to preparation of a second draft. These second drafts, along with *Mathematics and Democracy,* provided the foundation for the Forum. Following discussions at the Forum, several authors revised their papers yet again. The first section of this volume includes edited versions of these post-Forum revisions plus two additional papers written after the Forum that are complementary to the commissioned works.

NEED FOR WORK AND LEARNING

Four of these papers focus on the need for quantitative literacy, particularly in the context of citizenship and work, while eight address components of QL education: curriculum, pedagogy, articulation, and assessment. Of the eight, four deal directly with curriculum and four consider policy issues involving curricular relationships and assessment. Although thoroughly grounded in the realities of U.S. education, these papers explore a variety of paths to the goal of imbuing students with quantitative habits of mind in addition to conveying facts and procedures. As with all such

Bernard L. Madison is Professor of Mathematics at the University of Arkansas where he previously served as Chair of Mathematics and Dean of the J.W. Fulbright College of Arts and Sciences. During 1985–89, Madison directed the MS2000 project at the National Research Council, including the 1987 *Calculus for a New Century* symposium. Madison has worked in various roles for the Advanced Placement program, including serving as Chief Faculty Consultant for AP Calculus and as a member of the Commission on the Future of AP.

explorations, differences in terminology and emphases emerge, revealing both the intellectual richness and the complexity of this challenging issue.

The need for quantitative literacy is both personal and societal. Although personal needs are addressed to some extent in all the papers, four focus especially on the societal issues of citizenship and work. Two of these view QL and the workplace from very different perspectives. Linda Rosen (with Lindsay Weil and Claus von Zastrow) addresses QL from the standpoint of the National Alliance for Business, offering views from the business world concerning the need for QL education and the educational responses that have been made by businesses. Because QL is a nontraditional newcomer to education, the business response to it is predicted to be conservative. Arnold Packer, a pragmatic economist, approaches QL from the perspective of what mathematics everyone should know and be able to do. His approach is to evaluate skills in terms of their frequency of use and economic value in the workforce.

The third paper addressing societal issues, by historian Patricia Cline Cohen, views the need for QL from a historical perspective. She details how the U.S. government has relied on and promoted QL from the inception of constitutional rule in 1789. The fourth paper, by Anthony Carnevale and Donna Desrochers, analyzes the current need for QL education. The authors consider both the demands of democratic processes and the requirements of the current and future workforce.

Curriculum Issues

Four thought papers look specifically at the mathematics curriculum and its role in general education. Deborah Hughes Hallett, Jan de Lange, and Lynn Arthur Steen address various aspects of that curriculum, including some that often are classified under the rubric of statistics. Hughes Hallett writes of the college experience while de Lange offers an international perspective. Steen argues for a mathematics curriculum in grades 6 to 12 that would expand the current narrow focus on algebraic symbol manipulation. Finally, Randall Richardson and William McCallum discuss how to extend college QL education beyond mathematics courses to develop authentic contexts for mathematical concepts in other disciplines.

Policy Challenges

Policy challenges in various QL areas—articulation, assessment, relation to mathematics, and core curriculum—are the subjects of the final four thought papers. Michael Kirst addresses the complex political and policy issues surrounding articulation, that is, how QL education is affected by the decision making and transitions from secondary to higher education. Bernard Madison looks at articulation from within mathematics and analyzes features of the

current system of school and college mathematics that weaken QL education. Grant Wiggins discusses the unusual demands of assessing QL that are created by its contextual nature. Finally, Richard Scheaffer, aided by five statistics colleagues, positions many of the ideas in the other papers in the context of statistics education.

Part II: Forum Essays

The Forum program stimulated a wide-ranging discussion of the nature of QL; the relationships of QL to mathematics, statistics, and other disciplines; the consequences of innumeracy; possible improvements in QL education; and policy issues related to QL education. Perspectives expanded well beyond those presented in the background papers but continued to echo the themes of need and challenge. Varied voices spoke from broad and experienced viewpoints. For example, program participants included the presidents of major mathematical sciences professional organizations such as the American Mathematical Society (AMS), American Mathematical Association of Two-Year Colleges (AMATYC), American Statistical Association (ASA), Mathematical Association of America (MAA), and National Council of Teachers of Mathematics (NCTM).

Need for Work and Learning

Stronger mathematical education of teachers is central to QL in the view of National Academy of Science member Roger Howe. J. T. Sutcliffe, a high school mathematics teacher, not only supports stronger teacher education but also points to the constraints under which teachers work. Science dean and biologist David Brakke echoes the need for K–12 teacher education in QL but expands that in a call for colleges to continue and extend QL education. NCTM President Johnny Lott points to flaws in the K–16 mathematics curriculum that weaken QL education for all students, including future teachers.

Retired General Electric engineer William Steenken writes about the importance of QL to industry while Arnold Packer expands on his background paper, exhorting mathematicians to recognize the need for practical mathematical knowledge. Former astronaut and astronomer George Nelson discusses the nature of QL and compares it to science literacy.

Policy Perspectives

Although most participants at the Forum felt that education for QL should extend beyond mathematics and statistics, Jan Somerville cites policy issues surrounding college and university mathematics that impede progress toward a more useful mathematics education. She challenges mathematicians to take QL as a responsibility and to address more forcefully problems in mathematics education. Margaret Cozzens reinforces Somerville's views by identifying higher education policies and practices that hinder QL education. Judith Rizzo points to the need for stronger curricula and better prepared teachers, observing that our standards show that we already are strongly committed to QL. Sadie Bragg describes the special role of two-year colleges in general education and emphasizes how institutional policies can impact basic learning. In an essay addressing the importance of national networks, Susan Ganter discusses past and current successes of networks in mathematics curricular reform.

INTERNATIONAL PERSPECTIVES

In addition to the background paper by Jan de Lange, this volume contains a group of essays by authors from Brazil, Denmark, France, Great Britain, and the Netherlands, offering views of QL in those countries. Lynn Steen writes in his introduction to this section that "these glimpses of how mathematics educators in other nations are coming to terms with the new demands of numeracy, mathematics, and citizenship open a window on approaches that move well beyond those normally considered in U.S. curriculum discussions."

FORUM REFLECTIONS AND OBSERVATIONS

Three presentations at the Forum provided reflections on the central issues. Jeanne Narum opened the Forum with an analysis of the task ahead and, citing her experience with Project Kaleidoscope, urged collaboration in addressing QL. In a luncheon presentation, Rita Colwell, director of the National Science Foundation, challenged Forum attendees to produce national standards for QL and assessments that measure our progress toward attainment of QL goals. AMS President Hyman Bass, in his closing remarks, cautioned against major curricular changes until QL is better understood.

Although regrettably not recorded in the pages of this volume, Daniel Kennedy's hilarious monologue on "Why Johnny STILL Can't Add" entertained Forum participants after the midpoint dinner. For a brief respite, QL was replaced by a sterling example of "high humor" literacy.

The reflections at the end of this volume probably provide the best summary of Forum discussions. This is what various selected participants from a wide variety of backgrounds took away with them. Two themes dominate: (1) the relationship of QL to mathematics and statistics and (2) the perceived difficulty of improving QL education. AMATYC President Philip Mahler ties these two themes together, concluding that the difficulty in improving QL education requires that it must be extended beyond mathematics and statistics.

Gene Bottoms and Andrea Leskes focus on the need to improve school mathematics. Leskes suggests that viewing QL as sophisticated uses of elementary mathematics could allow schools to con-

centrate on improved understanding of elementary mathematics while colleges address more complicated uses. William Haver cautions that too much emphasis on how QL and mathematics differ could let mathematicians off the educational hook. Russell Edgerton acknowledges that the QL discussions made him more aware of the need for a curriculum that contributes to general learning goals. Peter Ewell muses about the struggle to define QL, the dominance of mathematics in Forum discussions, and the need for different messages for different audiences. Rob Cole worries about the narrowness of disciplinary thinking.

Jo Ann Lutz and Mary Jane Schmitt both speak of how the challenge of QL seemed to become more daunting as the Forum unfolded. Schmitt also points to the expansion of focus from education in grades 11 to 14 to "pre-K through grey." Don Small urges development of experimental QL education programs and suggests that reforming college algebra could provide a strong base for QL in colleges. Stephen Maurer, even though temporarily discouraged by the difficult task of QL education, left the Forum with a plan of action for Swarthmore. Edward Tenner notes the split between the experimentalist views of Small and Maurer and the more conservative view that QL is a long-term systemic challenge.

Many Faces and Common Themes

Mathematics and Democracy lays the groundwork for all the papers, essays, and reflections, providing common terminology, general definitions, and examples of quantitative literacy. Nevertheless, the thought papers and Forum proceedings exhibit considerable wrestling with the meaning of QL and offer a variety of interpretations and terminology. Some talk about mathematics and mathematical literacy as proxies for quantitative literacy while others draw finer distinctions between mathematics, mathematical literacy, numeracy, and QL. Many of the reflections on the Forum recognize that although a general understanding of QL is critical, precision in definition is unnecessary. The faces of quantitative literacy revealed in this volume create a mosaic of complex issues confronting a U.S. education system unaccustomed to dealing with competencies cutting across all academic disciplines and almost all aspects of everyday life. Yet these competencies are crucial for citizens living in a twenty-first-century democracy.

Common themes do run through many of the contributions to this volume. One is the need for better articulation and synergy between the components of the K–16 education system and between education and the rapidly changing political and economic environment. Kirst and Madison focus largely on articulation between school and college; Kirst analyzes political and policy issues while Madison aims specifically at circumstances within mathematics. Somerville and Lott both point to difficulties students face in the transition from to school to college mathematics. Haver and Small suggest specific ways in which college mathematics can ease some of those difficulties. Lutz cautions that current messages from colleges keep schools from emphasizing QL, and Maurer points to admission tests as an example of one such message. Other commentators address the need for different kinds of articulation.

Carnevale and Desrochers, Rosen, and Packer discuss the need for articulation between mathematics education and the workplace. Steenken expands on this need from the perspective of an engineer in industry. Hughes Hallett, de Lange, Scheaffer, and Richardson and McCallum all address the need for articulation between teaching mathematical and statistical concepts and using authentic contexts drawn from a variety of real-world sources. Further, they argue for the effectiveness of articulation between various college disciplines (Hughes Hallett calls this a "friendly conspiracy") in teaching the use of mathematics and statistics in numerous contexts. Cole and Edgerton expand on the need for QL to be a multidisciplinary effort. Leskes echoes the goal of teaching QL across the disciplines.

Closely aligned to the articulation theme is the complexity of the education system responsible for teaching quantitative literacy. The discussions in this volume point to numerous pressures within and on this system that make change difficult. Kirst speaks of the "Babel of assessments" facing students as they move through the mathematics curriculum. Madison describes the complex and overlapping system of mathematics at the boundary between school and college. In a Forum reflection, Schmitt observes that QL education should extend well beyond school and college to a host of adult education venues in the media, workplace, and community.

Wiggins writes about the difficulty of finding authentic contextual assessments. Steen discusses the formidable forces that shape the K–12 mathematics curriculum. Bottoms outlines five challenges for improving QL in the schools, including changing testing and textbooks and avoiding increased tracking. Cohen chronicles the historical development of QL and the forces that were in play in earlier eras. De Lange illustrates the difficulty of deciding what mathematics is important for QL and emphasizes the need for much closer ties between the curriculum and the culture in which it is taught. Tenner hypothesizes that only a minority of college faculty are potentially strong QL teachers and that they need to be convinced that QL is an intellectual challenge.

Rosen and Packer address the complex needs of a major component of U.S. culture, the workplace, and show how those needs are or are not being met by mathematics and quantitative education. Scheaffer confronts the doubly complex task of explaining how the relatively new and poorly understood discipline of statistics and statistics education fit into the haze of QL education.

Aside from the discussion—albeit mostly academic—about the need for a better definition of QL, the Forum papers and essays clearly point to two other needs:

1. Systematic evidence to support the call for stronger QL education; and

2. Clear descriptions of the levels of QL and of strategies for how they can be assessed.

Numerous anecdotes and the results of national and international tests point to low levels of QL, even among U.S. college graduates. Most people are familiar with this deficiency, but stronger evidence is needed about the consequences for society and for individuals. Although there is widespread agreement that a basic level of quantitative literacy should result from K–12 education and that levels of QL should continue to rise throughout higher education, neither the levels of QL nor assessments for these levels are yet identified in a form that commands widespread support.

Neither the background papers nor the Forum essays and reflections answer all the questions about the need for QL and how best to achieve it. They do, however, present valuable and informed views on quantitative literacy from a variety of perspectives. Together with *Mathematics and Democracy,* these views form a solid basis for furthering the national conversation on how to achieve quantitative literacy for all. As Peter Ewell observed, the Forum was helpful in "stirring the pot, which was exactly what was intended. The question now is how to keep the thing cooking without boiling over."

References

Madison, Bernard L. 2001. "Quantitative Literacy: Everybody's Orphan." *Focus* (6):10–11.

Steen, Lynn Arthur, ed. 2001. *Mathematics and Democracy: The Case for Quantitative Literacy.* Princeton, NJ: National Council on Education and the Disciplines.

Democracy and the Numerate Citizen: Quantitative Literacy in Historical Perspective

PATRICIA CLINE COHEN

"Political Arithmetick is an art daily growing more important in the United States," wrote the Massachusetts statesman Josiah Quincy in 1816. In a lengthy analysis of an innovative new book on American statistics published in the *North American Review*, Quincy expounded on the connections he saw between statistical knowledge and the duties of citizens and lawmakers in the fledgling American republic. Democratic government, as ordained by the Federal Constitution, made "a knowledge of our civil condition . . . something more than the gratification of mere curiosity." The careful accumulation of hard data about society—"authentic facts," "certain knowledge," "statisticks," in the language of Quincy's day—was essential information for a government whose goal was to promote the general welfare of its citizens. Hard data, Quincy declared,

> "are to be sought, and ought to be studied by all who aspire to regulate, or improve the state of the nation; and even by all who would judge rightly of their duties as citizens, and who are conscientiously scrupulous, even in private life, of so casting their influence into the scale of parties, as best to promote the general happiness and prosperity."[1]

Quincy's language sounds formal, antiquated, musty even, to modern ears, but his point about the growing importance of numbers to an informed citizenry was certainly farsighted. Over the two centuries that America has developed and matured under democratic institutions, numbers and quantities have achieved an overwhelming preeminence in the politics of public life. This is so because "Political Arithmetick" connects to democratic government in three distinct ways. First, the very political legitimacy of a representative democracy rests on repeated acts of counting: tallying people in periodic census enumerations to apportion the size and balance of legislative bodies, and tallying votes in varieties of elections to determine office-holding and public policies. Second, as Quincy suggested, a government whose goal is the general welfare of its citizens needs good aggregate information about those citizens on which to erect and assess public policy. It is no coincidence, then, that the word "statisticks" was coined in English in the 1790s (although what was meant by it was somewhat different from its meaning today). And third, the citizens of democratic governments also need good information, to assess their leaders' political decisions and judge them on election day. Voters certainly have always appraised the character and leadership qualities of candidates, but it is increasingly the case that candidacies in the modern era can be won or lost based on the unemployment rate, the crime rate, or the Dow Jones index. Our multitudes of numerical indicators summarize the complex economic, political, and social health of the country, and citizens need to be able to decode and decipher this modern-day "political arithmetic."[2]

To say that there is a vital link between numbers and representative democracy is not to suggest that this was fully understood from the founding days of the United States. The vast majority of citizens

Patricia Cline Cohen is Chair of the History Department at the University of California, Santa Barbara, where she has also served as Chair of the Women's Studies Program and as Acting Dean of Humanities and Fine Arts. Cohen specializes in U.S. women's history and early American history. She is coauthor of *The American Promise* and author of *A Calculating People: The Spread of Numeracy in Early America*, a cultural history of the diffusion of arithmetic skills and the propensity to use quantification in American culture in the 18th and early 19th centuries.

in 1789 had quite limited numeracy skills, skills that got exercised the most (if at all) in the world of commerce and trade, not in the world of politics. Although at the outset, the U.S. Constitution provided for a decennial census for apportioning the House of Representatives, the Congress took two decades just to begin to realize that the labor-intensive enumeration process could be augmented almost without cost to capture additional data that might be useful for a government to have. Even the apportionment function was carried out with considerable imprecision, showing us that a general faith in representative institutions in 1789 did not yet translate to anything so arithmetically concrete as one man, one vote.

We have moved, over two centuries, from a country where numeracy skills were in short supply and low demand, to one in which the demand is now very high indeed—and in which the supply, while greatly augmented, has not kept up with the need. This Forum is primarily focused on the present and the future, asking how much quantitative literacy is necessary to function in these beginning years of the twenty-first century. But it helps to look backward as well, to understand the development of the ideas linking quantitative literacy to citizenship in a representative democracy. By mapping out the spread of numeracy in specific arenas, we can begin to see what factors spurred the growth of quantitative literacy in American history. More than just arithmetic, the shopkeeper's skill, was highly valued in the early years of our democracy; leaders also championed the study of geometry as a pathway to the superior reasoning skills required by representative government. Our exploration of the practices of arithmetic and geometry instruction will quickly lead us to another important problem: the differential distribution of mathematical skills in past populations, which provides a further important clue to the question of how quantitative literacy bears on citizenship. And finally, we need to move beyond the naïve enthusiasm for "political arithmetick" characteristic of the early nineteenth century, which valued numbers for their seemingly objective, neutral, and therefore authoritative status, to see the symbolic and constructed uses of political numbers that can both convey and hide important information. As we all learned so dramatically in the election of 2000, "simple counting" in politics is never really simple.

This essay looks at three historical eras: the founding generation, from the 1780s to about 1810; the antebellum period, from the 1820s to the 1850s, when direct democracy came into full bloom and the country underwent a market revolution; and the late nineteenth century, when empirical social science became wedded to government and when new citizens—the newly freed slaves and the many thousands of immigrants—posed new challenges and choices for the developing education system. For each period I will sketch out features of the spreading domain of number in service to the state and then assess the levels of numeracy prevalent that

helped (or hindered) citizens from functioning effectively as citizens.

The Founding Generation: Who Counts

The writers of the U.S. Constitution embedded three ideas in their ingenious plan of government that implied and eventually fostered a relationship between quantification and politics. First, they chose to erect a representative government that acted on and represented people, not the states, as had the predecessor plan, the Articles of Confederation. The size of each state's population determined the composition of the House of Representatives and the number of electors in the electoral college that selected the president. Second, the Constitution inaugurated a regular and recurring census based on "actual enumeration," and the results would determine not only apportionment in the House and electoral college but also apportionment of direct taxes. And third, the framers handled the thorny problem of noncitizen inhabitants by counting slaves (circumspectly described as "other Persons" in contrast to the category of the "free") at a three-fifths ratio, which meant that slaves added weight, but not full weight, to the political power as well as the tax burden of slave states. (This was judged at the time to be a brilliant compromise between the North and the South; however, with relatively few instances of direct federal taxation before the Civil War—in 1798 and three times in the 1810s—the slave states derived constant political benefit without the counterbalancing pain of taxation essential to the three-fifths clause.)

These features of the Constitution suggest a numerical approach to governance, a way of imagining citizens as individuals who "count" or matter, as objects of, participants in, and paying supporters of government. But in the first several decades, scant attention was paid to direct democracy. (After all, these were the men who gave us the electoral college as a method of selecting the president.) The 1790 census no doubt substantially undercounted the population—Thomas Jefferson and George Washington both suspected that—but its precise accuracy was not a matter of great consternation at the time. Indeed, many of the people tallied in that census—women, children, servants, slaves, the unpropertied—although included for the headcount were never imagined therefore to be active participants in government. The narrow goal of the count was to yield proportional representation at a ratio of one representative to no fewer than 30,000 people, voters or not. The simplicity of the Constitution's mandate, however, was belied by the complexities of actually making a fair apportionment once the population was ascertained. Congress spent over five months on the problem, finding it both a politically and mathematically fraught question. What number of representatives, coupled with what divisor (in the ratio of representation), yielded the closest thing to proportional representation? And crucially, how would remainders be handled? Delaware, for example, had an enumerated population of 50,209 free people and 8,887 slaves, leaving it with one representative and a very large remainder no matter whether a divisor of 30,000 or 33,000 (the number finally chosen) was used. The final two opposing apportionment formulas were the work of Jefferson and Alexander Hamilton, which tells us right there that considerable political clout was at stake. But for much of the winter and early spring of 1792, members of Congress struggled with tedious repetitions of long division, testing out different divisors and trying to fathom the political consequences of different ways of treating the remainders. Little of this internal jockeying made the newspapers, which suggests that the "political arithmetick" of direct democracy was in its infancy then. Probably few citizens of Delaware ever drew the conclusion that their state had been shortchanged.[3]

Further, only a very few political thinkers saw that the innovation of a repeated census might be put to extended uses. Censuses before 1790, both in Europe and in the colonies, had been infrequent acts of monarchical power designed to assess military strength or taxation potential. Not surprisingly, then, enumerations historically had been met with suspicion and sometimes resistance. But in the U.S. case, counting people was a tactic to ensure representation, a good thing. Congressman James Madison served on the committee charged with drawing up the first "enumeration bill" in 1790. Madison proposed an expanded census, one that went beyond a basic tally of free and slave to further categorize people by race, by sex, and—for white males only—by age (those over 16, those under, a split that gauged military manpower). He also proposed that each employed person be tallied as doing either agricultural, commercial, or manufacturing work, arguing reasonably that "in order to accommodate our laws to the real situation of our constituents, we ought to be acquainted with that situation." In the end, however, Congress accepted the race, sex, and age additions but rejected the occupational categorization. As one representative said, it would "occasion an alarm" among the people, for "they would suppose the government intended something, by putting the union to this additional expence, beside gratifying an idle curiosity."[4]

When the 1800 census came up for drafting, two learned societies each petitioned Congress to enlarge the census to serve the cause of science. The Connecticut Academy of Arts and Sciences, located in New Haven, and the American Philosophical Society, in Philadelphia, each memorialized Congress with a plea to turn the census into a national gathering of "authentic facts." Such facts might include the age, nativity, occupation, and marital status of each person so that, over a run of years, future generations could chart the aggregate progress, health, and longevity of the citizens. But again Congress ignored these requests, not thinking them worth the bother.[5] The census was expanded a bit, in that the white population was now recorded in five age classifications for both sexes. The black population, however, whether free or slave, was not distinguished by any sex or age classification. Disparities like this one are very revealing, because they remind us pointedly of the constructedness of political numbers. Who gets counted and how: these are always political decisions. In all the U.S. censuses up to and including the 1840 count, blacks and whites were categorized under different age classifications, making it very difficult to compare their longevity or other vital rates.

The Connecticut Academy of Arts and Sciences undertook to do for Connecticut what it had failed to accomplish at the national level. It embarked on an ambitious survey of all Connecticut towns, with an instrument of 32 questions that probed for an account of the population, the numbers of houses and carriages, local manufactures, the number of clergymen and their salaries, and "instances of suicide in the last twenty years," among other things. The academy leaders failed in that task, too, finding that local respondents were mostly disinclined to collect the data; in the end, only two town studies were published.

The idea for a state-based survey came from a parallel survey project undertaken in Scotland by Sir John Sinclair, the man who came up with the word "statisticks" and defined it to mean "an inquiry into the state of a country, for the purpose of ascertaining the quantum of happiness enjoyed by its inhabitants, and the means of its future improvement."[6] "Statistick" first appeared in an American dictionary in 1803 with an enigmatic definition referring to Sinclair and his "statement of the trade, population, production [of Scotland] . . . with the food, diseases, and longevity of its inhabitants." By 1806, the word gained a clearer articulation in Noah Webster's first dictionary as "a statement or view of the civil condition of a people."[7] The word *state* was embedded in the term in two ways: facts about the state that could be plainly stated. Although such facts might take the form of numbers, this did not become an essential part of the definition for several more decades. By the mid 1820s, just over a dozen books had been published with the word "statistics" or "statistical" in the title, and another 17 not emblazoned with the word still had the character of reference books of authentic facts and numbers. Nearly all these books proclaimed the novelty of their shared project, assembling facts and figures for the aid of statesmen and citizens.[8]

The Founding Generation: Small Steps Toward Greater Numeracy

This slow but definite start to America's affinity for quantification in politics was paralleled by a similarly gradual embrace of arithmetic education in these early years.[9] The founding fathers in the 1790s were quick to form grand schemes to improve education; an educated citizenry was well understood to be the bulwark of a republican government, and there was no shortage of public-spirited plans formulated to improve the mental reasoning of the nation's youngest citizens and future voters. There also were good reasons in particular to address what had been an abysmal state of arithmetic instruction in the colonies. But, as ever, the fulfillment of these good intentions proved considerably harder to accomplish, in view of the costs to taxpayers of public education.

Arithmetic instruction in prerevolutionary America occupied a very narrow slice of what was already not a very generous provision of education before the 1790s. The South's few private schools and tutors educated only a small fraction of the gentry's children. It was in New England where literacy and numeracy were the most advanced, thanks to a patchwork tradition of district schools supported by local and state funds. But even there, significant obstacles kept arithmetic skills at bay, obstacles also at work in the South. The subject was identified with commerce, and generally only boys headed for the mercantile life troubled to learn it. It was demonstrably a difficult and arcane subject, requiring the writing and reasoning skills characteristic of children over age 11 or 12, so anyone whose education did not extend to the adolescent years skipped it entirely—thus, most girls missed out. Simple counting and adding in Arabic numerals below a hundred probably was routinely passed on from parents to children, eminently useful for handling small sums of money, paying taxes, toting up firkins of butter, selling excess eggs, measuring lumber and, in general, thinking about prices in the typically static colonial economy. But anything in the "higher branches" was not commonly taught, except to boys in vocational training.

A glance at any of the arithmetic textbooks used in the colonies reveals how truly convoluted and challenging this subject was. For two centuries, imported English texts had organized knowledge of the arithmetic arts into a catechism-like set of rules that relied on memory rather than reasoning. (The rules in different texts were not so regularized, however, that they found similar expression. Books even jumbled the order of presentation, bragging that no section depended on any previous section for completion.) Generally, a student first was introduced to Arabic numerals and then to the first four rules of addition, subtraction, multiplication, and division in whole numbers. Next, a text might repeat the rules in fractions, or repeat them afresh using denominate numbers— "named" numbers that expressed the elaborate and complex denominations of the English system of weights, measures, and money. Denominate arithmetic was undoubtedly the worst stumbling block in the acquisition of numeracy. Texts presented page after page of equivalencies in gallons and pints, bushels and pecks, pounds and ounces. Often the denominations of volume or size were specific to the item being measured: so, for example, a firkin of butter weighed 56 pounds whereas a firkin of soap weighed 64; a hogshead of beer contained 45 gallons whereas a hogshead of wine contained 63. Troy and apothecary ounces totaled 12 to the pound, whereas avoirdupois ounces equaled 16 per pound. Stu-

dents struggled with a rule called "reduction," learning to figure how many minutes in a week, how many ounces in a hundredweight, how many inches in 3 furlongs and 58 yards. Reduction was essential for the key problem of calculating the price of measured commodities in pounds, shillings, and pence.

The capstone of basic arithmetic arrived with the "rule of three": "Given three parts, to find the fourth" was the usual phraseology. This rule and its variations (single and double, direct and inverse) covered the basic commercial problem of proportional relationships. If a man pays 1s. 7d. to pasture a cow for one week, how much will it cost him to pasture 37 cows for two weeks? If nine men can build a house in five months, working 14 hours a day, in what time can nine men do it if they work only 10 hours per day? The solution required writing down the three known quantities in a certain order, multiplying the middle term by the last, and dividing the product by the first. Knowing the proper order and choosing the proper version of the rule were essential. Some books helpfully provided gimmicks to aid memory: "If more require more, or less require less, the question belongs to the Rule of Three Direct. But if more require less, or less require more, it belongs to the Rule of Three Inverse."[10]

Arithmetic was unrelentingly mercantile, and the chief method of instruction, up to about 1820, was the copybook. A teacher likely had just one text, and every student copied each rule into a manuscript copybook and worked a selected example for each rule. A student who passed through the major "rules" produced his own permanent record of the rules, essential for later reference in life. A large collection of arithmetic copybooks owned by Harvard University shows that the typical copybook ended with the rule of three. But printed textbooks and a few copybooks forged on, to the rules of fellowship, interest, compound interest, discount, tare and tret, and dozens more that covered seemingly unique business applications.

These textbooks and their derivative copybooks look quite impossible as teaching aids to us now. They eschew explanation, give minimal examples, invoke no repeat drills, and treat each type of problem as a universe unto itself, with nary a hint of logical connections between, say, subtraction and division, addition and multiplication, or fractions and decimals. The rule of three was about the only rule that attempted a form of generalization in abstract numbers and, as the copybooks show, many students were at sea in applying it to novel situations with the burdensome denominate numbers. Yet it is possible that having a multitude of seemingly distinct formulas actually improved marketplace calculation, precisely because a young merchant getting his footing in the world of trade did not try to reason things out but instead paged through his copybook looking for the exact rule that fit the situation. This was applied mathematics, and the point precisely was to give each application its own algorithm. In time, the young merchant would grow very familiar with the particular and limited kinds of calculations his type of business required, and the copybook would have served its purpose.[11] But such a form of training did little to enhance the generalized facility with numbers that we now call quantitative literacy.

This eighteenth-century picture of arithmetic training began to change in the 1790s, coincident with and explicitly connected to the arrival of republican institutions. Citizenship was a term newly invested with patriotic meanings, and leading statesmen contemplated the best pathways for creating an informed citizenry. Raising literacy rates was one obvious strategy, to improve the flow and reception of ideas and information; and reforming mathematics instruction to sharpen citizens' minds was another. No less a public figure than George Washington endorsed mathematics education as a civic benefit: "The science of figures, to a certain degree, is not only indispensably requisite in every walk of civilized life, but the investigation of mathematical truths accustoms the mind to method and correctness in reasoning, and is an employm. peculiarly worthy of rational beings."[12] Thomas Jefferson was on record with his support as well: "The faculties of the mind, like the members of the body, are strengthened and improved by exercise. Mathematical reasoning and deductions are, therefore, a fine preparation for investigating the abstruse speculations of the law."[13]

Jefferson sketched out an ambitious system of education for Virginia that would have provided three years of publicly supported schooling for all free boys and girls, covering reading, writing, and "common arithmetic" (probably to the rule of three). From there, the worthy boys (ones who could pay tuition plus a tiny fraction invited on scholarships) could progress to a Latin grammar school where "the higher branches of numerical arithmetic" would be taught. At the pinnacle, a college would educate the most deserving; here was where algebra and geometry would be encountered.[14] Notable in this plan was the provision for girls to be taught basic arithmetic. But the two lower levels of Jefferson's system were not built in his lifetime. Similar schemes for common school systems in other states were equally hard to implement because of the expense of public education. This meant that colleges—the handful that there were around 1800—generally needed to offer first-year courses in basic arithmetic to compensate for persistent deficiencies at the lower levels of instruction.[15]

Jefferson took another route, however, that had a much more immediate impact on numeracy in the 1790s. As secretary of state under Washington, he proposed a major reform in the monetary system of the nation in 1793, abolishing pounds and shillings in favor of decimal dollars, dimes, and cents. (Jefferson was equally inspired by French Enlightenment plans for the metric system, but that did not fly in the 1790s.) Ease of calculation was Jefferson's goal: "The facility which this would introduce into the vulgar arithmetic would, unquestionably, be soon and sensibly felt by the whole mass of people, who would thereby be enabled to compute for themselves whatever they should have occasion to buy, to sell, or measure, which the present complicated and difficult ratios place beyond their computation for the most part."[16]

By 1796, the mint was producing the new money, triggering the publication of dozens of new arithmetic textbooks with nationalistic titles, for example, *The Federal Calculator*, *The Scholar's Arithmetic: or, Federal Accountant*, *The Columbian Arithmetician*, and *The American Arithmetic: Adapted to the Currency of the United States*.[17] One book of 1796 spelled out explicitly the interconnections between common arithmetic, decimal money, and republican government:

> It is expected that before many years, nay, many months, shall elapse, this mode of reckoning [decimal money] will become general throughout the United States. . . . Then let us, I beg of you, Fellow-Citizens, no longer meanly follow the British intricate mode of reckoning. —Let them have their own way—and us, ours.—Their mode is suited to the genius of their government, for it seems to be the policy of tyrants, to keep their accounts in as intricate, and perplexing a method as possible; that the smaller number of their subjects may be able to estimate their enormous impositions and exactions. But Republican money ought to be simple, and adapted to the meanest capacity.[18]

In other words, bad governments prefer complicated money and innumerate citizens who cannot figure out how a tyrant can be fleecing them, while republican governments should make it possible for people of "the meanest capacity" to be able to decode the country's budget and tax policy.

The Antebellum Era: Numeracy Training Accelerates

Simplified decimal money alone did not drive the coming revolution in arithmetic training. Just after 1820, remarkable innovations and teaching techniques altered the look of arithmetic texts and heightened the social valuation put on numeracy. The underlying cause of this major change is not hard to identify: the rapid and unprecedented expansion of commerce in the years after 1815, when the War of 1812 ended. Economic historians call this the takeoff period of early capitalism, a time when more and more citizens eagerly committed themselves to (or found themselves enmeshed in) a market economy characterized by the rise of banking and economies of scale, the vast development of internal transportation, the introduction of water-powered factories, the sale of and speculation in western lands, wage labor, cyclical financial panics, and urbanization. Added to this, the years after 1820 brought a remarkable democratization of American politics, as state after state did away with property requirements, opened the franchise to all white men, and developed a sharply competitive party system that mobilized voters at the state and federal levels. (In the 1840 presidential election, an impressive 80 percent of eligible voters voted.) And, as noted at the opening of this essay, this was the period when a statistical approach to politics began to flourish, linking good government with vital data and measured economic strength. Both economic and political developments were accompanied by the growth of public education, leading to more schools, more teachers, surer state support, and a gradual bureaucratization of schooling with the development of state school systems starting in the 1830s, of which Horace Mann's leadership in Massachusetts is perhaps the best known. Within this new context, arithmetic education was spectacularly reconceived.

The most impressive change in arithmetic instruction came in the 1820s, when an entirely new approach to the field, based on inductive reasoning, challenged the heavy, memory-based books of the eighteenth century. The move started with a young Harvard graduate named Warren Colburn, who published a text of "intellectual arithmetic" for very young children, ages 4 to 8, that omitted all rules. The book instead consisted of pages of problems in addition, subtraction, multiplication, and division, with whole numbers and fractions, and for the first part of the book the numbers were written out as words, avoiding any explanation of Arabic numerals or the place system. In the next few years, Colburn extended his anti-rule method to another arithmetic text and to an algebra book.[19] By the late 1820s and well into the 1830s and 1840s, dozens of other text authors followed the Colburn method. Some two million copies of Colburn's first book were sold in its first 35 years and it was still in print in the 1850s, reportedly selling over 100,000 copies annually.[20]

Two distinct pedagogical techniques characterized this new approach. First, arithmetic began as a mental (or "intellectual") exercise, done in the mind without pencil and paper and without abstract symbols for numbers and operations. The idea here was to train the mind to reason with numbers, not to do problems by rote formula. An important side benefit was that mental arithmetic could be taught to children too young to read or write. Colburn's second and controversial innovation rested on his claim that children could develop their own calculation techniques, recapitulating mathematics through inductive reasoning. Set a student to work on an addition problem, Colburn advised,

> . . . without telling him what to do. He will discover what is to be done, and invent a way to do it. Let him perform several in his own way, and then suggest some method a little different from his, and nearer the common method. If he readily

comprehends it, he will be pleased with it, and adopt it. If he does not, his mind is not yet prepared for it, and should be allowed to continue his own way longer and then it should be suggested again.[21]

The rule of three was entirely omitted from all his books. "Those who understand the principles sufficiently to comprehend the nature of the rule of three, can do much better without it than with it, for when it is used, it obscures, rather than illustrates, the subject to which it is applied."[22] Colburn wanted to end children's slavish reliance on rules and rote learning and to teach them to think for themselves. "Most scholars soon acquire such a habit of thinking and reasoning for themselves, that they will not be satisfied with anything, which they do not understand, in any of their studies."[23]

This "new math" of the 1820s did not completely sweep the field of arithmetic instruction, of course. By the mid 1830s and increasing thereafter, a steady stream of criticism challenged the assertion that students could invent arithmetic wholly in their heads. Texts touting arithmetic by the "deductive" method appeared, presenting axioms and definitions to be memorized and applied. By the second half of the nineteenth century, the inductive method was remembered only as a failure. In the 1870s, the Paterson (New Jersey) superintendent of schools reflected that arithmetic was once "taught backward—reason before observation." Instead, fundamentals, number facts, and rote computation now took precedence over mathematical reasoning. "Reasoning upon facts is the work of a maturer mind," he wrote, something reserved for children age 12 and older.[24]

Nonetheless, Colburn's innovations had galvanized the field of arithmetic instruction, provoking scores of new textbook titles each taking one side or the other in this lively educational debate. (Schools and individual teachers usually chose their own textbooks, creating further incentive for new textbook authors to jump into the market.) After the 1820s, the catechism-like books of the eighteenth century, with their multitudes of terse, unintelligible rules each with a single example, were no longer published, having been rendered obsolete by the new books that outdid themselves in their efforts to connect to students. (The old books remained in use for some time, of course, even though they were no longer being republished in new editions.) Whether they called themselves inductive or deductive, mental or written, or analytic or synthetic, in a third axis of the debate, all the new books joined in an effort to promote solid and generalizable mathematical skills. Arithmetic still was valued for its business applications, but it also was valued for its ability to promote powers of reasoning. It was thought of now as a basic part of every school's curriculum, not a set-aside appropriate for future merchants alone.

Although more children were learning basic arithmetic and learning it better than ever before, coverage was uneven, of course, only reaching children who attended school; the days of mandatory school attendance lay far in the future. What is perhaps most striking about this early period of the flowering of numeracy is that it was, in theory, as available to young girls as it was to young boys. This was an unprecedented development. Before 1820, girls had only limited chances to become proficient in arithmetic. The spread of common schooling, the drop in the age at which formal arithmetic instruction began (from 11 to 12 down to 5 to 6), the disconnect between narrow vocational training and arithmetic, and—perhaps most significant—the large-scale entry of women into the teaching profession: all these factors combined to bring arithmetic instruction into the orbit of young women.

It was not an unproblematic development, however. It is ironic that, when at long last basic arithmetic education was routinely available to young girls in school, critics of that development began to assert that girls had a distinctly lesser talent for mathematics than boys. It is a gender stereotype that was actually rather new in the nineteenth century or, if not entirely new, appearing in a new and more precise form. In the eighteenth century, when proficiency with the rules of figuring was the province of boys bound for commercial vocations, any gender differential in mathematical skill could easily be understood as the product of sex differences in education. Women were less numerate than men, and they were also less often literate, but no one needed to conclude that women had an innately inferior capacity for reading the printed page just because fewer women could read. So too with numbers: the divide between the numerate and innumerate was traced to specific training and needs, not to sex-based mental capacity. And, to be sure, many female activities of the eighteenth century required, if not actual arithmetic performed via rules, then some degree of what we now see as part of a mathematical intelligence—counting, spatial relations, measuring, halving and doubling—as women went about cooking, weaving, knitting, and turning flat cloth into three-dimensional clothing without benefit of patterns.[25]

But in the early nineteenth century, when young girls finally had a chance to be included in formal arithmetic instruction, the perceived differences between the sexes were increasingly naturalized. Critics of arithmetic instruction for girls questioned whether girls needed it. "Who is to make the puddings and pies" if girls become scholars, one critic wondered. A state legislature objected to "masculine studies" in mathematics at one school, studies with no discernable bearing on the making of puddings and stockings. "What need is there of learning how far off the sun is, when it is near enough to warm us?" said a third.[26] Of course, there were champions of arithmetic instruction for girls. Most argued that a knowledge of household accounts was highly valuable for thrifty wives to have, but a few moved beyond the purely practical and staked their claim on the mental discipline and reasoning acquired through arithmetic and the higher branches of mathematics.

Geometry in particular became the real battleground in this debate in the 1820s and 1830s. Vaunted by European and American Enlightenment thinkers for its ability to teach citizens to reason, geometry had escaped the deadening pedagogy of rule-based commercial arithmetics. It rested on comprehensible axioms and definitions, mobilized in elegant, logical arguments. A handful of girls' academies took up the challenge of putting Euclid into the hands of students—Emma Willard's famous Seminary at Troy, New York, was one, and Catharine Beecher's school in Hartford, Connecticut, was another. Beecher saw geometry as a mental gymnastic, good for "disciplining and invigorating the powers of the mind."[27] But critics professed to be shocked, as seen in this reaction to the news in 1824 that a Philadelphia girl's school was taking up geometry: "The proper object of geometry is the development of the abstract properties and relations of space. In this science it cannot be expected that females will make much proficiency. Nor ought geometrical knowledge be considered as a necessary object of their pursuit."[28] The real concern for many was the blurring of sex roles and the creation of overly intellectual women that instruction in geometry implied, and the debate remained a lively one up until at least the 1850s. A middle course struck by one contributor to the debate helpfully suggested that no social harm would result if young women studied algebra and geometry, because their innate desire to be pleasing to men would keep them modest about their attainments. Similarly, their mothering instincts would remain unscathed: "Would [a mother] desert an infant for a quadratic equation?"[29] Of course not. But it took more than confidence in women's yearnings to be wives and mothers to quell this debate. In the end, it was the economic advantages of a female (cheap) labor force to fill public teaching positions that helped undermine the prejudices against women learning algebra and geometry.

The Antebellum Enthusiasm for Statistics

As the new arithmetic texts prospered and the higher branches became more familiar to many, so too did the use of numbers and statistics in American civic life. It is a chicken-and-egg question to ask which inspired which. Certainly the two phenomena were mutually reinforcing. A basic numeracy, along with a basic literacy, was fast becoming the hallmark of American public life. And this showed in the repeated uses of numbers and statistics that materialized in the newspapers, periodicals, and public debate of antebellum America.

Let me just itemize, quickly, some of the places in which a numerical frame of mind freshly and creatively took hold. The U.S.

Congress slowly shed its earlier reluctance to maximize the information derived from the census. The 1810 enumeration, launched during the failed embargo policies of Jefferson and Madison in the prelude to the War of 1812, was pressed into service as a way to learn about the actual state of manufactures and industry in the country. For the first time, data were collected that went beyond population, but the actual results were riddled with errors and many omissions. The 1820 census finally noted occupation, but again the effort was rudimentary, sorting all working adults into only three expansive categories. The 1830 census broadened the scope to further fine-tune age categories for the white population (but not the black) and to count the numbers of deaf, dumb, and blind in the population; here we see the start of federal interest in social statistics. But it was in 1840 that Congress completely succumbed to the siren song of statistics. The census population schedule expanded to 74 columns, adding new inquiries about the number of insane and idiot Americans, the number of scholars and schools, a tally of literacy, and a headcount of revolutionary war pensioners, a category associated with direct government expense. A second schedule also filled in by all enumerators contained 214 headings and answered Congress's blanket call for "statistical tables" containing "all such information in relation to mines, agriculture, commerce, manufacturers, and schools, as will exhibit a full view of the pursuits, industry, education, and resources of the country." From this massive aggregation, a person could learn the number of swine, of retail stores, of newspapers, of the bushels of potatoes and 200 more economic "statistics" (i.e., descriptive numbers) for every census district in the United States.

This deluge of statistics was eagerly awaited by the reading public. A variety of statistical almanacs first appeared and gained popularity in the 1830s, and they were eager to carry news of America's progress to their readers. The *American Almanac and Repository of Useful Knowledge* was an annual Boston publication dating from 1830, which was devoted to statistics, defined as "an account of whatever influences the condition of the inhabitants, or the operations of government on the welfare of men in promoting the ends of social being, and the best interest of communities."[30] This almanac filled its pages with miscellaneous figures—on banks, canals and railroads, pupils and schools. Other annual publications had a strictly political focus, such as the *Politician's Register,* begun in 1840, and the *Whig Almanac and United States Register,* begun in 1842; both recorded elections back to 1788 for many localities and provided county-level data for recent elections, giving readers information to strategize future campaigns.[31] We take this kind of data for granted now, but it was newly publicized information in the years around 1840—not coincidentally, the year when electoral participation was at an unprecedented high, a high that was sustained for another five decades.

Another rough but very innovative act of political quantification arrived on the scene in the 1850s, the straw poll of voters. Jour-nalists roamed the public thoroughfares, targeting mixed assemblages of people, often passengers on a steamboat or a passenger railroad, to ask about voter preference in an upcoming election. Interestingly, women passengers usually were not excluded from such polls even though they were not voters, but their votes were tallied separately from men's (which is how we can know that women were asked). These 1850s straw polls were the first American efforts to quantify public opinion.[32]

Antebellum newspapers, the everyday reading of many thousands of Americans, studded their columns with facts and figures. A very typical small item, from the New York *Herald* of 1839, titled "Railway and Stagecoach Travelling," drew on "a return of the mileage and composition duties on railway and stage carriages respectively" to show that over the previous two years, 4,800,000 fewer persons had traveled by stage while 14,400,000 more persons had traveled by railway.[33] No meaning or analysis was attached to these data; they simply stood alone, in manifest testament to the railroad revolution that all the *Herald*'s readers knew was underway. Mileage of railroad tracks was another favorite and frequent boast. But newspaper readers of the 1830s would not have been able to learn the total number of lives lost in steamboat explosions and accidents over that decade (unless they added up the losses reported for each accident, a rather shocking sum that historians have been able to reconstruct).

Not all statistical reports were cheery and boastful. The antebellum era has been tagged the "era of reform" by some historians for the rich variety of civic movements dedicated to eradicating social problems. Although the federal and state governments were not yet counting and publicizing the numbers of inebriates, prostitutes, or runaway slaves, other associations were—the temperance, moral reform, and abolitionist movements. A faith in the unimpeachable truth of numbers was part of the landscape now, and the most powerful way to draw attention to and gain legitimacy for a political or social goal was to measure and analyze it with the aid of arithmetic, giving the analysis the aura of scientific result.

It was in the 1850s that statistics were finally harnessed to opposing sides of the most pressing political division in the history of the United States, the conflict over slavery that led to the Civil War. In this decade-long debate, we can most clearly see the political constructedness of numbers and their mobilization to serve both symbolic and instrumental functions. Although it is very unlikely that anyone—a voter, a member of Congress—changed opinions about the sectional crisis based on quantitative data, it is instructive to see how both sides tried hard to harness the numbers to endorse their own predilections.

The quantitative dueling started in the congressional debate over the 1850 census. This was the first census designed to gather information on the individual level rather than the household, and the initial proposal included revealing individual-level data about slaves. Although relegated to a separate slave schedule, slaves were to be identified by name, age, sex, color, and place of birth. In addition, the proposal included asking for the number of children ever born of each woman, whether alive or dead now, and then a measure of the "degree of removal" from white or black in race. Southern congressmen powerfully objected to this level of data collecting, which would enable significant comparisons of blacks and whites as to fertility, longevity, and family formation. An acrimonious floor fight resulted in the removal of a significant part of the schedule. In the end, slaves were listed by number, not name, and place of birth and number of children were omitted, along with the explosive question on racial admixture. Political maneuvering had blocked the collection of data that would have furthered potentially invidious comparisons between North and South.[34]

Remaining parts of the 1850 census lent themselves to the North-South debate, however. In 1857, an antislavery southerner named Hinton Helper published *The Impending Crisis of the South,* a book that used the agricultural and social statistics of the census to argue that the South was trailing behind the North in every conceivable measure of economic productivity, wealth, education, and general progress. The fault, Helper declared, was slavery. Helper's book created quite a stir, and many northern and southern commentators wrestled with the questions it provoked. If slavery was bad, what about menial wage labor in the North? If the South's economy was ruined, why were there more paupers in New England than in the South? One critic pointed to Helper's mistake of comparing plain numbers from the census without recasting the data to take account of state sizes, a mistake in the "rule of simple proportion" that "any schoolboy can calculate."[35] But since Helper's error had eluded him and most of his supporters and critics, it is doubtful that a typical schoolboy in the United States would have had sufficient quantitative literacy to recognize the problem.

Arithmetic and Statistics in the Late Nineteenth and Twentieth Centuries

The post–Civil War era finally brought a full melding of statistical data with the functioning of representative government. A century after the first census of 1790, no one any longer suggested that an expanded census would alarm the people or merely gratify idle curiosity. The government had accepted an ongoing obligation to monitor the vital signs of the nation's health, wealth, and happiness. The census bureau was at last turned into a permanent federal agency, lodged for a time in the Department of Labor and later the Department of Commerce. The rapid urbanization and industrialization of the country suggested the agenda for national

statistics collection, with a new focus on urban problems, immigration, labor conditions, and standards of living. Unlike mid-century censuses, which had been run by men with no particular training in mathematics, the later census officials, such as Carroll Wright and Francis Amasa Walker, came from the new ranks of professionally trained economists and statisticians. Statistics was no longer limited to descriptive number facts; work by European thinkers such as Adolphe Quetelet, Francis Galton, and Karl Pearson had pushed the field into an increasingly sophisticated mathematical methodology. Federal censuses still were used to apportion Congress, but that was a minor sideline to a much larger enterprise engaged in measuring social indicators that would be helpful not only to legislators but to external commercial agencies and businesses as well, including universities, private research organizations, and trade associations.[36]

This growing sophistication of government statistical surveillance was not matched by a corresponding improvement in quantitative literacy on the part of the public. Unlike the early nineteenth century, when a public enthusiasm for numbers and arithmetic developed along with a statistical approach to civic life, in the early twentieth century the producers of statistics quickly outstripped most consumers' abilities to comprehend. The number crunchers developed more complex formulations while the arithmetic curriculum stagnated—this despite two further major attempts to reform the mathematics curriculum, first in the 1910s to 1920s and again in the 1950s to 1960s.

In the earlier phase of reform, a new breed of specialist—the professional mathematics educators in the university—addressed the problem of a rapidly growing student population assumed to have limited abilities. Foreign immigration and African-American migration combined with new compulsory schooling laws shifted the demographics of American schools. The percentage of youth ages 14 to 17 who attended school went from 10 percent in 1890 to 70 percent by 1940; the decades of maximum change were the 1910s and 1920s. When primarily middle- and upper-middle-class students had attended high school or academy, higher mathematics was typically served up in two or three standard courses, algebra, geometry, and trigonometry. But when the children of immigrants, emancipated slaves, and industrial workers arrived on the high school's steps, the wisdom of teaching the higher branches for the intellectual development they promised was increasingly called into question. A leading educational theorist, Edward Thorndike, reversed the truism of the early nineteenth century and argued that mathematics did *not* encourage mental discipline. Vocational education and the manual arts became prominent themes in educational circles, promoting the line that instruction should be geared to likely job placement. Several states removed all mathematics requirements for graduation and, predictably, enrollments declined. One study of Baltimore's schools in the 1920s explicitly recommended that algebra and geometry be withdrawn from the curriculum for worker's children because of their "lack of practical value" and that they be replaced by a two-year course that would teach mathematics "needed as a working tool in industry." In 1905, a Milwaukee trade school for mechanics endorsed mathematics only as a subject taught via practical problems that arose in the context of the specific mechanical tasks at hand.[37] The history of arithmetic education and blacks in the post-emancipation period is one yet to be written, although its outlines can be guessed at in light of the manual arts training promoted by black and white educational leaders. The details of how the most basic numeracy was imparted to a population just on the threshold of literacy will likely be an important story, however, in view of persistent race differentials in mathematics achievement in late twentieth-century America.[38]

In the second period of curricular reform, the 1950s to 1960s, university educators along with mathematics professors joined to revamp the K–12 mathematics curriculum in a climate of Cold War competition with the Soviet Union over scientific brainpower. The result was the widely publicized "new math" program that attempted to introduce set theory and discovery methods into the elementary school curriculum. In the judgment of current researchers, the new math resulted in a lot of sound and fury but made much less of a dent in actual mathematics instruction, in part because teachers were not nearly so enthused about the new or so ready to abandon the old methods of instruction.[39] Further, the new math tended to the abstract and thus had little effect in promoting the kind of quantitative literacy related to political or civic life.

Conclusion

This brief survey of quantitative literacy and citizenship in the nineteenth century has tried to demonstrate that although there is a natural affinity between numerical thinking and democratic institutions, that affinity was not necessarily predicated on quantitative sophistication on the part of citizens, at least not at first. Representative democracy originated in a numerical conception of the social order, under the U.S. Constitution. That same document ordained that government should "promote the general welfare and secure the blessings of liberty," a mandate that around 1820 was increasingly answered with a turn toward "authentic facts" and statistics. Statistics soon became compressed into *quantitative* facts, an efficient and authoritative form of information that everyone assumed would help public-spirited legislators govern more wisely. Schools, both public and private, correspondingly stepped up arithmetic instruction for youth, bringing a greatly simplified subject to all school-attending children and making it possible for them to participate with competency both in the new market economy and in the civic pride that resulted from the early focus on quantitative boasting.

As basic numeracy skills spread, so did the domain of number in civic life. The unsophisticated empiricism of early statistical history yielded to a more complex political terrain where numbers were enlisted in service of political debates and strategizing. At mid-century, the level of quantitative mastery required to keep up with debates based on numbers was still within the reach of anyone schooled in long division and percentage calculations. At a deeper level, the quantitative savvy required to challenge numbers (for bias, for errors in measurement and counting, for incorrect comparison of figures, for selective use of numbers) was not well developed, either in the producers or consumers of numbers. Choices about what to count and what not to count might be made naively, or purposefully and politically, as in the decision not to collect comparable demographic data on blacks and whites in the census.

Since the late nineteenth century, statistics has become a branch of mathematics and a powerful tool of the social sciences, but there has been little corresponding change in the arithmetic curriculum delivered to the vast majority of school-attending children. A much higher percentage of children attend primary and secondary school now compared with the late nineteenth century, which would suggest that the diffusion of civic numeracy also should be higher than a century ago. But at that crucial time of vast demographic change, back around 1890 to 1920, educators too often responded by scaling back or abandoning requirements such as algebra and geometry, setting them to the side with other subjects, such as Latin, now deemed unnecessary and even inappropriate for the children of immigrants and workers. Vocational tracks with courses on bookkeeping proliferated in the 1920s and garnered high enrollments mainly from female students preparing for clerical jobs. Aside from that, however, little thought was given to what might replace the once-standard higher mathematics curriculum of nineteenth-century academies. Noncollege-bound students continued to be sidelined and shortchanged in mathematics preparation so that now, something as basic as reinstating algebra as a high school graduation requirement (as recently happened in California) leads some to predict that graduation rates will tumble. Both sides in the current "math wars" debate acknowledge that the mathematical competencies of U.S. high school students are worrisomely low.[40] And quite apart from the math wars issue, high schools have not taken on the task of developing courses specifically aimed at teaching a kind of practical, context-based "political arithmetic" that would help students learn to evaluate the types of numbers that are routinely invoked in political life.

Our political system today uses and produces numerical data at a rapid clip, and the numbers are often in dispute or contradiction. Both the politicians and the voters may be in over their heads when it comes to evaluating different projections on the future of Social Security, the differential and future effects of tax cuts, the flow of immigration into the country, the rising or falling of student test scores, and the gyrations of the stock market as summarized in a few one-number indexes reported hourly on the radio. The danger is that we may not realize we are in over our heads. The attractiveness of numbers and statistics in the early- and mid-nineteenth century arose from their status as apparently authoritative, unambiguous, objective bits of knowledge that could form a sure foundation for political decisions. That may have been naïve, but gains in numeracy enabled some, at least, to learn to question numbers, to refine them, and to improve on their accuracy. Now, however, numbers are so ubiquitous and often contradictory that some fraction of the public readily dismisses them as "damned lies."[41]

The recent bandying about of the term "fuzzy math" furthers suspicions about numbers; when used in the political context, it seems to condemn arithmetic and "political arithmetic" alike. Wrenched from its origins as a legitimate if esoteric mathematical term dating from the 1960s, fuzzy math was first appropriated and rendered perjorative by the critics of curriculum reform in the mid 1990s, most famously and nationally by then-National Endowment for the Humanities (NEH) chair Lynne Cheney in a 1997 *Wall Street Journal* essay. It was lifted to national attention by George W. Bush in the first presidential debate in the fall of 2000, when Bush used it to characterize Al Gore as a number-benumbed pedant who was, in Bush's charge, eliding the truth with numbers. In its most recent turnabout, the term has been slapped back on Bush by the *New York Times* columnist and economist Paul Krugman, whose book *Fuzzy Math: The Essential Guide to the Bush Tax Plan* excoriates the Bush administration's arithmetic on tax relief.[42]

So what is to be done? Statistics are not the perfect distillation of truth that early nineteenth-century statesmen thought they were, but neither are they the products of fuzzy math that can be safely disregarded or disparaged. Statistical reasoning and the numbers it produces are powerful tools of political and civic functioning, and at our peril we neglect to teach the skills to understand them in our education system. Some of this teaching needs to happen in arithmetic and mathematics classes, but some of it must be taken up by other parts of the curriculum, in any and every place in which critical thinking, skepticism, and careful analysis of assumptions and conclusions come into play.

On my campus (the University of California at Santa Barbara) and no doubt many others, two programs developed in the last decade or two aimed to generalize basic skills. The first, "Writing Across the Curriculum," devised ways to implant intensive writing experiences in courses well beyond the expected domains of the English department or writing program—say, in engineering and the sciences. Additionally, composition teachers taught writing courses keyed to the science and social science curricula. And in a related fashion, language instruction and practice branched out from the confines of courses on vocabulary and grammar to attach themselves to relevant subject matters. A Western Civilization course thus might have one section taught in French or German, with a portion of the readings also in that language. The idea was to demonstrate the utility and importance of language skills (foreign or English) by crossing the parochial disciplinary boundaries that tend to structure academia. In a parallel way, quantitative literacy needs to be generalized across the curriculum, not only at the college level but in all the earlier grades as well.

The subject matter of history can no doubt play an important role in this process. A list of ideas for units or topics in a U.S. History course (see Appendix A) shows a few ways in which quantitative literacy skills can be called on to deepen and enrich our understanding of some classic and central events in our nation's history. At the same time, teaching units like these would enhance students' quantitative skills, helping to answer that age-old question asked in many mathematics courses, "hey, are we really ever going to need this stuff?" Quantitative concepts are indeed embedded in our civic culture, and quantitative literacy on the part of citizens is greatly needed to make democratic institutions work. It is a worthy goal to make those connections explicit in history and government courses, by showing how numbers, both flawed and accurate, have played a role in past debates.

Appendix A: Promoting Quantitative Literacy in U.S. History Courses

The suggestions below illustrate ways in which typical U.S. history survey courses in high school or college can be enhanced with quantitative ideas. These ideas all link to large events that are routinely taken up in such courses, but rarely do instructors linger over them, perhaps because they seem too complex or abstruse. My suggestion is that we should deepen these stories to draw on (and enhance) students' skills in quantitative reasoning. By exploring the quantitative dimension of these situations, students can better understand what the participants in these events thought they were doing and can better evaluate options for policy or action.

1. Teach the writing of the Constitution to emphasize the quantitative implications and underpinnings of democracy. Was it "one man, one vote" at the beginning? Is it now? How does apportionment work? What does it matter what method is chosen? And what would that mean anyway?

2. Teach a detailed unit on the 3/5 clause as a North-South compromise. Trace it out over the next 70 years: How much extra political clout did the South have in Congress because of this clause? (In 1820, at the time of the Missouri Compromise, the South had 17 more representatives than it

would have had if representation had been based only on the free population.)

3. Focus on the electoral college: Why was it set up the way it was? Does it favor the inhabitants of small or large states? Where did the "winner take all" idea enter, and why?

4. Study the rise of popular voting for the presidency. How do we combine a popular election for the presidency with the electoral college?

5. Study tariff policies in the early republic. Why was there a tariff at all? What social, economic, or political objectives were served by tariffs, beyond the raising of revenue for the government? Did tariff makers have adequate information about the country's economic circumstances to make reasoned tariff policy? (Recall Andrew Jackson's politically strategic campaign promise to be in favor of "a judicious tariff.") Focus on the tariff of abominations of 1828, which led directly to the nullification controversy of 1832, a major showdown on federal versus state power.

6. Consider national land policy during the nineteenth century with respect to the selling of the national domain. How should government handle such a valuable resource? How did the government, at various times, set up land sales? What were the origins of the rectilinear survey idea? How were the survey lines run? What were the procedures on size of parcels? Who gained benefits and who did not?

7. How did women gain literacy and numeracy? What was at stake in this development? How did post-emancipation blacks gain literacy and numeracy? What was at stake? Why had it been illegal in most southern states to teach slaves to read? Who stood to gain from promoting numeracy for blacks? Who stood to gain by obstructing it? How did immigrant groups new to America gain fluency in English, literacy, and numeracy? Again, what factors promoted or obstructed the gaining of this knowledge?

8. What has been the average life expectancy over our country's history? How is that number arrived at? How has it changed over time? How does it vary by race, by sex, by region, and why? Who first tried to frame this question and answer it, and why? Why was/is it worth answering?

9. What is the history of poverty in America? How has poverty variously been defined and measured? What was at stake, say, in enumerating paupers in nineteenth-century censuses? Or idiots and the insane?

10. Ditto for the history of wealth. How has wealth been measured? What about income? How have historians talked about or defined economic classes, and why? How legitimate is it for us to impose some quantitative notion of wealth to stratify a past population when perhaps the members of that population did not think about their own community that way at all? (For example, compare the wealth distribution of a Puritan village, based on land records, versus that same town's sense of its own hierarchy as embedded in the church seating chart, in which other factors besides wealth, or in place of wealth, determined a person's social location.)

11. In the late nineteenth century and later, where did quantitative knowledge come from? Who generated it? Who processed it? Who abstracted it? Who defines the standard measures—of weight and quantity, of economic indicators—and what difference might that make?

12. Who invented the measurement of "unemployment" and when? What was that measure based on? This could be done with any number of common indicators we now use. The idea is to get students to understand the historical forces that go into constructing numbers and measures. What were the mechanisms and procedures for data collection? Who collected data, and to what end? What kinds of data were available? Where should we best look for dispassionate, objective data—politicians, the census bureau, university experts, journalists, media conglomerates?

Notes

1. "A Statistical view of the Commerce of the United States of America; its connection with agriculture and manufactures, and an account of the publick debt, revenues, and expenditures of the United States... By Timothy Pitkin..., *The North American Review and Miscellaneous Journal* 3(9): (1816): 345–54. The published review was unsigned, but the copy digitized on Cornell University's Making of America Web site includes attributions for many articles in this volume, added in an early nineteenth-century cursive hand. "J. Quincy" was written at the head of this piece, on p. 345; "Josiah Quincy" also was on a similar but very long review in the same volume, a review of Moses Greenleaf's *Statistical View of the District of Maine* (pp. 362–426). The federalist Josiah Quincy (1772–1864) had a distinguished career in politics and higher education. He served in the U.S. Congress for Massachusetts from 1805–1814, in the state senate from 1815–1821, as a judge in 1821–1823, as mayor of Boston from 1823–1829, and finally as president of Harvard University from 1829–1845.

2. The phrase "Political Arithmetick" was first used by the English economist Sir William Petty in the late seventeenth century to describe what seemed to others to be an unorthodox combination of high-level statecraft with arithmetic, which was then seen as a "vulgar

art" beneath the notice of leaders because of its associations with the world of commerce. Petty promoted the expression of all political and economic facts in terms of "Number, Weight, and Measure." William Petty, *Political Arithmetick* (London, 1690), reprinted in Charles Henry Hull, ed., *The Economic Writings of Sir William Petty*, 2 vols. (Cambridge, UK: At the University Press, 1899), I: 244.

3. Margo J. Anderson, *The American Census: A Social History* (New Haven, CT: Yale University Press, 1988), 15–16. In the end, remainders were ignored, in accordance with Jefferson's plan; Hamilton's plan had provided for extra seats distributed to the states with the largest remainders.

4. Quoted in Patricia Cline Cohen, *A Calculating People: The Spread of Numeracy in Early America* (New York, NY: Routledge, 1999), 159–60.

5. Cohen, *A Calculating People*, 161–62.

6. John Sinclair, *The Statistical Account of Scotland* (Edinburgh, 1798), vol. 20, xiii.

7. S.v. "statistick," John Walker, *A Critical Pronouncing Dictionary and Expositor of the English Language* (Philadelphia, 1803); "statistics," Noah Webster, *A Compendious Dictionary of the English Language* (New Haven, 1806).

8. A list of 31 of these books appears in Cohen, *A Calculating People*, 254, n.3.

9. See Patricia Cline Cohen, "Numeracy in Nineteenth-Century America," forthcoming in George M. A. Stanic and Jeremy Kilpatrick, eds., *A History of School Mathematics* (Reston, VA: National Council of Teachers of Mathematics, 2003).

10. Nicholas Pike, Pike's *Arithmetick* (Boston, 1809), 101. Small print helpfully elaborated that "more requiring more, is when the third term is greater than the first, and requires the fourth term to be greater than the second."

11. I had not considered this possibility until I read Zalman Usiskin's essay, "Quantitative Literacy for the Next Generation," in *Mathematics and Democracy: The Case for Quantitative Literacy*, Lynn Arthur Steen, ed. (Princeton, NJ: National Council on Education and the Disciplines, 2001), 79–86.

12. George Washington to Nicolas Pike, author of the first American arithmetic text, June 20, 1788, quoted in George Emery Littlefield, *Early Schools and Schoolbooks of New England* (New York, NY: Russell and Russell, 1905), 181.

13. Thomas Jefferson to Co. William Duane, October 1812, quoted in Florian Cajori, *The Teaching and History of Mathematics in the United States* (Washington, D.C.: Bureau of Education Circular, 1890), 35.

14. "Bill for the More General Diffusion of Knowledge," 1779, Virginia State Legislature; and Thomas Jefferson, *Life and Selected Writings*, Adrienne Koch and William Peden, eds. (New York, NY: Modern Library, 1944), 262-63. Plan discussed in Richard D. Brown, *The Strength of a People: The Idea of an Informed Citizenry in America,*

1650–1870 (Chapel Hill, NC: University of North Carolina Press, 1996), 75–76.

15. Harvard made common arithmetic a requirement for admission in 1802; on colleges, see Cohen, *A Calculating People*, 123.

16. Thomas Jefferson, "Second State of the Report of Weights and Measures," April–May 1790, in Julian P. Boyd. ed., *The Papers of Thomas Jefferson*, vol. 16 (Princeton, NJ: Princeton University Press, 1961), 631.

17. *The Federal Calculator, or American Schoolmaster's Assistant and Young Man's Companion* (actually just an 1803 version of the older Thomas Dilworth book from England with federal currency added); Daniel Adams's *The Scholar's Arithmetic: or, Federal Accountant* (1801); William B. Allen's *The Columbian Arithmetician; or New System of Theoretical and Practical Arithmetic* (1811); and Oliver Welch's *The American Arithmetic: Adapted to the Currency of the United States* (1813).

18. Erastus Root, *An Introduction to Arithmetic for the Use of Common Schools* (Norwich, CT: 1796), preface.

19. Warren Colburn, *First Lessons, Or, Intellectual Arithmetic on the Plan of Pestalozzi* (Boston, 1821); *Arithmetic Upon the Inductive Method of Instruction* (Boston, 1826) and *An Introduction to Algebra upon the Inductive Method of Instruction* (Boston, 1826).

20. Theodore Edson, "Warren Colburn," *American Journal of Education* 2 (1856), 302.

21. Colburn, *Arithmetic Upon the Inductive Method of Instruction*, 4–5.

22. Colburn, *Arithmetic Upon the Inductive Method of Instruction*, 7.

23. Colburn, "Lecture XI, On the Teaching of Arithmetic," *The Introductory Discourse and Lectures Delivered in Boston Before the Convention of Teachers, Annual Meeting* (Boston: American Institute of Instruction, 1830), 283.

24. E. V. DeGraff, *The School-Room Guide* (Syracuse, NY: C. W. Barden, 1882, 11th ed., first published 1877), 184.

25. See Cohen, *A Calculating People*, 139–49, for a fuller treatment of this gendered development.

26. All quoted in Cohen, *A Calculating People*, 146–147.

27. Catharine Beecher, "First School Closing Address," October 18, 1823, folder 314, Beecher Collection, Schlesinger Library, Harvard University, Cambridge, Mass.

28. *The Portfolio* (Philadelphia) 17 (1824): 456.

29. *Western Academician and Journal of Education and Science* (Cincinnati) I (1837): 438.

30. Joseph E. Worcester, *The American Almanac and Repository of Useful Knowledge*, I (1930), 139.

31. *The Politician's Register* was published in Baltimore by G. H. Hickman; *The Whig Almanac* was the work of Horace Greeley, editor of the New York *Tribune*.

32. Susan Herbst, *Numbered Voices: How Opinion Polling Has Shaped American Politics* (Chicago: University of Chicago Press, 1993), 74–79.

33. New York *Herald*, April 17, 1839.

34. Margo J. Anderson, *The American Census*, 40–41.

35. Margo J. Anderson, *The American Census*, 53–55; Cohen, *A Calculating People*, 222–24. Quote is from Samuel M. Wolfe, *Helper's Impending Crisis Dissected*, quoted in Anderson, 55.

36. The story of the industrial era's censuses is well told in Anderson, *The American Census*, ch. 4.

37. George M. A. Stanic and Jeremy Kilpatrick, "Mathematics Curriculum Reform in the United States: A Historical Perspective," *International Journal of Educational Research* 17 (1992), 409–11; Herbert M. Kliebard, *Schooled to Work: Vocationalism and the American Curriculum, 1876–1946* (New York, NY: Teachers College Press, 1999), 93, 156.

38. No research that I am aware of yet addresses this question for the late nineteenth century. See Danny Bernard Martin, *Mathematics Success and Failure Among African-American Youth: The Roles of Sociohistorical Context, Community Forces, School Influence, and Individual Agency* (Mahwah, NJ: Lawrence Erlbaum Associates, 2000); James D. Anderson, *The Education of Blacks in the South, 1860–1935* (Chapel Hill, NC: University of North Carolina Press, 1988); and Donald Spivey, *Schooling for the New Slavery: Black Industrial Education, 1868-1915* (Westport, CT: Greenwood Press, 1978).

39. James T. Fey and Anna O. Graeber, "From the New Math to the *Agenda for Action*," forthcoming in Stanic and Kilpatrick, eds., *A History of School Mathematics*.

40. Diana Jean Schemo, "Test Shows Students' Gains in Math Falter by Grade 12," *New York Times*, August 3, 2001. Perhaps the most striking finding in this report is that only a quarter of all eighth graders scored at or above the "proficient" level on the mathematics portion of the National Assessment of Educational Progress test last spring. (The scores fell into four groups, below basic, basic, proficient, and advanced.) For a long-range view of these issues, see David L. Angus and Jeffery E. Mirel, *The Failed Promise of the American High School, 1890–1995* (New York, NY: Teachers College Press, 1999).

41. For the most recent articulation of the famous aphorism (attributed variously to Mark Twain or Benjamin Disraeli), see Joel Best, *Damned Lies and Statistics: Untangling Numbers from the Media, Politicians, and Activists* (Berkeley, CA: University of California Press, 2001), 5.

42. The Oxford English Dictionary, 2nd edition (1989), credits mathematician Lotfi A. Zadeh for the term "fuzzy" in mathematics, dating from 1964. It was in use in the California debate over curriculum reform in 1995, appearing in a *Los Angeles Times* article of December 19, 1995, by Richard Lee Colvin: "Parents Skilled at Math Protest New Curriculum, Schools: Vocal minority, many in technical fields, deride 'fuzzy' teaching. But reformers call them elitist." Lynne Cheney's *Wall Street Journal* article deriding "fuzzy math" appeared June 11, 1997, and it sparked a flurry of other newspaper usages in the following months, according to a LEXIS-NEXIS database search. Bush's debate use occurred on October 3, 2000; Paul Krugman's book was published in May 2001 by W. W. Norton (NY).

The Democratization of Mathematics

ANTHONY P. CARNEVALE
DONNA M. DESROCHERS

Mathematics has been one of the primary engines in both the intellectual and material development of human society, especially in western civilization. Because of mathematics' broad influence, mathematics education impacts societies in both profound and practical ways. The development of mathematical and scientific knowledge that represents a reality beyond particular cultures and political systems is a central element in the world's shared social condition. Mathematical reasoning is transferable to any culture without loss of effectiveness; it does not depend on subjectivity, culture, or religion. The brute power of mathematical reasoning in human history comes from its practical utility. In combination with scientific experimentation, technology, and market economies, mathematical reasoning is a taproot of our material progress, which is still the driving force in restructuring the world's economic, cultural, and political systems.

Unfortunately, neither the need to understand mathematical reasoning as a distinctive approach to knowledge nor the practical need for applied mathematical skill is fully served by our current education system.[1] From school to college, mathematics follows an isolated trajectory of increasing difficulty and abstraction whose implicit purpose is to select and prepare the best mathematics students for graduate education in mathematically intensive fields. The isolation of mathematics is part of a larger pattern of academic specialization that creates virtually impregnable barriers between the discrete disciplinary silos of mathematics, science, and the humanities. Specialization obscures the animating ideas in those studies that are crucial to cultural literacy and democratic pluralism in modern societies. It discourages the development of an interdisciplinary "general curriculum" that fosters an appreciation for the healthy tensions between the rationalist perspective of mathematics and science and the subjective and spiritual perspectives of the humanities.[2] In addition, the isolation of the mathematics curriculum impedes broad dispersion of the practical uses of mathematics, thus erecting artificial barriers to learning and the development of applied disciplines.[3]

A more accessible mathematics curriculum is critical to closing the growing gap in the opportunity to learn and earn. Success in high school mathematics from algebra through calculus partially determines access to selective colleges, even among students who do not intend to pursue programs of study that require advanced mathematics. In similar fashion, higher levels of abstract mathematics are required for access to certain professions, even when high-level mathematical procedures are unnecessary in the day-to-day work of those professions.

Mathematics needs to become more accessible if it is to fulfill both its cultural and economic roles. Accessibility requires curricula to move beyond coverage of discrete operations to a deeper and more applied understanding. To fully understand mathematics as a key idea in our intellectual and cultural history, the walls that separate the disciplinary specialties in mathematics, science, and the

Anthony P. Carnevale is Vice President for Education and Careers at Educational Testing Service. Previously, he served as Vice President and Director of Human Resource Studies at the Committee for Economic Development and as Chair of the National Commission for Employment Policy. Carnevale has written numerous books and articles on competitiveness and human resources, most recently *The American Mosaic: An In-depth Report on the Future of Diversity at Work* and *Tools and Activities for a Diverse Work Force.*

Donna M. Desrochers is a Senior Economist at Educational Testing Service. Previously, she served as an economist at the Bureau of Economic Analysis and at the Center for Labor Market Studies. Desrochers' research examines how changes in the economy impact the education and training needs of students and workers. She has co-authored several articles and reports, most recently *Help Wanted. . .Credentials Required: Community Colleges in the Knowledge Economy* (2001).

humanities need to be lowered. Moreover, to fully exploit mathematics as a practical tool for daily work and living, mathematics needs to be taught in a more applied fashion and integrated into other disciplines, especially the applied curricula that now dominate postsecondary education.

Mathematics and Economic Opportunity

Quantitative reasoning is both a key element implicit in growing modern economies and a key asset for people who work in them. The economic value of mathematical reasoning has increased inexorably since around 3000 B.C., when the priests of Sumer, in present-day Iraq, began to use mathematical procedures to develop an agricultural calendar. Over time, the subsequent improvements in agriculture efficiency created food surpluses that freed up human labor for more productive pursuits (McNeil 1999). The resultant material progress stimulated increasing social complexity that, in turn, both generated and required ever-higher levels of mathematical reasoning abilities among the general population (Greenfield 1998; Neisser 1998; Schooler 1998).

The synergy between social complexity and reasoning ability continues. In Great Britain, scores on the Raven Progressive Matrices test showed that score levels that included the bottom 90 percent of the population born in 1877 included only the bottom 5 percent of the population born in 1967 (Flynn 1998). These increases in basic reasoning ability have occurred in spite of the fact that the highest fertility rates persist among the lowest scorers.

The value of mathematical reasoning has surged at each of the great economic divides: in the shift from agriculture to an industrial economy and most recently in the shift from an industrial to a knowledge economy. In the latest economic shift, the increasing value of reasoning abilities has ratcheted up the educational ante for good jobs from high school to postsecondary education. In 1959, only 19 percent of prime-age workers (ages 30 to 59) had any college education and, until the early 1980s, many good jobs were available for high school graduates and even high school dropouts, especially for men looking for blue-collar industrial jobs. Remarkably, however, since the 1980s when the new information economy took hold, the wage advantages of college-educated workers have continued to increase even as the supply of those workers has continued to grow. For example, even though the share of college-educated workers in the labor force increased from 37 percent in the 1980s to almost 60 percent in 2000, the wage premium for those with at least some college education over those with high school or less jumped from 43 percent to a whopping 73 percent over the same time period (Carnevale and Fry 2001).

Mathematical ability is the best predictor of the growing wage advantages of increased postsecondary educational attainment (Murnane, Willet, and Levy 1995). Improvements in mathematical skills account for at least half of the growing wage premium among college-educated women and is the most powerful source of the wage advantages of people with postsecondary education over people with high school or less. Moreover, although the wage premium for college-educated workers has increased across all disciplines, it has increased primarily among those who participated in curricula with stronger mathematical content, irrespective of their occupation after graduation (Grogger and Eide 1995).

Those with stronger quantitative skills thus earn more than other workers. Data from the National Adult Literacy Survey (NALS) show that workers with "advanced/superior" mathematical literacy similar to that of the average college graduate earn more than twice as much as workers with "minimal" quantitative skills similar to average high school dropouts. Those with "advanced/superior" mathematical literacy earn almost twice as much as workers with the "basic" quantitative skills typical of below-average high school graduates. Moreover, the importance of quantitative skills in labor markets will grow in the future. Almost two-thirds of new jobs will require quantitative skills typical of those who currently have some college or a bachelor's degree (see Figure 1).

Success in the new information economy also appears to require a new set of problem-solving and behavioral skills. These skills, especially problem-solving skills, emphasize the flexible application of both mathematical and verbal reasoning abilities in multifaceted work contexts across the full array of occupations and industries. Such skills most often require the versatile use of relatively basic mathematical procedures more akin to "numeracy" and "quantitative literacy" than to higher knowledge of advanced mathematical procedures.

Who Pays for Innumeracy?

The growing importance of college-level cognitive skills, especially mathematical skills, in allocating economic opportunity is especially significant in the United States, where poorly educated individuals, not employers or governments, pay the price of educational inequality. Individuals who do not acquire college-level cognitive skills are forced into low-wage and low-benefits jobs. This is quite different from continental European labor markets, which have inherent incentives to educate and train all workers in the hope that their productivity will justify the earnings and benefits guaranteed by the European welfare states.

With no earnings or benefits guarantees, America is increasingly divided into math-haves and math-have-nots. Of course, teaching mathematics is not just about dollars and cents, but the inescapable reality is that ours is a society based on work and knowledge.

Figure 1: Quantitative Literacy and Job Opportunity, 2000-2010

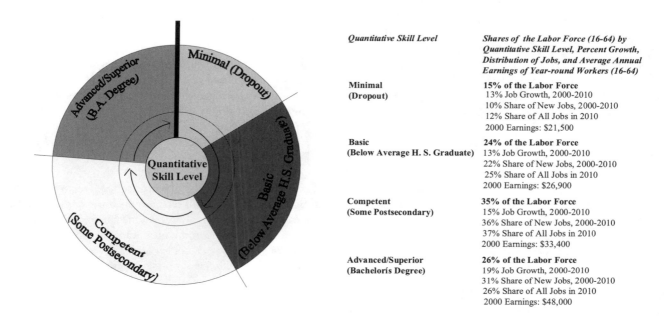

Quantitative Skill Level	Shares of the Labor Force (16-64) by Quantitative Skill Level, Percent Growth, Distribution of Jobs, and Average Annual Earnings of Year-round Workers (16-64)
Minimal (Dropout)	**15% of the Labor Force** 13% Job Growth, 2000-2010 10% Share of New Jobs, 2000-2010 12% Share of All Jobs in 2010 2000 Earnings: $21,500
Basic (Below Average H. S. Graduate)	**24% of the Labor Force** 13% Job Growth, 2000-2010 22% Share of New Jobs, 2000-2010 25% Share of All Jobs in 2010 2000 Earnings: $26,900
Competent (Some Postsecondary)	**35% of the Labor Force** 15% Job Growth, 2000-2010 36% Share of New Jobs, 2000-2010 37% Share of All Jobs in 2010 2000 Earnings: $33,400
Advanced/Superior (Bachelorís Degree)	**26% of the Labor Force** 19% Job Growth, 2000-2010 31% Share of New Jobs, 2000-2010 26% Share of All Jobs in 2010 2000 Earnings: $48,000

Source: Authors Analysis of National Adult Literacy Survey, 1992; Current Population Survey, 2001; BLS Employment Projections, 2000-2010.

Unlike many of the continental European systems, there are minimal earnings and benefits guarantees for the unemployed or the underemployed in the United States. Even among those who are fully employed, wages and benefits depend on skill. We know that those who cannot get or keep good jobs are trapped in working poverty, underemployed, or unemployed. Eventually many of them drop out of the political system and withdraw from community life. In some cases, they may create alternative economies, cultures, or political structures that are a threat to the mainstream. If educators cannot fulfill their economic mission to help our youth and adults achieve quantitative literacy levels that will allow them to become successful workers, they also will fail in their cultural and political missions to create good neighbors and good citizens.

Higher levels of quantitative literacy increase both individual and national income. Sweden is one of the most quantitatively literate countries in the world. If the levels and distribution of quantitative skills in the United States mirrored those of Sweden, a back-of-the-envelope calculation suggests that we could increase GDP by $463 billion and reap as much as $162 billion in additional federal, state, and local tax dollars.[4]

Mathematics and International Economic Competitiveness

Our ability to produce mathematically literate citizens is also critical to the performance of the American economy in global competition. Although data from the National Assessment of Educational Progress (NAEP) show that American performance on mathematics is improving, our scores on international tests are consistently sub-par. The recent Third International Mathematics and Science Study (TIMSS) is the latest in a steady drumbeat of reports showing that U.S. students do not measure up globally. Among 38 nations tested in TIMSS, we are significantly behind 14, even with 6, and doing significantly better than 17. You do not have to have the test scores of a rocket scientist to know that in the new high-tech economic world mathematics and science education is a key asset in global economic competition.

But, if the United States is so bad at mathematics and science, how can we be so successful in the new high-tech global economy? If we are so dumb, why are we so rich?

Just look at the numbers: Japanese students are among the front-runners in the TIMSS study, but the average purchasing power of American families is 40 percent greater than the average purchasing power of Japanese families. In general, members of the European Union outperform us on TIMSS. In 1998, however, the U.S. per capita income towered over that of the European Union nations—$32,413 versus roughly $25,000 in West Germany, Belgium, Denmark, and the Netherlands and roughly $22,000 in Italy, France, Sweden, and the United Kingdom (Mishel, Bernstein, and Schmitt 2001). During the same period, U.S. unemployment has been consistently less than half the European level.

How can we reconcile our educational failures in mathematics and science and our economic success in the high-tech global economy? The first answer is that although the United States may not have, on average, the world's best overall stock of mathematically skilled graduates, because of our size we have more top students—and our economic agility allows us to use their abilities more effectively.

Our sheer size, therefore, allows us to be both mediocre in mathematics and science and number one in the world economy. The U.S. population, for instance, is roughly four times the size of France, Italy, or the United Kingdom and three times the size of Germany. Our student population is only twice as large as the Japanese school-age population but our size advantage still prevails. In the TIMSS data on eighth-grade students, the Japanese ranked fifth in mathematics and we ranked eighteenth. Sixty-four percent of Japanese eighth-graders scored in the top quartile of international benchmarks in mathematics compared with 28 percent of U.S. students. But because our eighth-grade population is twice as large as the eighth-grade population in Japan, there are 970,000 U.S. students in the top international quartile compared with 928,000 Japanese eighth-graders.

Although more is not always better, in this case it often is. For instance, we have four times as many workers as France, Italy, or the United Kingdom. Four pretty good engineers tackling a business problem often outperform one very good engineer working alone. Similarly, four companies in the software business competing directly against each other in the highly competitive U.S. product market are likely to produce better software than a single company elsewhere.

A second advantage that allows the United States to get away with relatively low levels of mathematical and scientific literacy is the flexibility that allows us to make better use of what talent there is. In the United States, minimally regulated labor markets allow employers enormous agility in hiring, paying, and allocating workers, and also allow workers more job flexibility. Pay varies with performance, and there are virtually no wage, benefits, or job guarantees. Our flexibility optimizes returns on capital investments, human and machine. With no substantial safety net, individuals, not employers or governments, pay the price of underinvestment or obsolescence of human capital.

America's characteristic flexibility also means that employers do not need to rely on the nation's homegrown mathematics and science talent. Immigration is a major source of talent among technical professionals. For instance, more than 40 percent of all engineers and almost half of all civil engineers are foreign born (National Science Foundation 2002). In addition, U.S. companies are free to produce offshore if they cannot find the talent at home at the right prices.

In Europe and Japan, by comparison, access to jobs and pay is highly regulated by skill certification and seniority. Jobs are protected shelters from economic and technological change. There is a place for everyone in the European and Japanese economies—and everyone stays in his or her place. The results? Job security and structural rigidity in a world of economic and technological changes.

The problem with the current American strategy in global competition is that our advantages will not last. We cannot remain a first-rate economic power with second-rate mathematical and scientific literacy. In global economies, all forms of advantage are temporary. The European and Japanese versions of highly planned economies surged in the 1970s but lost out to American flexibility in the 1980s. Eventually, our competitors will narrow our economic lead as they learn how to create their own versions of agility and scale. At that point, the competition will really come down to who has the best human capital—especially in a world in which people are no longer nation-bound and in which technology and financial capital ignore national boundaries as they hop across borders from one entrepreneurial opportunity to the next.

The Demographic Twist

If we are to retain the lead in the global economic race and the good jobs that go with it, we will at some point have to rely on homegrown human capital for our competitive edge. Eventually, we will have to close the education gap; however, because of demographic shifts we face at home, that may be surprisingly difficult.

A simple thought experiment demonstrates the likelihood of a shortage of workers with college-level quantitative literacy. We know that retirements begin aggressively after age 55, especially for men, and that retirement ages have been declining steadily. By 2020, about 46 million baby boomers with at least some college education will be over 55 years of age. Over the same period, if we maintain current attainment rates in postsecondary education, we will produce about 49 million new adults with at least some college education—a net gain of about three million (Carnevale and Fry 2001).

Historical and projected increases in the share of jobs that will require at least some college-level mathematical literacy far exceed this small increase in the college-educated population, however. Official projections on the share of jobs that will require at least some college education through 2020 are unavailable, but the U.S. Bureau of Labor Statistics projects a 22 percent increase by 2010 in such jobs. If the trend continues, we will experience a net deficit in workers with mathematical skills at or above the "some college" level of more than 10 million workers by 2020 (Carnevale and Fry 2001).

The Curriculum Mismatch

One way to close the emerging gap that will arise with the retiring baby boom is to align the secondary school curriculum more closely with college requirements and labor market needs. The current structure of the secondary school mathematics curriculum creates a mismatch between college admission requirements and what students choose to study once they enter college. College entry requirements tend to demand at least three years of mathematics—preferably geometry, algebra I, and algebra II; selective colleges usually expect trigonometry, calculus, and statistics as well. Advanced Placement (AP) courses in mathematics are a plus in getting accepted at selective colleges. In 2001, there were 181,000 enrollments in AP Calculus and 41,000 in AP Statistics. By way of comparison, there are roughly 150,000 seats for first-year students in the nation's top 146 colleges.

Once they enter postsecondary education, the vast majority of students increasingly avoid the highly quantitative academic silos of mathematics, science, and engineering in favor of less-quantitative curricula with a more applied focus. Of the 1,184,000 bachelor's degrees conferred in 1998, roughly 175,000 were in mathematics (12,000), science, and engineering. More than 200,000 were in the liberal arts, literature, social science, history, and humanities. The remaining two-thirds of bachelor's degrees were awarded in applied majors outside traditional academic disciplines. For example, there were 233,000 bachelor's degrees in business; 17,000 in parks, recreation, leisure, and fitness studies; 50,000 in communications; 52,000 in the visual and performing arts; 17,000 in home economics; and 25,000 in protective services (U.S. Department of Education 2000). The same pattern is seen in the expansion of applied associate degrees, certificates, certifi-

cations, and customized training in two-year colleges (Carnevale and Desrochers 2001). Of the 555,000 associate degrees conferred in 1996, 115,000 were awarded in the liberal arts and sciences, general studies, and humanities and only 758 were conferred in mathematics (U.S. Department of Education 2000).

The apparent mismatch between high school mathematics and college degrees raises two natural questions about mathematics education: Are mathematics courses creating artificial barriers to college entry? And are the majority of college students who do not continue their mathematics education getting enough mathematics? Perhaps these are the wrong questions. Advocates for a shift in focus toward quantitative literacy and numeracy over the traditional abstract curriculum and teaching methods would argue that Americans are not taking too much mathematics but are taking the wrong kind of mathematics in high school and not enough applied mathematics in the majority of college majors.

There also appears to be a mismatch between the mathematics students take in high school and the mathematics used on the job. Mathematical skills are the best general proxy for demonstrating the increasing economic returns to reasoning ability in the new economy. It is much less clear, however, that the content and methods of the current mathematics curriculum are aligned with the uses of mathematics in the world of work. Most Americans seem to have taken too little, too much, or the wrong kind of mathematics. Too many people do not have enough basic mathematical literacy to make a decent living even while many more people take courses in high school such as geometry, algebra, and calculus than ever will actually use the mathematical procedures taught in these courses.

The pattern of too little, too much, or the wrong kind of mathematics seems to persist in college. Most people abandon mathematics after high school even though a vast majority of jobs require increasing levels of quantitative literacy. The same holds even in mathematics and science disciplines: postsecondary institutions produce more Ph.D.s in quantitative disciplines than are required to fill college teaching positions, but not enough to fill K–12 mathematics and science teaching positions or enough to meet private sector needs for technically qualified managers and other professionals (Romer 2000).

A substantial share of Americans have too little mathematics. Almost 40 percent of the workforce does not have sufficient quantitative literacy for jobs that pay more than $26,900, on average (see Figure 1). These people tend to be in job categories that are growing more slowly than average and in which inflation-adjusted wages are declining. Their quantitative literacy is similar to that of a high school dropout or below-average high school graduate. At best they can perform a single arithmetic operation such as addition or subtraction when the numbers are given and the operation

Table 1.

Mathematical Literacy Paradigm from the National Adult Literacy Survey

Skill Level	Approximate Educational Equivalence	NALS Level	NALS Competencies (Quantitative)	NALS Examples (Quantitative)
Minimal	Dropout	1	Can perform a single, simple arithmetic operation such as addition. The numbers used are provided and the operation to be performed is specified.	—Total a bank deposit entry
Basic	Average or below-average high school graduate	2	Can perform a single arithmetic operation using numbers that are given in the task or easily located in the material. The arithmetic operation is either described or easily determined from the format of the materials.	—Calculate postage and fees for certified mail —Determine the difference in price between tickets for two shows —Calculate the total costs of purchase from an order form
Competent	Some postsecondary education	3	Can perform tasks in which two or more numbers are needed to solve the problem and they must be found in the material. The operation(s) needed can be determined from the arithmetic relation terms used in the question or directive.	—Use a calculator to calculate the difference between the regular and sale price —Calculate miles per gallon from information on a mileage record chart —Use a calculator to determine the discount from an oil bill if paid within 10 days
Advanced	Bachelor's or advanced degree	4	Can perform two or more operations in sequence or a single operation in which the quantities are found in different types of displays, or in which the operations must be inferred from the information given or from prior knowledge.	—Determine the correct change using information in a menu —Calculate how much a couple would receive from Supplemental Security Income, using an eligibility pamphlet —Use information stated in a news article to calculate the amount of money that should go to raising a child
Superior	High-achieving, college-educated populations	5	Can perform multiple operations sequentially, and also can find the features of problems embedded in text or rely on background knowledge to determine the quantities or operations needed.	—Use a calculator to determine the total cost of carpet to cover a room —Use information in a news article to calculate the difference in time for completing a race —Determine shipping and total costs on an order form for items in a catalog

Source: Carnevale, Anthony P., and Donna M. Desrochers. 1999. *Getting Down to Business: Matching Welfare Recipients to Jobs that Train.* Princeton, NJ: Educational Testing Service; Barton, Paul E., and Archie LaPointe. 1995. *Learning by Degrees: Indicators of Performance in Higher Education.* Princeton, NJ: Educational Testing Service.

described— determining the difference in price for theater tickets to two different shows, for instance (see Table 1).

Those who get the best jobs have taken the most mathematics. We estimate that three-fourths of those in the top-paying 25 percent of jobs have at least one year-long high school credit in algebra II. More than 80 percent have taken geometry. Twenty-seven percent of those in the top-paying jobs have at least a semester of pre-calculus and roughly 20 percent have taken calculus. Among the rest of those in the top half of the pay distribution, more than half have taken algebra II and more than two-thirds have taken geometry in high school. In the bottom half of the distribution of earnings in American jobs, roughly three-quarters have at least a year-long credit in algebra I, 63 percent have geometry, and slightly fewer than half have algebra II.

Clearly, algebra II is the threshold mathematics course taken by people who eventually get good jobs in the top half of the earnings distribution. And the more mathematics beyond algebra II, the better the odds of eventually landing a job in the top 25 percent of the earnings distribution. Yet even a casual analysis of the distribution of occupations demonstrates that relatively few of us— fewer than 5 percent—make extensive use of geometry, algebra II, trigonometry, or calculus on the job. In the year 2000, there were 146 million people in the workforce. Roughly three million were in "computer and mathematical occupations," including actuaries and statisticians. There were roughly 1.5 million engineers and architects and 1.2 million life, physical, and social scientists. In addition, there were 132,000 secondary school science teachers and 180,000 secondary school mathematics teachers (Hecker 2001). In spite of these realities, in 1998, 75 percent of high school students took geometry, 63 percent took algebra I, 62 percent took algebra II, and 18 percent took calculus (U.S. Department of Education 2000).

The mismatch between high school mathematics courses and the quantitative literacy required on the job suggests that a large share of Americans have either too much mathematics or the wrong kind. What mathematics skills are required for good jobs in the new economy? The threshold appears to be the skills associated with people who have some postsecondary education. These workers tend to have "competent" mathematical literacy—level 3 on the NALS scale. These also are the jobs that are expected to add the most new positions over the next decade and that tend to pay $33,400, on average (see Figure 1). Workers whose mathematical skills are similar to those of people with some postsecondary education can, typically, perform quantitative tasks to solve problems when the appropriate numbers and operations are not given directly but can be determined from the words used in the problem. An example would be the calculation of miles per gallon using a mileage record chart (see Table 1).

People in the most highly paid jobs tend to have the overall mathematical literacy skills of those who are advanced or superior (at levels 4 and 5 in the NALS hierarchy), skills typical of college graduates. The quantitative literacy characteristic of people with bachelor's degrees or better does not, on average, rise much above independent application of basic mathematical operations in complex situations (see Table 1). Yet people with this level of quantitative literacy are in jobs that pay $48,000, on average, per annum. This is the second fastest-growing set of jobs (see Figure 1).

It appears that the requirement for mathematical literacy in labor markets (and by implication in society) is one of an ascending ability to use basic mathematical operations with increasing independence and in situations of increasing complexity. This suggests that the way we teach mathematics may not be aligned with the uses we make of mathematics in most jobs.

Does the fact that only 5 percent of us use advanced mathematics on the job mean that we should stop teaching algebra, geometry, trigonometry, or calculus in high schools? Not necessarily. In the current educational curriculum, these higher-level courses are the means by which people learn higher-level reasoning skills even if they are not directly applicable on the job. For instance, the core competencies of computing, measuring, and manipulating shapes as well as the ability to solve problems by understanding factors and their relationships and the ability to assess the likelihood of events are consistent with the core competencies implicit in algebra, geometry, trigonometry, calculus, and statistics. Too many students, however, get bogged down in the abstract procedures that remain the focus of much of the current mathematics curriculum. Others know the formulas and procedures but do not understand what they know well enough to use mathematics outside mathematics class. We certainly should not throw out the current curriculum without a superior alternative in place, but ultimately we will need a curriculum that teaches these higher-level quantitative reasoning skills in a more applied and accessible context in which the goal is both knowledge and understanding.

How Did the Mismatch Arise?

The current mismatch between the core mathematics curriculum and our growing need for quantitative literacy is primarily an accidental product of recent history. Prior to World War II, elementary and secondary education included both academic and vocational tracks culminating in the "comprehensive" high school that prepared most students for work and a few for college. The college preparatory curriculum emphasized the traditional core subjects of mathematics, science, and humanities. For the most part, colleges extended studies in these disciplines beyond the introductory core curriculum as preparation for the professions and college teaching.

In the first few decades following World War II, this core academic curriculum experienced explosive growth. First, the Cold War and then Sputnik made sorting the best mathematicians and scientists an urgent priority in the K–16 system. Because the liberal arts curriculum was viewed as a cultural and political bulwark against communism, the humanities were supported along with mathematics and science, but to a lesser degree. The federal government fully funded university research and development in mathematics and science. Student aid increased massively, beginning with the GI Bill of Rights and culminating in the National Defense Education Act. The baby boom expanded the 18- to 24-year-old student population to outsized proportions. Public funding and demography created a tidal wave of new demands for college. The rising tide raised all the boats in the traditional college curriculum. The government provided the financial means for college and, in the 1960s, offered added motivation because the Vietnam conflict gave every male a good reason to stay in school and go to college. Unprecedented economic growth provided funding and robust job markets for college graduates from 1946 through 1973.

As a consequence, between 1946 and the mid-1970s, a massive education system was built around the core set of discrete disciplines in mathematics, science, and the humanities whose implicit purpose was to reproduce the college professoriate at the top of each disciplinary hierarchy. The rapid expansion in college faculty jobs and the growth of federally funded, university-based research and development justified the disciplinary pipelines that ran from middle school to graduate school.

In the 1970s, all the economic, demographic, and geopolitical forces that created the American Golden Age, and the Golden Age of higher education, lost momentum. The Cold War receded as communism began to collapse under the weight of its own inherent contradictions. As the Vietnam conflict wound down, young men no longer needed college deferments. The baby boom became the baby bust ending the ready supply of 18- to 24-year-old students. The postwar economic boom gave way to stagflation. As college-educated baby boomers flooded the job market, the wage premium attached to traditional college degrees was cut in half. Education became a mature industry, no longer subject to exponential growth (Menand 2002). To fill the empty seats left by the graduating baby boomers and to be more responsive to market realities in the stagflationary 1970s, postsecondary education moved toward vocationalism in its curriculum and toward nontraditional adults in its student population.

Throughout the 1970s, higher education managed to maintain enrollment levels. The college wage premium never fell below 30 percent and the demand for college-level talent, especially in vocational majors, continued to grow. After the Volker recession wrung the inflation out of the economy in the early 1980s, growth resumed and "skill-biased technology change" accelerated economic restructuring. With this restructuring, the college wage premium grew rapidly both in traditional college-level jobs and also in a growing share of jobs that previously did not require college. The share of prime-age adult workers with at least some college jumped from 2 in 10 in 1959 to 6 in 10 in the late 1990s. Even more stunning is the fact that the wage premium for college-educated workers, compared with high school educated workers, has increased by 70 percent since the 1980s, even though the supply of college-educated workers increased by 60 percent. As a result, even though the number of high school graduates declined by 700,000 between 1979 and 1991, college enrollments only dropped by 14,000 students. In the late 1990s, the college-age population began to surge again. Over the period between 1979 and 2000, this population declined by 250,000 students but admission standards and enrollments increased substantially and acceptance rates declined.

Since the late 1990s, the number of college-age youth has surged again and will not peak until 2015 (Carnevale and Fry 2000). This demographic surge, in combination with the high college wage premium, will create enormous pressure to align mathematics curricula with job requirements.

Matching Curriculum to Needs

The recognition of the need for a broader and more applied mathematics curriculum has grown appreciably since the 1970s as a result of new occupational skill requirements and new forms of work organization. The vast majority of new jobs requiring postsecondary education created since the 1970s emerged in service occupations (e.g., management, business services, education, health care, computer services) that did not require advanced mathematical operations but whose incumbents did need quantitative literacy at the level of people who had at least some postsecondary education (see Table 1). The shift toward a high-skilled service economy required more and better integration of quantitative and verbal reasoning abilities. Problem solving in high-skilled service jobs is embedded in complex social interactions that mix both quantitative and verbal reasoning (Carnevale and Desrochers 2001; Carnevale and Rose 1998). Consequently, employers and educators began focusing on analytic, problem-solving, and critical thinking skills in the 1970s, and national assessments of quantitative literacy were developed in the 1970s and 1980s.

The landmark report *A Nation at Risk,* issued in 1983, called for high standards for all students in mathematics as well as curricula that would teach students to "apply mathematics in everyday situations" (U.S. Department of Education 1983). The call for more applied and accessible curricula has been a persistent theme in education reform, but it has proven far easier to outline more rigorous mathematics standards for all students than to develop and implement effective new curricula.

Ironically, with notable exceptions, the traditional mathematics curriculum increasingly dominates secondary education and admission to postsecondary institutions. Indeed, the "back-to-basics" tone of education reform tends to strengthen the traditional academic silos in high school. Studies show that 56 percent of students completed at least three years of mathematics in 1998, compared with only 14 percent in 1982 (Roey et al. 2001).

The growing share of students who complete the traditional mathematics curriculum at least through algebra II represents both a remarkable achievement and a new opportunity. The next step in making the mathematics curriculum more accessible will be to shift toward a more applied context. A stronger emphasis on applications should improve teaching and learning for all students and will align high school mathematics more closely with college studies, work, daily life, and citizenship.

The sequence of abstract high school mathematics courses that prepares students for advanced degrees in mathematics and science is still crucial to our advanced economy, but moving the entire school-age population through the academic hierarchy from arithmetic to calculus as a sorting strategy for producing elite mathematical talent required of a small share of college majors and fewer than 5 percent of the workforce does not match well with our more general needs for applied reasoning abilities and practical numeracy. Even now students take more mathematics courses in elementary and secondary school than any other subject except English, but the narrowly focused sequence of courses from arithmetic to calculus surely is not the only way to produce reasoning abilities and does not necessarily lead to a more applied quantitative literacy (Steen 1997; Steen 2001).

The Democratization of Mathematics

The remedy for the widening cultural, political, and economic gulf between those who are literate in mathematics and those who are not is the democratization of mathematics. Democratization does not mean dumbing down. It means making mathematics more accessible and responsive to the needs of all students, citizens, and workers. The essential challenge in democratizing mathematics applies to the sciences and humanities as well. The challenge is to match curricula to cultural, political, and economic goals rather than continuing the dominance of discrete disciplinary silos.

Jacques Barzun ends his history of the last 500 years of western civilization with a disturbing vision of the future. Barzun foresees the globalization of western culture, with the exception of fierce pockets of resistance both within and outside the advanced economies. He invents a fictional historian who, looking back from the year 2300, writes:

> The population was divided roughly into two groups; they did not like the word classes. The first, less numerous, was made up of men and women who possessed the virtually inborn ability to handle the products of techne and master the methods of physical science, especially mathematics—it was to them what Latin had been to the medieval clergy. . . . It validated their position over the masses who by then could neither read nor count. . . . He, and more and more often she, might be an inventor or a theorist, for the interest in hypothesis about the creation of the cosmos and the origin of life persisted, intensified, from the previous era. The sense of being close to a final formulation lasted for over 200 hundred years. . . . It was from this class—no group—that the governors and heads of institutions were recruited. . . . On the workaday plane, the dictates of numerical studies guided the consumer, the parent, the old, and the sick. (Barzun 2000, 799)

Barzun's scenario is disturbing because it comes a little too close to home. As we begin the twenty-first century, the juggernaut of western science, mathematics, and technology seems to be increasingly compartmentalized and closed off from the mass of citizens at home and abroad. Many people live and work in a world that is driven by mathematical and scientific forces beyond their understanding or control. When these forces are embodied in new technologies and disseminated by market economies, they often are experienced as a threat to job security as well as to established traditions and institutions.

The wall of ignorance between those who are mathematically and scientifically literate and those who are not can threaten democratic cultures. The scientifically and mathematically illiterate are outsiders in a society in which effective participation in public dialogue presumes a grasp of basic science and mathematics. Their refuge is a deep mistrust of technocratic elites that often leads to passive withdrawal from public life or an aggressive and active opposition to change. In extreme cases, withdrawal leads to alienation and a retreat to various forms of secular nihilism or religious fundamentalism that explicitly reject the mathematical and scientific rationalism at the heart of western culture (Castells 1997; Gellner 1992). Citizens who are resigned to being cogs in some incomprehensible machine are not what the founders of the American republic had in mind, nor does such a society put its best foot forward in the global cultural dialogue.

From a purely economic point of view, the prospects for reforming the current mathematics curriculum to encourage broader numeracy are promising—perhaps inevitable. Expanding the pragmatic reach of mathematics and science as a tool for work has powerful backing. It serves our material interests in economic growth and individual economic opportunity. It is powered by the relentless invisible hand of market forces that increasingly disciplines educational investments according to their economic returns. In the new economy, quantitative literacy has increasing value. Increasing efficiency in the production and dissemination of mathematics education is now being driven by powerful market forces and by the authority of governments that pay the bills.

In the short haul, pragmatic economic needs and career requirements are probably a healthy spur to reform in mathematics education, but the alignment of mathematics education with economic requirements can miss the mark and go too far. The ultimate goal in making mathematics more accessible is democratization not commodification. Advances in mathematical reasoning abilities need to serve our individualistic culture and our participatory politics as well as our economy. Over the long haul, we will need to be vigilant to ensure that the economy does not hijack mathematics education.

The advocates for quantitative literacy already are leading the way toward a more accessible mathematics curriculum that serves both economic and cultural purposes. We need to continue support for their work. They offer a more engaged approach that would teach the ability to use mathematics seamlessly in varied social contexts and in different communities of practice (Ewell 2001). According to the mathematical historian Joan Richards, "When teaching mathematics is seen as a way of teaching people how to think, it can no longer be isolated" (Richards 2001).

Notes

1. The debate over whether mathematics should be taught as an abstract deductive system or in a more applied fashion sets up a false choice between purists and advocates of quantitative literacy and numeracy. The validity of mathematics is founded on deduction but it develops, and is most easily understood, in applied contexts. Similarly, the distinction between mathematical and verbal reasoning is also artificial. In the real world, reasoning is a cognitive soup of words and numbers that assumes the shape of social contexts. (Cole 1996; National Research Council 2000; Scribner 1997; Scribner and Cole 1997).

2. The most powerful call for a "general curriculum" comes from a study released in 1945, sponsored by James Conant at Harvard, officially entitled *General Education in a Free Society* and unofficially known as the "Red Book." The report argued for interdisciplinary learning to foster an appreciation of the pluralism of ideas—the rational, subjective, and spiritual—at the heart of western culture. The general curriculum was viewed as an antidote to single-minded ideologies and fanaticism. In 1945 that meant communism and fascism. In the twenty-first century, it applies to the global clash of cultures. The development of a general curriculum remains difficult in the context of specialization in the academic disciplines and the rise of vocationalism.

3. Teaching and learning that takes advantage of the synergy between applied and abstract knowledge can be deeper and more accessible, if done properly (see Barton 1990; Berryman and Bailey 1992; National Research Council 1998; Resnick and Wirt 1995; Schoen and Zubarth 1998; Steen 1997; Steen 2001; Wood and Sellers 1996).

4. Data from the International Study of Adult Literacy shows that workers in Sweden have the following distribution of quantitative literacy: Level 1 (lowest): 5 percent; Level 2: 17 percent; Level 3: 40 percent; and Level 4/5 (highest): 38 percent. In contrast, the distribution of workers' quantitative literacy in the United States is much lower: Level 1 (lowest): 16 percent; Level 2: 24 percent; Level 3: 33 percent; and Level 4/5 (highest): 27 percent (OECD 1995). To estimate the increases in GDP and taxes that would occur if we had a quantitative literacy distribution similar to Sweden's, we first calculated the number of workers in the United States at each literacy level and, second, applied the distribution of literacy in Sweden to the total number of workers in the United States to estimate how many workers would fall at each skill level if the United States' quantitative literacy levels resembled Sweden's. Taking both of the distributions, we multiplied the average earnings of U.S. workers at each skill level by the number of workers at each level and summed to get aggregate earnings. The difference in aggregate earnings using the U.S. and Swedish distribu-

tions provided an estimate of the potential increase in GDP. We then multiplied the estimated increase by 35 percent to capture the additional federal, state, and local taxes that would be paid by these more-skilled workers.

References

Barton, Paul E. 1990. *From School to Work*. Princeton, NJ: Policy Information Center, Educational Testing Service.

Barton, Paul E., and Archie LaPointe. 1995. *Learning by Degrees: Indicators of Performance in Higher Education*. Princeton, NJ: Policy Information Center, Educational Testing Service.

Barzun, Jacques. 2000. *From Dawn to Decadence: 1500 to the Present: 500 Years of Western Cultural Life*. New York: HarperCollins.

Berryman, Sue E., and Thomas R. Bailey. 1992. *The Double Helix of Education and the Economy*. Institute on Education and the Economy, Teachers College. NY: Columbia University Press

Carnevale, Anthony P., and Donna M. Desrochers. 1999. *Getting Down to Business: Matching Welfare Recipients to Jobs that Train*. Princeton, NJ: Educational Testing Service.

Carnevale, Anthony P., and Donna M. Desrochers. 2001. *Help Wanted . . . Credentials Required: Community Colleges in the Knowledge Economy*. Princeton, NJ: Educational Testing Service.

Carnevale, Anthony P., and Richard A. Fry. 2000. *Crossing the Great Divide: Can We Achieve Equity When Generation Y Goes to College?* Princeton, NJ: Educational Testing Service.

Carnevale, Anthony P., and Richard A. Fry. 2001. "The Economic and Demographic Roots of Education and Training." Washington, DC: Manufacturing Institute, National Association of Manufacturers.

Carnevale, Anthony P., and Stephen J. Rose. 1998. *Education for What? The New Office Economy*. Princeton, NJ: Educational Testing Service.

Castells, Manuel. 1997. *The Information Age: Economy, Society and Culture: Volume II. The Power of Identity*. Oxford, UK: Blackwell.

Cole, Michael. 1996. *Cultural Psychology: A Once and Future Discipline*. Cambridge, MA: Harvard University Press.

Ewell, Peter T. 2001. "Numeracy, Mathematics and General Education." In *Mathematics and Democracy: The Case for Quantitative Literacy*, edited by Lynn Arthur Steen, 37–48. Princeton, NJ: National Council on Education and the Disciplines.

Flynn, James R. 1998. "IQ Gains Over Time: Toward Finding the Causes." In *The Rising Curve: Long-Term Gains in IQ and Related Measures*, edited by Ulric Neisser, 25–66. Washington, DC: American Psychological Association.

Gellner, Ernest. 1992. *Postmodernism, Reason and Religion*. London: Routledge.

Greenfield, Patricia M. 1998. "The Cultural Evolution of IQ." In *The Rising Curve: Long-Term Gains in IQ and Related Measures*, edited by Ulric Neisser, 81–23. Washington, DC: American Psychological Association.

Grogger, Jeff, and Eric Eide. 1995. "Changes in College Skills and the Rise in the College Wage Premium." *Journal of Human Resources* 30(2) (Spring): 281–310.

Hecker, Daniel E. 2001. "Occupational Employment Projections to 2010." *Monthly Labor Review* 124(11) (November): 57–84.

McNeil, William H. 1999. *A World History,* 4th ed. New York: Oxford University Press.

Menand, Louis. 2002. "College: The End of the Golden Age." In *New York Review of Books* 48(16): 44–47.

Mishel, Lawrence, Jared Bernstein, and John Schmitt. 2001. *The State of Working America. 2001.* (Table 7.7, p. 374). Ithaca, NY: Cornell University Press.

Murnane, Richard, John Willet, and Frank Levy. 1995. "The Growing Importance of Cognitive Skills in Wage Determination." *Review of Economics and Statistics* (May): 251–266.

National Research Council. 1998. *High School Mathematics at Work.* Washington, DC: National Academy Press.

National Research Council. 2000. *How People Learn: Brain, Mind, Experience, and School.* Washington, DC: National Academy Press.

National Science Foundation. 2002. "Characteristics of Doctoral Scientists and Engineers" (Table 5). Retrieved January 31, 2002, at http://www.nsf.gov/sbe/srs/srs01406/start.htm.

Neisser, Ulric, ed. 1998. *The Rising Curve: Long-Term Gains in IQ and Related Measures.* Washington, DC: American Psychological Association.

Organization for Economic Cooperation and Development (OECD), Centre for Educational Research and Innovation. 1995. *Literacy, Economy, and Society: Results of the First International Adult Literacy Survey.* Ottawa, Canada: Statistics Canada.

Resnick, Lauren, and John Wirt. 1995. *Junking School and Work: Roles for Standards and Assessments.* San Francisco, CA: Jossey-Bass.

Richards, Joan L. 2001. "Connecting Mathematics With Reason." In *Mathematics and Democracy: The Case for Quantitative Literacy,* edited by Lynn Arthur Steen, 31–36. Princeton, NJ: National Council on Education and the Disciplines.

Roey, Stephen, Nancy Caldwell, Keith Rust, Eyal Blumstein, Tom Krenzke, Stan Legum, Judy Kuhn, and Mark Waksberg. 2001. *The High School Transcript Study Tabulations: Comparative Data on Credits Earned and Demographics for 1998, 1994, 1990, 1987, and 1982 High School Graduates.* National Center for Education Statistics. NCES 2001–498. Washington, DC: U.S. Government Printing Office.

Romer, Paul M. 2000. "Should the Government Subsidize Supply or Demand in the Market for Scientists and Engineers?" NBER Working Paper 7723. Cambridge, MA: National Bureau of Economic Research.

Schoen, H. L., and S. Zubarth. 1998. "Assessment of Students' Mathematical Performance." Core Plus Mathematics Evaluation. Iowa City, IA: University of Iowa.

Schooler, Carmi. 1998. "Environmental Complexity and the Flynn Effect." In *The Rising Curve: Long-Term Gains in IQ and Related Measures,* edited by Ulric Neisser, 67–79. Washington, DC: American Psychological Association.

Scribner, Sylvia. 1997. *Mind and Social Practice: Selected Writings of Sylvia Scribner.* Cambridge, UK: Cambridge University Press.

Scribner, Sylvia, and Michael Cole. 1997. *The Psychology of Literacy.* Cambridge, MA: Harvard University Press.

Steen, Lynn Arthur, ed. 1997. *Why Numbers Count: Quantitative Literacy for Tomorrow's America.* New York: College Entrance Examination Board.

Steen, Lynn Arthur, ed. 2001. *Mathematics and Democracy: The Case for Quantitative Literacy.* Princeton, NJ: National Council on Education and the Disciplines.

U.S. Department of Education. National Center for Education Statistics. 2000. *Digest of Education Statistics.* Washington, DC: U.S. Government Printing Office.

U.S. Department of Education. The National Commission on Excellence in Education. 1983. *A Nation at Risk: The Imperative for Educational Reform.* Washington, DC: U.S. Government Printing Office.

Wood, T., and P. Sellers. 1996. "Assessment of a Problem-Centered Mathematics Program: Third Grade." *Journal for Research in Mathematics Education* 27(3): 337–53.

What Mathematics Should "Everyone" Know and Be Able to Do?

ARNOLD PACKER

This essay presents ideas for teaching what some people are now calling "quantitative literacy." Some of the ideas are old hat—project-based collaborative learning, teaching in context, and using computers. Some are radical—banning the use of x and y as variable names until after college algebra. An early step is to determine whether a "canon of empirical mathematics problems" can be defined, doing for quantitative literacy what the canon of literature does for cultural literacy. Some will argue that this quest departs too radically from current mathematics education to be feasible, but the current algebra curriculum has its own canon. An amusing book, *Humble Pi,* sets it out: age problems, canoe problems, planes meeting in mid-continent, and so on.[1] Why not a comparable set for quantitative literacy?

As befits an essay on empirical mathematics (a term I prefer to quantitative literacy), a table of specific types of examples is provided. It also is appropriate to cite some data. Over the last few years, inner-city Baltimore students were taught quantitative literacy in their algebra courses. They outperformed traditionally taught students by a wide margin. They took and passed Algebra II at a greater rate, received higher grades, were absent less, and were more likely to graduate and to go on to college.[2]

This essay concludes that it is better to teach mathematics inductively. Let students first learn the power of mathematics in specific examples. Later, they can appreciate mathematics' power to generalize. The inductive approach is more likely to succeed than the current deductive process, in which general rules are taught first and applications—selected from the canon noted in *Humble Pi*—are of secondary importance.

The Challenge

The first order of business is to demonstrate that mathematics education is inadequate to today's challenge. The challenge exists because of mathematics' growing importance for both economic and citizenship reasons. It is no accident that, along with reading, mathematics is one of the two subjects that always are required on standardized tests. This implies that it is important for everyone, not only for those few who "love" the subject and grow to see the beauty in it.

Two hundred years ago, only merchants, engineers, surveyors, and a few scientists were mathematically literate. Merchants had to calculate the price of cloth "2 yards 1 foot 4 inches square at 3 pence 2 farthings the square foot."[3] Military engineers had to determine the angle needed for a cannon to project a missile over a moat. Surveyors had to lay out site lines. Isaac Newton needed to invent calculus to solve his physics problems. How many Americans are now mathematically literate is an arguable question. By some estimates, it is less than one-fourth: that is how many adults achieve levels of 4 and 5 in the National Adult Literacy Survey (NALS) and International Adult Literacy

Arnold Packer is Chair of the SCANS 2000 Center at the Institute for Policy Studies, Johns Hopkins University. An economist and engineer by training, Packer has served as Assistant Secretary for Policy, Evaluation, and Research at the U.S. Department of Labor, as co-director of the Workforce 2000 study, and as executive director of the Secretary's Commission on Achieving Necessary Skills (SCANS). Currently, his work is focused on teaching, assessing and recording the SCANS competencies.

Survey (IALS) studies,[4] levels at which they can perform two or more sequential operations or tasks of similar complexity.

But the rigors of international competition have changed policy-makers' views on the issue. Ten years ago, the first President Bush and the governors (including then-Governor Bill Clinton) met in Charlottesville, North Carolina to set education goals. By the year 2000, U.S. students were to be first in the world in science and mathematics. But now we are well past 2000, and by any measure we have not met that goal. National Assessment of Educational Progress (NAEP) scores in mathematics (for 17-year-olds) in 1996 were only 3 percent higher than in 1982. The average NAEP score was 307, meaning that the average 17-year-old can compute with decimals, use fractions and percentages, recognize geometric figures, solve simple equations, and use moderately complex reasoning. The averages among blacks (286) and Hispanics (292) were below 300, meaning the ability to do no more than perform the four arithmetic operations with whole numbers and solve one-step problems.[5] Over half of the students entering the California State University system need to take a "developmental" mathematics course. Over one in four college freshmen feels a need for tutoring or remedial work in mathematics. This compares to one in 10 for English, science, and foreign language.[6]

Teaching is part of the problem. International comparisons of mathematics teaching find U.S. methods to be inferior to those used by Japanese or German teachers. The nation faces a severe shortage of primary and secondary school mathematics teachers and an overabundance of those trained to be college mathematics teachers. In 1998, 18 percent of high school mathematics teachers did not have a major or minor in the subject.[7] At the same time, only 2 percent of college freshmen expect to major in the physical sciences. This 2 percent includes only 0.5 percent in mathematics.[8] Mathematics teachers are disconnected from other faculty in many schools and colleges.[9] As a result, mathematics lacks context and other courses lack mathematics.

Although they may not know the reasons why, generations of American students have been convinced that something was amiss with mathematics classes. Many a parent has heard their teenage children complain, "I hate math; it's boring and hard. Why do I have to learn math, it's so useless. . . ." Many parents are sympathetic. They themselves finished their last required mathematics course in high school or college with expressions of relief, not commitments to take another mathematics course as an elective.[10]

These parents often are mathematically inadequate at their own jobs and in other aspects of their lives. They do not understand statistical quality processes, cannot follow political candidates who speak of "weighted averages,"[11] and cannot make sense of alternative strategies for financing their own retirement. They would express wonderment if by some small chance they ever met

a mathematician who spoke of mathematical beauty (although seeing *A Beautiful Mind* might have an impact). Our society pays a high cost for the general lack of mathematical competence.

What is wrong? The way middle school teachers teach fractions provides a clue. They teach their students to add fractions by:

First finding the lowest common denominator.

Then converting all fractions to that denominator.

Then adding the numerators.

Finally, reducing the answer, if possible.

Nobody does that outside the schoolroom. Imagine a school cafeteria in which the selected items totaled three quarters and three dollars and four dimes. The schoolroom method would be to change all these in for nickels. Or go to the shop. Maybe the problem is adding one foot and 8 and 1/16 inches to 6 and 1/4 inches. Would any carpenter change it all into sixteenths? It is a very rare situation when anyone needs this method, say to add odd fractions such as fifths and sevenths.

Mathematics teachers might say they want a "general solution" so that students could add twentieths and sixteenths. A thoughtful student might respond, "Yeah . . . like when?" We are generally using the decimal system (for money or where the metric system prevails) or the English system of measurement. The practical result is *not* a universe of students who can solve a universe of fraction problems. Instead, it is a great many students who learn (about the sixth grade) that they "can't do math" and demonstrate that truth by being unable to solve either the cafeteria or shop problems.[12]

Nor is the general abstract approach to mathematics necessarily a big favor for those who "love" mathematics or science. "No scientist thinks in equations," Albert Einstein said. Einstein employed visual images and muscular feelings. The mathematician S. M. Ulam said that he uses "mental images and tactile sensations to perform calculations, replacing numerical values with the weights and sizes of imagined objects." Joshua Lederberg becomes "an actor in a biological process, to know how [to] behave as if I were a chromosome."[13]

Evidence from mathematics assessments is consistent with the theories (and data) from cognitive science: it is better to build abstract thinking on a concrete base. Adding ethereal fractions or solving $3x = 9$ by eliminating references to concrete objects or phenomena removes the connection to nonsymbolic ways of thinking about mathematics. For too many, the bloodless abstraction makes it impossible to learn the subject. Others can remember, via rote recall and long enough to pass the final, how to plug in numbers and chug through the formula.[14] Do not, however, ask either the passing or failing students to apply the technique to a real-life problem. Weeks after the final, they cannot even remember that the formula exists. They have no way to recall the formula from long-term memory. Imagine asking most adults the formula for solutions to the quadratic equation or, worse yet, what real-life process is described by the equation. Nor does the problem disappear as students take higher-level courses: ". . . undergraduates never learn how calculus relates to other disciplines, much less the real world."[15] The situation is untenable for two kinds of students: those who do not like mathematics and those who do.

Thomas Berger of Colby College, former chair of the Committee on the Undergraduate Program in Mathematics of the Mathematical Association of America, speaks of the "mathematization of society" as symbolic models become the basic tools of engineers, medical researchers, and business executives.[16] These models, however, simulate real-world processes and systems. They are used to allocate resources, design technology, and improve system performance. Mathematization increases the significance of higher-level skills for most citizens. Successful workers, citizens, and consumers need to know how to solve problems, analyze data, and make written and oral presentations of quantitative results.

How does the traditional pre-calculus curriculum serve these purposes? How valuable, actually, is calculus? Even mathematicians often replace calculus with finite mathematics to take advantage of computer technology.[17] The same technology can handle both the traditional tasks of manipulating formulas and performing long computations. Spending too much time teaching humans to solve problems better handled by machines is not a wise strategy when there is so much to know.

Conceptualizing how a problem can be stated mathematically has become (and, indeed, always was) more valuable than factoring a polynomial or taking a derivative. The tasks most college graduates face demand quantitative literacy (a.k.a. empirical mathematics)—a way with numbers and comfort replacing concrete realities with symbols—without forgetting the reality beyond the symbols. In other words, banish x and y from mathematics class at least until the completion of college algebra. Use, instead, letters (even Greek letters) that stand for something students can understand or picture: v for velocity, d for distance, P for price, n for number, p for profit, and so on.

This idea is not so radical. In his introduction to *Why Numbers Count,* Lynn Arthur Steen referred to scientific mathematics in which mathematical variables always stand for physical quantities—"a measurement with a unit and implicit degree of accuracy."[18] In the same volume, F. James Rutherford said,

" . . . citizens need to possess certain basic mathematical capabilities *understood in association with* relevant scientific and technological knowledge."[19]

Mathematicians, of course, want their students to understand mathematics' power to solve general problems, ones that are not rooted in a specific problem. That point can be made and demonstrated near the end of the mathematics course. Teach that the equation for velocity can be used in many contexts relating to change. True generality can be saved for those mathematics students who still will be taking mathematics courses in their junior year in college. (Indeed, there might be more such students if mathematics were less abstract in the earlier years of school.) *Make each year of mathematics instruction worthwhile in itself, not just preparation for the next mathematics course.*

Many critics of this point of view believe it does not credit the power of abstract mathematics to be generally applicable. But—as guns don't kill but people with guns do—mathematics does not apply itself: mathematically competent individuals do. Individuals require enough competence and creativity to structure a problem mathematically and to know when and how to use the tools. On that basis, the current approach to achieving widespread mathematical competence is failing. The real issue is whether mathematics should be taught inductively—from the concrete to the abstract—or the other way around, as it often is today. The answer can be found empirically, not theoretically. Which approach will meet education's goals of productive workers, engaged citizens, and well-rounded individuals who continue to learn after graduation?

Quantitative Literacy: Goals and Objectives

What mathematics should "everyone" know and be able to do? The National Council of Teachers of Mathematics (NCTM) has been attempting to answer this question for more than a decade as council members developed mathematics standards. Wisely, NCTM included the ideas of real-world problem solving and being able to communicate in the language of mathematics. Its report, however, is built around standard mathematical topics, algebra, geometry, calculus, statistics, and so on. The problems were what we might expect: Solve $x^2 - 2x - 7 = 0$, or derive the equation describing the motion of a Ferris wheel car. Few individuals work on either of these problems outside of a school situation. One helpful criterion is to restrict problems to those that American workers get paid to solve, those that American citizens should have informed opinions about, or those that American consumers actually need to solve.

Consider the challenge posed by Berger's mathematization of society. What if Berger's problem were stated in the language of mathematical optimization? (Surely, mathematicians should applaud using their discipline to analyze this problem.) In the workplace, industrial psychologists analyze the frequency and criticality (sometimes called importance) of tasks and the various skills needed to carry them out. The human resources department then either hires folk with the more important skills or trains staff in those skills. Transfer this thinking to the school situation in which the challenge is how best to prepare students for their life beyond the schoolhouse walls. Think first of the student's professional life. The optimizing school would seek to maximize the benefit that is a function of:

1. The frequency of having any particular job or career;

2. The probability that any particular problem will arise in that job;

3. The criticality of having the appropriate mathematics skills to solve the problem; and

4. The economic importance of solving the problem properly.

The mathematics curricula should seek to maximize the benefits under the constraints of time, talent, and materials.[20] The trick is figuring out the problems that students exiting formal education after grade 14 have a significant likelihood of having to solve in their careers. In an earlier paper, I estimated that advanced mathematical content was required in about 4 percent of jobs; that is the percentage of engineers, scientists, computer analysts, financial analysts, and accountants in the labor force.[21] I also suggested that the weighted probability of a problem arising should be 1 percent or more before it should be put in the canon of problems that all students should be able to solve. Applying this criterion to curricula would mean that 1.5 million persons would have to encounter a problem in their lifetimes before it was worth including in the canon.

As noted before (and repeated for emphasis), careers and work are not the only economic reasons for taking mathematics. In a consumer society, successful individuals make wise consumption, saving, and investment decisions. The equation needs to be supplemented, therefore, with the probability of making decisions in these domains, the frequency with which the decisions will be made over a lifetime, the criticality of mathematics for making the decisions wisely, and the economic cost of the decisions.

Education also has responsibility for preparing students for their roles in noneconomic domains. A democracy needs citizens who participate with awareness and understanding; surely this is a mandatory objective of publicly funded education. Citizens should be able to understand the *New York Times,* the president's State of the Union speech, and the school district's budget. Comprehending statistics and reading charts and tables are essential. There are also personal reasons for knowing some mathematics. Now we have to add the importance of encountering problems in these two noneconomic domains to the benefit equation. Instead of only economic costs, political and social costs need to be considered.

The challenge is to identify important, frequently encountered problems that cannot be efficiently solved without using mathematics. In other words, the challenge is to identify a canon of mathematical problems analogous to the canon in literature. David Denby, film editor for the *New York Times,* wrote a controversial book about his midlife experience of returning to Columbia University to revisit the literature canon of the Western world. He read literature from Homer and the Bible to Virginia Woolf.[22] Can anything similar to the literary canon be described for mathematics? What problems have been, and will be, relevant for centuries and across cultures?[23]

Well, some problems have been around for a while. We can imagine that the Egyptian pharaohs had problems of budgeting and scheduling construction of the pyramids. The biblical story relates Abraham's negotiating the price for the cave of Machpelah as a burial place for him and Sarah. Penelope's suitors would have benefited from knowing something about the rate of change in the area of the cloth she was weaving. Similar problems will be around for the next new millennium if humans last that long.

The classes of problems also should remain fairly constant across cultures and up and down the organizational ladder. Problems of budgeting apply from the fourth grade to the CEO (and, of course, to the president and Congress). The problem only becomes more complex as variables multiply and uncertainty enters the equations. Of course, the way budget and schedule problems are solved changes—King Tut did not have a spreadsheet or Harvard Project Planner. With computers, mathematicians may choose linear programming rather than calculus to solve numerical optimization problems.

A Scheme

E. D. Hirsch is widely known for his educational canon. He lists things students should know at each grade level. I will try to avoid such laundry lists and suggest, instead, a structure in which types of problems can be placed or developed. This structure can accommodate a range of difficulties for each of the problem types. Some examples in the range are suitable for different school grades. A second grader may, for example, be taught something about schedules while mathematics post-docs may struggle with variations of the traveling salesman problem. The particular examples we put forth are suitable for grades 11 to 14 in school and for college.

The structure builds on the SCANS taxonomy, a set of competencies developed in 1991 by the Secretary's Commission on Achieving Necessary Skills (SCANS).[24] These competencies—a better term is problem domains—are quite broad and were intended to accommodate a full range of situations from entry-level to CEO. The five SCANS domains and the subdomains that require quantitative literacy are:

- *Planning problems.* Allocating money (budgeting), time (scheduling), space, and staff.

- *Systems and processes problems.* Understanding, monitoring, and designing social, physical, or business systems.

- *Interpersonal problems.* Working in teams, negotiating, teaching, and learning.

- *Information problems.* Gathering and organizing data, evaluating data, and communicating, both in written and oral form.

- *Technology problems.* Using, choosing, and maintaining equipment of any type.

Solving problems in any domain requires a foundation of basic (reading, writing, listening, speaking) and higher-order (problem-solving, decision-making, creativity, and mathematical) skills and personal qualities such as integrity, sociability, and self-management. Performing in a real situation often demands solving problems in more than a single domain.

The SCANS categorization must be approached with care and common sense. It is an abstract structure imposed on an endlessly complex reality to help organize examples. The categories are only reasonably comprehensive and relatively disjointed. In the table at the end of this essay, many problems could easily fall into different box from the one into which they were put.

Other structures can be, and have been, devised. The U.S. Department of Labor developed O*Net, the New Standards group developed Applied Academics, and a number of states and occupational groups developed their own standards. The manufacturing and sales and service sectors developed standards under the guidance of the National Skills Standards Board. Equip for the Future (EFF), a project of the National Institute for Literacy, has extended similar standards to define the literacy needs for work, citizenship, and parenting. Basically, all these standards are variations on the same theme and crosswalks have been developed to link them. All the good ones strike a balance between an endless unstructured list of examples and an almost equally endless list of narrow categories. The best structures acknowledge that human memories are generally limited to recalling a list of five to seven items.

I chose the SCANS taxonomy for the following four reasons:

1. It is the best-known and most widely used structure available.[25]

2. It is one of the only structures that have widespread recognition across the academic and occupational standards that have been developed in the United States and other countries.

3. It is easily modified to suit standards developed under other structures, such as state standards for mathematics.

4. It is easily extended to roles other than career and work.[26]

Four "roles" are used to fill out the structure. For most students and policymakers, the role of work and careers is of foremost concern. If not for this role, mathematics departments would be competing for students with literature and art departments, not with computer sciences. Unlike most school-based problems, real work-based problems usually cannot be solved in a few minutes but take hours of sustained effort. Preparation for this role requires that students engage in long-term projects. The ability to carry out such tasks has been noted by a recent National Academy of Sciences effort to define computer literacy and fluency.[27] Academy member Phillip Griffiths, director of the Institute for Advanced Studies in Princeton, speaks to the need for the mathematically competent to function in various SCANS domains. "We asked . . . [about] . . . science and engineering PhD's. The employers told us that . . . they find shortcomings: . . . communications skills . . . appreciation for applied problems . . . and teamwork. . . . Skills like project management, leadership . . . interpersonal skills . . . computer knowledge." Students will have to work in teams, use computers to solve problems, and make oral and written presentations if Griffith's requirements are to be met.

Many mathematics teachers may decry my emphasis on work and careers, so I want to acknowledge, once again, the importance of other domains (without relinquishing the idea that the primary force behind the nation's emphasis on mathematics is economic). Individuals also require mathematics to succeed in their second important role as consumer. Some buying problems can and must be solved quickly and on the spot. Comparing the price per ounce for similar products sold in differently sized bottles, understanding discounts, approximating a large restaurant or hotel bill are examples. Other problems, such as comparing retirement or health plans or comparing mortgage rates may take more time (although the Internet can speed things up).

Citizenship, the third role, is a noneconomic role, one that is mandatory if public funds are to be used for education. Informed discussions about the adequacy of Social Security, the growth rates of spending and taxing, health policy, science policy, and a host of other topics are impossible for the mathematically illiterate.

Finally, mathematics can provide personal pleasure. This is the personal role. Pleasure can take the form of appreciating pure mathematics itself, reading about a variety of subjects that require mathematical or computer literacy for full understanding, or employing mathematics for leisure activities from astronomy to sailing to carpentry.[28] In this domain, mathematics educators will have to compete with music, arts, and physical education.

Thoughts on Breadth Versus Depth and Pedagogy

Some believe that students, after learning all the mathematical topics in the current curriculum, can put them together for applications such as those contained in the Appendix. That belief is not based on empirical data. Students—and, unfortunately, many mathematics teachers—simply cannot do it. People learn how to put together budgets by making a budget. Projects are necessary. This raises the hoary problem of coverage. It brings up the optimization problem stated earlier: how to provide the most value to the student and society under constraints of time and resources.

Massachusetts Institute of Technology mathematics professor Arthur Mattuck pointed out that teaching through modeling is difficult. Models must be sophisticated to capture interest. The more time spent building and understanding the model the less time for coverage. "In the end," he said, "very little mathematics gets done."[29] One response to Mattuck is this: "What if covering Taylor's expansion rather than a more interesting modeling project means that fewer students will take the next mathematics course?"[30] This clearly illustrates the trade-off.

Brain research has shown again and again that retention of information requires context. Unless a student can provide a mental map, developed by making connections, memory of facts or skills will soon dissipate. This holds true whether people are trying to remember names, formulas, or how to solve a differential equation.

The dilemma of coverage was highlighted in the Third International Mathematics and Science Study (TIMSS) international comparison of mathematics teaching and learning. American textbooks are thick, Japanese thin. We cover more topics lightly and they cover fewer topics in depth. Japanese students surpass those of most other countries in international mathematics assessments. We are in about the middle of the pack.[31]

The lessons of TIMSS apply as well to empirical mathematics. Learning how to solve the problems shown in the Appendix will take more time and is unlikely to be done well unless certain other topics are eliminated or at least postponed until higher college levels when career choices are clearer. Recall, yet again, that we are trying to maximize usefulness under constraints of time, money, and talent.

Even if the curriculum is revised to fit, pedagogy will have to change. Managing groups of students working collaboratively on a project is different from lecturing. Computers and the Internet will probably be part of the instructional materials. Teachers who offer these sorts of classes find it to be more work but more rewarding than using traditional methods. Creating projects is time consuming. Most mathematics teachers do not have the time or inclination (or talent) to create realistic projects. Electronic and paper libraries (such as the Harvard Case Studies) have and can be created.[32]

Coverage of mathematics topics will also have to be reduced if the culture of mathematics is to fit into the limited time that can be devoted to the subject. If all students are going to understand mathematicians' discovery processes,[33] there will be less time to understand the discoveries themselves. Consider, for example, the fifth-grade lesson $C = \pi D$. It is much less interesting than $C/D = \pi$. With the latter, students learn that someone discovered π by showing that the ratio C/D is invariant with different-sized circles. It maybe worth dropping the definition of a rhombus to teach the lesson of π.

Finally, assessment will have to change. Multiple-choice, fill-in-the-blank, and even 10-minute problems still will have a place but other assessments will be required. Some of these will be formative assessments that teachers provide as students work through the project or make presentations. As in writing with word processors, multiple drafts will be required. Each will have to be assessed and returned for improvement. That is quite a difference from "you got it wrong, let's move on."

Each of the above will take resources, from political leadership to money. Imbuing all students with quantitative literacy cannot take place without additional instructional materials, substantial teacher training, and new assessment instruments. Why is this investment justified? Because current approaches are failing too many students. Their careers and our society will suffer from it. Teachers in technical college programs complain that students cannot do mathematics. We have enough history to know that students are not going to change. We must, therefore, change what and how we teach mathematics.

Appendix: Empirical Mathematics

Computers take derivatives and integrals, invert matrices for linear programming, and perform other algorithms much better than humans. I have written elsewhere about the end of algorithmic work as a means of making a livelihood in the United States.[34] American workers cannot accept a wage low enough to compete with a computer. Workers do, however, require enough mathematics and creativity to structure a problem so that mathematics can be used. They also need sufficient quantitative capacity to know when tools are not working right or have been improperly used.

This appendix, whose structure is shown in the accompanying table, offers a first stab at a canon of empirical mathematical problems. The table lists mathematical tools for each of the five SCANS competencies and each of the four adult roles. Some of the entries in the table do not include all the tools needed because they have been noted frequently in other boxes. For example, the four arithmetic functions are needed to solve many problems that an American will face, so they are not listed repeatedly. When the phrase "concept of . . . " is used in the table, it means just that—knowing the concept of rate of change and change in the rate of change (acceleration) does not require knowing how to take the second derivative. The same thought applies to linear programming and to the idea that minimums and maximums occur when the derivative is zero or inflection when the second derivative is zero or that an integral takes the sum over an interval.

The main part of the appendix consists of examples of important tasks arranged according to the SCANS taxonomy. The mathematical models described are expected to be developed and expressed in spreadsheets, graphics packages, etc. Students would be asked to estimate "rough numbers" to ensure that the models have been properly specified and the numbers properly entered.

Planning

BUDGET:

Worker: Using a spreadsheet with algebraic formulas, develop a budget for a retail store, construction project, manufacturing operation, or personal services (e.g., dental) office. The budget should include wages, benefits, material (or inventory), rent, and interest costs on borrowed funds.

Consumer: Using pencil and paper (with a calculator) and given a set of criteria and prices, develop a monthly budget for a family of four. Develop a budget for a party.

Citizen: Given an agency or organization budget for the past five years, write a two-page letter explaining and criticizing it.

Include information on the growth or decline of the budget components themselves and as shares of the total. Relate to other variables, such as inflation and population growth.

Personal: Be able to understand the effects of budgets on historical events. Was the Athenian budget for its navy an excessive burden?

SCHEDULE:

Worker: Using a spreadsheet (or other software) with algebraic formulas, develop a schedule for a construction project, advertising campaign, conference, medical regime, or software project. Require conversions from hours to workweeks. Understand the difference between activities done in sequence and simultaneously. Understand PERT and Gantt charts.

Consumer: Using pencil and paper without a calculator, plan a party or a meal. Convert hours to minutes.

Citizen: Understand why it takes so long to build a road or school.

Personal: Appreciate why Napoleon was beaten by the weather and Russia.

SPACE:

Worker: Using a computer graphics package, lay out a storeroom or office space in three dimensions. Develop a graphic for a brochure. Lay out material for a garment or a steel product. Lay out a restaurant or hotel space. Place paintings in a gallery.

Consumer: Look at a builder's plans and modify them. Understand your own living space.

Citizen: Understand plans for a public building.

Personal: Appreciate good design in products and buildings. Hang paintings in your house.

STAFF:

Worker: Using a matrix and database, assign staff to functions. In unusual situations, you may use linear programming to match skills and requirements matrices.

Consumer: Contract out a renovation project for your house.

Citizen: Understand a school's staffing requirements.

Personal: Understand staffing requirements in a historical setting. Assign players in a Little League baseball game or in the local orchestra.

Systems and Processes

UNDERSTAND:

Worker: Read and understand a flowchart for a production or paperwork process. Read organization charts. Read diagrams explaining how technology functions.

Consumer: Read a flowchart and follow the directions to install a new piece of software or an exercise machine.

Citizen: Read government organization charts. Understand a flowchart for legislation as it passes through Congress.

Personal: Grasp the organization of a military campaign. Understand a diagram explaining how technology functions or a scientific process unfolds. Understand the culture of mathematics and the process of mathematical discovery.

MONITOR:

Worker: Use techniques of statistical process control to monitor a manufacturing process or patient or customer complaints.

Consumer: Understand statements about the quality of the products or services purchased.

Citizen: Understand environmental safeguards.

Personal: Monitor changes in a local garden.

DESIGN:

Worker: Develop an information (or other) system flowchart and build a mathematical model to simulate its operation. Develop a statistical process-control system.

Consumer: Design a system for keeping the pipes in a summer house from freezing.

Citizen: Help a local school district design a school safety system.

Personal: Design a system for maintaining a diet and exercise regime.

Interpersonal

NEGOTIATE:

Worker: Negotiate the price of a product or project and be able to think on your feet, including manipulating numbers mentally. Participate in a labor-management negotiation.

Consumer: Be able to understand a construction contractor's or mechanic's proposal and negotiate a fair agreement.

Citizen: Understand a government negotiation.

Personal: Understand a historically important negotiation.

TEACH AND LEARN:

Worker: For teachers, help students do quantitative work in non-mathematical subjects.[35] For workers, teach co-workers or customers the mathematics needed to carry out a task or use a product. Should know enough mathematics to absorb training.

Consumer: Should know enough mathematics to learn how to use a product when taught by a salesperson. Should be able to teach a spouse how to use a product.

Citizen: Should be able to explain and debate policy issues when quantitative issues are involved.

Personal: Should be able to discuss topics when quantitative issues are involved.

Information

GATHER AND ORGANIZE:

Worker: Create a filing system for parts or customer information. Build a database.

Consumer: Create a filing system for tax information. Use a database. Organize an on-line checking system.

Citizen: Use a file to find out about government services in your district. Organize a file for a school's PTA.

Personal: Use a Dewey decimal and an on-line library system to find a book and information.

EVALUATE:

Worker: Use a statistical package to evaluate data. Read relevant statistical studies and come to a judgment.

Consumer: Evaluate advertising claims. Read an annual report from a firm whose stock you hold.

Citizen: Evaluate political claims.

Personal: Judge the likelihood of an event or story (UFO) being true.

COMMUNICATE:

Worker: Write a report about a quantitative issue, including tables and charts. Make a presentation on the material to more senior colleagues.

Consumer: Read and listen to such reports critically and be able to ask intelligent questions.

Citizen: Make a presentation or write a report for the school board.

Personal: Carry out a conversation about a quantitative issue. Engage in a chat room about a quantitative issue of interest such as astronomy.

Technology

Use:

Worker: Use equipment, such as a numerically controlled machine tool, to produce a part.

Consumer: Use a computer.

Citizen: Use a county's Internet address to find tax data.

Personal: Use a chat room to engage in discussion.

Choose:

Worker: Analyze alternative medical, construction, manufacturing, or computer equipment and recommend a purchase.

Consumer: Analyze alternatives for video on demand, home security systems, or computers.

Citizen: Analyze a county's or school board's decision to purchase technology, from fire engines to computer systems. Be able to judge whether the antimissile system makes sense.

Personal: Analyze a historic technology decision, from the longbow to atomic energy.

Maintain:

Worker: Follow maintenance instructions for a piece of industrial equipment.

Consumer: Follow maintenance instructions for a consumer product.

Citizen: Participate, as part of a volunteer fire department, in maintenance of the fire engines.

Personal: Maintain rare books or valuable paintings when temperature and humidity must be controlled.

Mathematics Required to Solve Frequently Occurring Problems in Four Roles and Five SCANS Competencies[36]

Problem Domains	Planning • Budget • Schedule • Space • Staff	Systems and Processes • Understand • Monitor • Design	Interpersonal • Negotiate • Teach and learn	Information • Gather and organize • Evaluate • Communicate	Technology • Use • Choose • Maintain
Worker Role	Four arithmetic operations, estimation, geometry, algebra, exponential functions, spreadsheets, conversions. Concept of trade-offs. Awareness of tools such as linear programs and calculus for making trade-off decisions.	Model-building. Concept of first and second derivative and of integral, average, and standard deviation.	Mental arithmetic, fractions, percentages.	Create and read graphs, tables, and explanatory text.	Read graphs, tables, and explanatory text, Concept of trade-offs. Geometry.
Consumer Role	Four arithmetic operations, geometry, exponential functions, spreadsheets. Concept of trade-offs.	Concept of first and second derivative and of integral, average, and standard deviation.	Mental arithmetic, fractions, percentages.	Read graphs, tables, and explanatory text.	Read graphs, tables, and explanatory text. Geometry.
Citizen Role	Four arithmetic operations, geometry, concept of trade-offs.	Concept of first and second derivative and of integral, average, and standard deviation.	Mental arithmetic, fractions, percentages.	Read graphs, tables, and explanatory text.	Read graphs, tables, and explanatory text. Geometry.
Personal Role	Geometry, concept of trade-offs.	Concepts of calculus and statistics. History of mathematical discovery.		Read graphs, tables, and explanatory text.	Geometry.

Notes

1. Michael K. Smith. *Humble Pi: The Role Mathematics Should Play in American Education* (Amherst, NY: Prometheus Books, 1994).

2. John Faithful Hamer and Anna-Liisa Aunio, "The Technology Literacy Challenge and the Baltimore Initiative: Integrating School and Work on the Information Highway Final Evaluation Report" (2001).

3. Theodore M. Porter, "The Triumph of Numbers: Civic Implications of Quantitative Literacy," in *Why Numbers Count,* Lynn Arthur Steen, ed. (New York, NY: College Entrance Examination Board, 1997), 1–10.

4. John Dossey, "National Indicators of Quantitative Literacy," in Steen, *Why Numbers Count,* 45–59.

5. "Do You Know the Good News About American Education?" (Washington, DC: Center on Education Policy, 2000): 13.

6. "This Year's Freshmen: A Statistical Profile," *Chronicle of Higher Education*, 28 January 2000, A50.

7. "Do You Know the Good News About American Education?" (Washington, DC: Center on Education Policy, 2000): 27.

8. "This Year's Freshmen: A Statistical Profile," *Chronicle of Higher Education,* 28 January 2000, A50.

9. See http://www.stolaf.edu/other/ql/intv.html.

10. Ibid.

11. As arose in the Bradley-Gore debates in the discussion of rival health insurance premiums.

12. Lynn Arthur Steen pointed out that adding odd fractions is preparation for adding mixed algebraic fractions. The preparation can, in my judgment, wait until students reach such algebra problems (if ever). The cost, in students who become convinced that "mathematics is not for them" is too high to justify the benefit.

13. Robert S. Bernstein and Michele Root-Bernstein, "Learning to Think With Emotion," Chronicle *of Higher Education,* 14 January 2000, A64.

14. An anecdote from Steve Childress of New York University: I just finished grading an exam I gave to graduate students seeking admission to our Ph.D. program. One of the questions I asked (the subject was complex variables) was of a standard kind requiring the calculation of a "residue." Now there are various ways of doing this, certain formulas that are useful in individual cases, but the heart of the matter is that you are seeking a certain coefficient in a series and this can usually be obtained directly by expanding the series for a few terms. My problem could be solved in several lines by this direct approach. I was astounded to see that almost everyone applied a certain formula that, in this problem, led to impossibly complicated mathematics. I asked around about this and learned that we had just instituted a kind of prep course for the exams, and that the instructor had given them a problem of this type and solved it with that special

15. Robin Williams, "The Remaking of Math," *Chronicle of Higher Education,* 7 January 2000, A14.

16. Ibid.

17. http://www.stolaf.edu/other/ql/intv.html.

18. Lynn Arthur Steen, "Preface: The New Literacy." In *Why Numbers Count,* Lynn Arthur Steen, ed. (New York, NY: College Entrance Examination Board, 1997), xv–xxviii.

19. F. James Rutherford, "Thinking Quantitatively about Science." In Steen, *Why Numbers Count,* 60–74. Italics in the original.

20. Arnold Packer, "Mathematical Competencies that Employers Expect," In Steen, *Why Numbers Count,* 137––54.

21. Ibid.

22. David Denby, *Great Books: My Adventures with Homer, Rousseau, Woolf, and Other Indestructible Writers of the Western World* (New York, NY: Simon and Schuster, 1996).

23. We hope that the mathematics canon will be less controversial that Denby's literature canon. On the other hand, that may be an unreasonable hope.

24. See *"What Work Requires of School* (1991) and *Learning a Living* (1992) (Washington, DC: U.S. Department of Labor).

25. http://www.stolaf.edu/other/ql/intv.html.

26. The author of this essay was executive director of SCANS.

27. National Academy of Sciences, *Being Fluent with Information Technology* (Washington, DC: National Academy Press, 1999).

28. I recall my quantitatively literate mother using her skills to figure out when important events—such as births, marriages, and deaths—occurred.

29. Arthur Mattuck, "The Remaking of Math," *Chronicle of Higher Education,* 7 January 2000, A15.

30. I heard one engineering dean wonder if his course in electronics was not the best recruiting tool the School of Business had for transfers to its program.

31. That is, we do not shine even on the disaggregated topics. As to real problem solving, it is not even tested.

32. I, and many others, have been involved in creating CD-ROMs to relieve teachers of the task of project construction.

33. Something advocated by NCTM and emphasized to me by Ivar Stakgold in a private telephone conversation.

34. Hudson Institute, "The End of Routine Work and the Need for a Career Transcript," Hudson Institute Workforce Conference (Indianapolis, IN: September 23–24, 1998).

35. Mathematics teachers would presumably have taken mathematics courses beyond this level.

36. See Appendix for examples of the entries in this table.

formula (in a case where it worked easily)! This is the crux of the problem I see from day to day, from freshmen on up.

Quantitative Literacy in the Workplace: Making It a Reality

LINDA P. ROSEN
with LINDSAY WEIL
and CLAUS VON ZASTROW

Business cares deeply about education because the United States can thrive only with a well-educated populace. Indeed, business is deeply invested in improving education for all young people, especially in helping them acquire the increased knowledge and skills required to meet twenty-first-century demands. In this agenda, business is not alone—educators, policymakers, and the general public share the same goal. Despite their concerted effort, however, student achievement remains inadequate. Rather than dwell on disappointment, business leaders and others continue efforts to revitalize education. This essay explores one vital component of the goals for education in the twenty-first century—that of quantitative literacy for all.

Although there is no firm consensus on the meaning of quantitative literacy, there is at least growing agreement that existing practices in mathematics education do not adequately address this competency as it is required in the workplace. Many new jobs demand highly developed computational skills coupled with strong skills in critical thinking, problem solving, and logical reasoning. Moreover, given the increasing pace of technological progress, future jobs will require greater adaptability to new systems and processes: employees must be prepared to apply quantitative principles in unforeseeable contexts. Although the level of sophistication may differ from job to job, the need for adaptability will characterize low-skill as well as high-skill jobs. There is a growing awareness, therefore, that our nation's young people must master something more complex than the mathematics curriculum as it is now frequently taught.

Absent a widespread understanding of the steps needed to achieve this mastery, however, businesses are unlikely to include any systemic attempts to achieve quantitative literacy. The challenge, then, is how to bring quantitative literacy into the business agenda for education reform.

The Changing World

The competitive pressures of today's global economy are forcing U.S. firms to restructure the work they do and how they do it. These changes in the workplace frequently demand more from employees than ever before; workers not only must be able to read, write, and use mathematics but they also must have strong problem-formulation and problem-solving skills. In 1950, for example, 80 percent of jobs were classified as "unskilled," whereas an estimated 85 percent of jobs today are classified as "skilled."[1] Decisions once reserved for management—including how to organize responsibilities,

Linda P. Rosen is an educational policy consultant. Previously, she was Senior Vice President for programs at the National Alliance of Business. Prior to that she served as mathematics and science advisor to Education Secretary Richard Riley and as executive director of the "Glenn Commission" on mathematics and science teaching, whose report, *Before It's Too Late,* was issued in September 2000. Earlier, Rosen served as executive director of the National Council of Teachers of Mathematics (NCTM) and associate executive director of the Mathematical Sciences Education Board (MSEB).

Claus von Zastrow is Director of Institutional Advancement at the Council for Basic Education. Previously, he was Director of Post-secondary Learning at the National Alliance of Business.

Lindsay Weil is Education and Marketing Manager at the Character Education Partnership. Previously, she was Program Manager at the National Alliance of Business.

how to improve procedures and increase profitability, how to maintain quality control—are now also routinely expected of nearly all employees.

Unfortunately, the U.S. labor force is not always poised to meet these changing expectations. An annual survey by the American Management Association, released in May 2001, indicated that 41 percent of the responding companies require basic skills tests of job applicants, with slightly more testing in mathematics than in reading. Eighty-five percent of these companies indicated that they do not hire skills-deficient applicants. The 2001 results showed that more than one-third of job applicants tested in reading and mathematics lacked the necessary skills to perform even entry-level jobs. In particular, the assessment of spreadsheet and database management skills—attributes of quantitative literacy—identified 26 percent of the applicants as lacking the necessary knowledge and skills.[2]

The corporate community has reacted to these findings in an effort to develop a workforce qualified for jobs along the skill spectrum:

- Business leaders have made significant investments in training programs. *Training Magazine* reported that in 1999, nearly $62.5 billion was spent on training.[3] Although exact allocations are difficult to document, anecdotal information suggests that a substantial portion was spent helping employees master basic skills that they should have acquired in high school, thus effectively forcing business to pay for our schools' failure to educate some members of the workforce.

- Despite challenging political odds, the business community successfully lobbied Congress to enact H-1B visa bills enabling the entry of nearly a million temporary, nonimmigrant, highly skilled computer workers between 1998 and 2004. Lawmakers were persuaded that jobs would otherwise go unfilled by an American workforce lacking the necessary expertise, thus endangering U.S. competitiveness in the global economy.

Projections about future needs only heighten corporate concern. An estimate that 60 percent of all new jobs in the early twenty-first century will require skills possessed by only 20 percent of the current workforce is one such cause for alarm.[4] Similarly, projections that 20 million jobs will be added to the U.S. economy by 2008 have raised questions about the vitality of the educational pipeline to support such growth.[5] Although the full impact and length of the current economic downturn are not yet clear, the business community is paving the way for future growth even as it takes steps to deal with existing challenges.

Corporate Involvement in Education

These signs have persuaded the business community to adopt a proactive, rather than reactive, stance on education. Instead of relying only on remediation or recruitment abroad, business leaders are increasingly committing themselves to improving U.S. education: that is, to raising the knowledge and skill levels of all young people prior to their entry into the workforce. Business leaders do not expect the need for specialized training to diminish, given the technology-driven workplace in which the only constant is change. But they do expect that adult workers no longer will be impeded in their acquisition of new knowledge by lapses in their understanding and mastery of prior knowledge. Here are five examples of major business-led reform efforts.

STATE REFORM

Advocacy: In collaboration with the nation's governors, over the past five years several CEOs[6] have served as members of Achieve, Inc., including participation in four national education summits. These corporate leaders have committed themselves and their companies to improving student achievement, increasing investments in and accountability for teachers, and promoting regular assessments that are comparable across schools and districts.

Implementation: The business community—through state and local business coalitions—plans to work with state education officials to implement No Child Left Behind, the reauthorized Elementary and Secondary Education Act (ESEA). These efforts may include dissemination of information about the legislation, mobilization of business leaders to participate in strategic planning, identification of effective practices for business involvement, and providing public officials with the business perspective on roadblocks and implementation successes.

INFLUENCING FEDERAL POLICY

K–12 Education: In January 2001, over 70 leading U.S. corporations and business organizations from across the economy formed the ad hoc Business Coalition for Excellence in Education (BCEE) to work with the president and Congress on the reauthorization of the ESEA. Guided by a set of 10 policy principles, leading CEOs presented a unified business voice on recommended legislative language to help ensure that an effective bipartisan bill was signed into law. These principles offer a road map of the educational issues that are most important to the business community. (See the Appendix for a complete list of the principles.)

Postsecondary Education: With the reauthorization of the Higher Education Act, the Workforce Investment Act, and the Carl D. Perkins Vocational and Applied Technology Education Act scheduled for the next session of Congress, the business community will likely again coalesce around a set of principles to guide its recommendations for shaping the legislation.

ENHANCING THE TEACHING PROFESSION

In 2001, four business organizations—the Business Roundtable, the National Alliance of Business, the National Association of Manufacturers, and the U.S. Chamber of Commerce—released a report entitled *Investing in Teaching*.[7] Calling for a renaissance in teaching, the report describes:

- A new model of teacher preparation and professional development;

- A new model of teacher pay tied to performance and a new employment compact; and

- A new school environment that provides teachers with the freedom and flexibility to achieve results.

The business community is now partnering with educational leaders, policymakers, and other stakeholders to bring these models to fruition.

INDIVIDUAL COMPANY INITIATIVES

Individual companies invest significant resources and staff to provide grants, scholarships and fellowships, and executives-on-loan, among other options, to programs at the national, state, and local level. To name just a few:

- The Johnson & Johnson Bridge to Employment program provides mentoring opportunities, internships, job shadowing, teacher externships, guest lecturers for high school science classes, and curriculum development in eight communities across the country.

- Micron Technology devotes considerable staff time and energy to K–12 programs that demonstrate the importance of mathematics to twenty-first-century careers.

- Charles Schwaab offers conferences for student attendees to learn about quantitative literacy in the finance industry. A keynote speaker and various professionals typically describe their jobs and what is takes to be successful in their careers.

SETTING BENCHMARKS

The American Diploma Project (ADP), recently launched by Achieve, the National Alliance of Business, the Fordham Foundation, and the Education Trust, has three goals:

1. To develop and solidify demand—from higher education and employers—for standards-based high school assessment data in admissions and hiring processes;

2. To assist states in revising and/or strengthening their current standards-based systems; and

3. To develop national high school graduation benchmarks in English language arts and mathematics that all states may use to calibrate the quality and rigor of their standards and assessments.

Through this project, the business community seeks to identify, among other skills, the quantitative literacy that is fundamental to success in the workplace. The intent is to define benchmarks in terms of academic skills and courses that must be mastered in secondary school.

IMPLICATIONS

These business initiatives all address education, yet only the last one overtly addresses quantitative literacy, and then only in the context of school mathematics. Although the business community has demonstrated its sincere and long-standing commitment to education reform, the issue of quantitative literacy is almost absent from its education agenda. Furthermore, business leaders are not looking for new issues to champion, especially when substantial progress on existing issues remains elusive. Advocates for greater quantitative literacy, therefore, cannot expect business to take any position on the issue—much less to promote it in its principles for education reform—unless they themselves raise business awareness of the issue's importance. To do so, they first have to formulate a useful definition of quantitative literacy, one that clearly addresses the business demand for necessary knowledge and skills and one that is widely understood.

What Is Quantitative Literacy?

THE BUSINESS PERSPECTIVE

What does the phrase "the business perspective" mean? Clearly, the business community is not monolithic and we must always use caution with generalizations—perhaps even more caution when describing an issue such as quantitative literacy, which has yet to receive widespread attention from the business community.

When asked to describe quantitative literacy, a quality manager from General Electric characterized it as "the ability to conceptualize work, identify metrics for gathering data, and understand how to utilize data to take action to improve performance." By contrast, the head of organizational development at Quaker State Penzoil characterized it simply as the ability to apply "basic addition, subtraction, multiplication, and division skills to various situations on the job." A study of the skills and competencies needed in the environmental technologies industry contained aspects of both these characterizations:

Mathematics as applied in the workplace, and mathematics as taught in schools and colleges, can be very different. Most mathematics problems in the workplace involve applications of what is typically referred to as "basic arithmetic," i.e., addition, subtraction, multiplication, and division. However, these problems can vary considerably in their complexity and associated levels of mathematical reasoning. Many jobs require complex, high levels of mathematical reasoning, even though they do not require high level mathematical concepts found in geometry, trigonometry, or calculus. For example, adding production figures is very straightforward, but knowing when and how to calculate the average production for the day is more difficult; it is a two-step mathematical calculation and requires knowing both what an average is as well as how it is calculated. Even more complicated is understanding how and when to take into consideration scrap or waste, in order to calculate "net" production. . . . [8]

Are these conceptions necessarily different? While GE emphasized reasoning, Penzoil emphasized computation, two facets of current workplace responsibilities and of quantitative literacy. And, although the environmental technologies illustration unites reasoning and computation, it employs the word "mathematics" rather than quantitative literacy.

This is not to argue that the representatives of GE, Penzoil, or the environmental technologies industry agree or disagree about quantitative literacy. Indeed, the assertion of active agreement or disagreement implies far more awareness and discussion of quantitative literacy than currently exists in the business community. There is, in fact, no shared business-wide vocabulary about the issue, or a consensus on what constitutes quantitative literacy. Yet, progress in building a more quantitatively literate workforce depends on such consensus. Many businesses successfully "reinvented" themselves over the past decade by a deliberate process of change management motivated by a clear vision of new goals. Without such a clear, quantifiable vision, many business leaders hesitate to pursue change.

Although the business community has thus far shown little interest in developing a widely shared understanding of quantitative literacy, there are admittedly workplace efforts underway that could yield a common definition, perhaps by inference, perhaps as an unintended by-product.

Assessing Skills for Employment Readiness: The American College Testing (ACT) WorkKeys® program[9] offers a set of scales developed so that:

- Employers can identify and develop workers for a wide range of skilled jobs;

- Students and workers can document and advance their employability skills; and

- Educators can tailor instructional programs to help students acquire the skills employers need.

Yet the WorkKeys "Applied Mathematics" scale is primarily arithmetic, with virtually no reference to the reasoning skills sought by the GE quality manager. Although this scale might be appropriate for some entry-level jobs in some industries, its usefulness across the economy has not yet been demonstrated. Thus, its utility as the basis for a workplace definition of quantitative literacy is questionable at best.

Skills Standards: The National Skills Standards Board (NSSB) was created in 1994 to "build a voluntary national system of skill standards, assessment and certification systems to enhance the ability of the U.S. workforce to compete effectively in a global economy."[10] These standards were intended to define the work to be performed, how well the work must be done, and the level of knowledge and skill required. Although a description of quantitative literacy in the workplace might emerge from this initiative, this potential is far from being realized, because:

- The rate of change in the workplace has outpaced the development of the standards, rendering them almost obsolete by the time of release.

- The "least common denominator" often emerged from the process of developing standards, with the corresponding result of scant buy-in from different constituencies in the workplace.

THE EDUCATION PERSPECTIVE

In contrast to the business community, education groups offer more concrete definitions of quantitative literacy, even though they sometimes refer to these definitions under the rubric of "mathematical literacy."

One important definition serves as a foundation for the Programme for International Student Assessment (PISA), a first-of-its-kind international study of 15-year-old students' ability to apply reading, mathematics, and science literacy in real-world contexts. PISA characterizes mathematics literacy as "an individual's capacity to identify and understand the role that mathematics plays in the world, to make well-founded mathematical judgements and to engage in mathematics, in ways that meet the needs of that individual's current and future life as a constructive, concerned, and reflective citizen."[11]

In *Mathematics and Democracy: The Case for Quantitative Literacy*,[12] the National Council on Education and the Disciplines outlines several elements of quantitative literacy:

- Having facility with simple mental arithmetic; estimating arithmetic calculations; reasoning with proportions; counting by indirection;

- Using information conveyed as data, graphs, and charts; drawing inferences from that data; recognizing disaggregation as a factor in interpreting data;

- Formulating problems, seeking patterns, and drawing conclusions; recognizing interactions in complex systems; understanding linear, exponential, multivariate, and simulation models; understanding the impact of different rates of growth;

- Understanding the importance of variability; recognizing the difference between correlation and causation;

- Recognizing that seemingly improbable coincidences are not uncommon; and

- Using logical thinking; recognizing levels of rigor in methods of inference; checking hypotheses; exercising caution in making generalizations.

IMPLICATIONS

Attainment of quantitative literacy requires the ability to reason, to make sense of real-world situations, and to make judgments grounded in data. The description of lifelong literacy—"learning to read" and "reading to learn"—could provide a good model for the development of a similarly effective characterization of quantitative literacy. This model must capture the notion that people who acquire quantitative literacy gain a foundation for future learning, one that enables them to adapt to the demands of an increasingly technological world.

Still, the business and education communities have yet to close ranks around a single, well-known conception of quantitative literacy that could motivate a reform agenda advocated by both parties. What is emerging, however, is a consensus that there is *something new* needed by an educated adult, something more than arithmetic proficiency. Business leaders are seeing the problem; they have not yet seen the solution.

Who Needs Quantitative Literacy?

Rapid technological change has dramatically altered the American business landscape. The invention of the microprocessor, with its ability to move vast amounts of information, has prompted a technological explosion. Innovations stemming from more advanced technology, remote satellite communication systems, fiber optic cables, encryption, biotechnology and genomic discoveries, laser scanners, and the Internet have launched the marketplace in multiple, often uncharted, directions. As a result, a company's competitive advantage rests with its workers' ability to interpret data, make decisions, and use available technology. This is true, to some degree, of almost all jobs along the skill continuum, even though each calls for different levels of quantitative literacy.

Although some jobs are becoming more complex, computers and related technologies are simultaneously eliminating many traditional jobs. With the assistance of technology, one person, in dramatically less time, now can accomplish tasks that once were carried out by a team of people. ATMs have replaced bank tellers, on-line databases have replaced travel agents, and computer-operated machines have replaced factory laborers.

JOB GROWTH AND DECLINE

Projections from the Bureau of Labor Statistics for 1995–2008[13] confirm that the majority of shrinking occupations are those that are being replaced by technologies. Jobs performed by installers or operators are in the greatest decline: typesetting machine operators, railroad brake and signal machine operators, peripheral equipment operators, sewing machine operators, machine tool cutting operators, woodworking operators, and switchboard operators. Office automation and the increased use of word processing equipment by professionals and managerial employees also have led to a decline in individually paid word processors and typists, proofreaders and copy markers, payroll and time clerks, bank tellers, and bookkeeping and auditing clerks.

The four fastest growing occupations—computer engineers, computer support specialists, systems analysts, and database administrators—demand strong mathematical skills, complex problem solving, a facility with the use of technology, and the ability to evaluate data to anticipate future challenges. In other words, they require quantitative literacy.

Desktop publishing specialists and legal assistants, the next two fastest growing occupations, also follow this pattern. Incumbents in such jobs must have the ability to use technology to record and represent data and the ability to think logically and implement multilevel solutions to problems.

Other projected high-growth occupations require quantitative literacy. Home health aides, medical assistants, social and human service assistants, and physician assistants—often thought of as low-skill workers requiring a minimum of formal education—need to think logically and devise multilevel solutions to complex problems. Such skills, especially in health care, require significant quantitative skills as a frame of reference for administering correct dosages of medicine, gauging physical reactions, and judging the interaction of various treatments.

IMPLICATIONS

Although gainful employment is not the sole purpose of education, it is a necessary and expected outcome. Education therefore must be influenced by changes in the workplace. That some types of jobs disappear and new ones emerge is certainly not a new phenomenon; neither is the fact that education evolves to reflect the changing employment market.

The accelerating rate of change in the workplace, however, heightens the challenge. Mathematics education reform in the late 1980s criticized the lingering vestiges in school mathematics of a "shopkeeper curriculum" left over from the previous century for a nation no longer dominated by shopkeepers. We cannot afford the luxury of such a slow response, if we ever could.

The pervasiveness of quantitative literacy among jobs showing the greatest growth—and the reasonable assumption that the trend will continue—requires the education system to respond accordingly by incorporating quantitative literacy into schooling. In its frequent calls for "critical thinking" abilities or "real-world" skills, the business community has long been moving toward something resembling a conception of quantitative literacy. Still, a vast gulf separates this intuitive sense of new skill requirements from the advocacy of education reforms that can actually result in a quantitatively literate citizenry.

What Is Business Doing to Address Quantitative Literacy?

The answer is simple—not enough.

IN EDUCATION

Business involvement in education, as described earlier, is focused on policy. Calls for higher student achievement are often accompanied by calls for rigorous course work. What should comprise that rigorous course work—in mathematics or any subject—is not discussed in detail. Instead of addressing specific pedagogical or curricular questions in which it has little expertise, the business community focuses on broader issues in terms of outcomes:

- Algebra for *all* students;

- A world-class secondary school curriculum, as defined by the Third International Mathematics and Science Study (TIMSS); and

- A widening of the pipeline for scientists and engineers.

Although laudable, these recent business-led efforts to improve student achievement in mathematics do not necessarily advance the cause of quantitative literacy. Certainly, the business community's long-standing call to align curriculum, assessments, and teacher preparation with high-quality, rigorous academic standards promises to bring about much-needed gains in student achievement. Real progress toward widespread quantitative literacy, however, will require even more fundamental changes.

IN BUSINESS

Even in their own employee training programs, businesses do little to encourage quantitative literacy.

Effectiveness: Reports from the American Society of Training and Development, The Work in Northeast Ohio Council, and the National Association of Manufacturers indicate that training programs are effective—up to a point.[14] These studies provide evidence that corporate training programs can improve employee performance, firm productivity, product quality, and even company profitability. Indeed, such evaluations help business justify the expenditure. Over the long term, however, such gains in productivity and profitability will inevitably remain limited as long as the training is restricted to narrowly defined skill areas.

Course Content: Two types of corporate training programs—remedial and computer-based—could, but apparently do not, include quantitative literacy. Remedial programs tend to teach basic arithmetic and fail-safe formulas with little emphasis on problem solving. Employees are rarely taught to identify quantitative relationships in a range of contexts and settings, to consider a variety of approaches to manipulate those quantitative relationships, or to make data-based decisions on the job. As a result, few employees acquire even rudimentary quantitative literacy on successful completion of such a program.

With businesses incorporating more technology into their daily operations, the majority of workplace training—both formal and informal seminars—is computer related. Indeed, according to *Training Magazine,* nearly 40 percent of all workers receive formal training from their current employers.[15] These classes run the gamut from the use of spreadsheets to the use of advanced statistical analysis software such as SPSS.

Despite this universal access to computer training, such classes apparently have little impact on quantitative literacy. Existing computer training programs may fail to build strong quantitative literacy because they devote scant attention to the connection between computer applications and real-world scenarios. Because accessing technology does not necessarily depend on a person's ability to reason with the inputs or results, very few computer-related training courses are contextualized. Consequently, training providers focus their instruction on algorithmic usage at the expense of exploring the power of technology and the ways in which it can be applied in a variety of situations. The end result: workers gain only rudimentary knowledge of quantitative literacy through use of computer technology.

IMPLICATIONS

The candid answer to the question—What is business doing to address quantitative literacy?—remains: apparently very little, at least little that consciously addresses the challenge.

We could attribute this inaction to uncertainty about effective ways to broaden training or to participate meaningfully in educational discussions about curriculum. There could be a reluctance to invest the time and money without a clear means of measuring results. Business might be dismayed by the lack of a clear course of study that leads to quantitative literacy, or by many other training issues competing for attention and support in the business world.

Moreover, there is no clear leverage point to rally around. When students are not yet achieving at acceptable levels in traditional course work, the prospect of fighting for a new, somewhat amorphous concept with far-reaching curricular implications is daunting.

Most important, business leaders routinely measure investments of time, resources, and commitments against the potential "return on the investment." Without a clear understanding of the means and ends of quantitative literacy—the ways in which young and adult learners acquire the knowledge and skills, and the payoff for such acquisition—business will not likely make any serious investment.

This is not cause for discouragement but rather a window of opportunity.

Setting Greater Expectations

There is no better way to improve business' chance for success than by developing well-prepared, job-ready workers who think on their feet, learn on the job, and take on new challenges. Although these qualities may be commonplace among the highest tier of employees in innovative industries, they do not characterize the workforce writ large.

Our failure to produce a more quantitatively literate workforce presents our nation with an important civic and economic challenge. The business community has a critical role to play in assisting educators and the public in restructuring education in response to the needs of the modern workplace and the requirements of today's society. If we want to promote a palpable

increase in quantitative literacy, we must adopt an aggressive strategy designed to improve the knowledge and skills of the current and future workforce.

The following six action steps provide corporate America with a blueprint for meeting this challenge:

1. Participate with education and workplace researchers to better document the existing level of and anticipated need for quantitative literacy in the workplace.
The vibrancy of the U.S. economy—despite the recent downturn—and the high level of innovation throughout history suggests that there has always been a cadre of people with the necessary skills and verve. Yet, a greater proportion of the workforce needs quantitative literacy to sustain and grow business in the twenty-first century.

There seems to be little readily available data that could inform new policies to support broader acquisition of quantitative literacy. This is ironic, because in such a data-driven field, experts who promote quantitative literacy apparently have not gathered the ammunition to support the need expressed in their rhetoric.

Without data, questions pivotal to policy decision making end up unanswered. For example: What proportion of the population lacks quantitative literacy skills? What proportion of jobs requires quantitative literacy? What can business expect as a return on investment for implementing quantitative programs? Is it more cost effective to achieve quantitative literacy through the educational pipeline or through workplace training or through both? What are the educational characteristics of programs that would yield quantitative literacy?

The inability to answer such questions has impeded, and will continue to impede, progress in developing realistic options and programs that demonstrate results.

2. Work with schools and colleges and among companies to raise general awareness about the importance of quantitative literacy in today's workplace.
Most businesses do not recognize quantitative literacy in the workplace, making it difficult to design and support efforts to increase it. Because many use computational capabilities as a proxy for quantitative skills, they often develop and support educational programs that may rest on faulty assumptions. Quantitative literacy may even manifest itself differently from industry to industry, from occupation to occupation, from task to task, further complicating the situation.

As more data about quantitative literacy are gathered, and businesses analyze the demand for quantitative literacy in the workplace, they will be better equipped to formulate a cogent message to students, employees, educators, policymakers, and peer companies about the true implications of quantitative literacy in today's workplace. Such a public information campaign is needed to institutionalize quantitative literacy as a fundamental goal of the educational pipeline.

Because some information about workplace skills is proprietary and may bear on a company's competitive advantage in the marketplace, impartial business organizations and researchers may be best positioned to aggregate data on quantitative literacy and share it among interested stakeholders. A broad group of stakeholders, however, should work together to raise the level of awareness and understanding of quantitative literacy.

3. Provide leadership and support to achieve quantitative literacy among elementary and high school students.

A specific and workable conception of quantitative literacy should provide a foundation for long-term initiatives to improve U.S. secondary school education.

Ultimately, the typical business manager has a right to be perturbed when he or she pays twice to educate an employee—first through taxes for public education that did not fully succeed, and again through direct expenditures for that employee. While recognizing the need to shore up the skills of the current workforce, business must promote improvement in public schools as a means of increasing the skills of future generations.

Indeed, this need to promote improvement must extend beyond mere advocacy for higher standards to include a call for fundamental reforms to the way we teach mathematics. Business leaders regularly argue that even students who perform well in mathematics courses are often not prepared to function effectively in today's workplace because they lack versatility and flexibility in dealing with real-world obstacles. They become stymied by challenges for which there are no prescribed textbook solutions. Young people must learn this versatility and flexibility in school, long before they enter the workforce.

Business is particularly well equipped to make a powerful case for quantitative literacy in elementary and secondary schools, but first it must acknowledge that widespread quantitative literacy will not necessarily result from requirements that students take more mathematics courses. To effect more meaningful changes over the long term, business must become more fully engaged with the content and delivery of those courses.

4. Engage education and training partners to help upgrade the quantitative literacy of the workforce based on identified quantitative needs.

Although efforts to create a new generation of quantitatively literate Americans will promote a stronger economic future, the business and education communities cannot simply write off the current generation of workers. Businesses should capitalize on and modify existing training infrastructures to produce a more quantitatively literate workforce.

Large corporations are centralizing their education and training functions under a "Chief Learning Officer" (CLO) to bring a sense of strategy, purpose, and efficiency to far-flung educational and professional development functions. In such corporations, economies of scale allow this specialization of the CLO. Of course, the vast majority of U.S. companies are small and do not have the resources to conduct detailed job task analyses nor the expertise to choose the right mix of course work for their employees. There is no shortage of vendors and salespeople plying their wares to the small-business owner or human resources director. Unless there is a clear, functional skill needed by employees, however, a harried manager is likely to avoid the subject of education and training altogether.

Yet a small company may be able to gain access to external expertise by tapping the resources of a local small-business resources center, community college career development center, or continuing education division of a local college or university. These organizations not only offer specific training courses but they also can link a small business to planning and assessment tools, and possibly management consultants, who can help map out a company-wide employee development plan, which should include a focus on the range of quantitative literacy needed by employees. No matter what means they use, businesses must ensure that the planned curriculum is consonant with something more than arithmetic proficiency.

5. Invest Money Wisely and Measure Return on Investment.

Business needs to know that the money it invests is providing the skills that workers need. Whether this investment targets young people prior to employment or broadens and deepens their knowledge thereafter, business will rightfully insist on frequent measures of success. Increasing global competition and mounting educational challenges demand wise corporate investments that demonstrate educational achievement and workforce quality. Thus, employers must engage in regular, meaningful evaluation of their efforts.

6. Develop a Road Map for Continuous Improvement.

To create a mechanism for gauging the return on its investment, business requires an ambitious yet reasonable plan for improvement. If it simply strains after lofty goals, it will certainly fail. And it will—just as certainly—abandon the effort.

Rather, business leaders and educators must establish a succession of clear and attainable objectives, all of which must lead to the ultimate goal of ensuring that every U.S. citizen achieves a high level of quantitative literacy. Piecemeal success does not necessarily add up to a measurable national improvement—every localized initiative must support a much larger vision.

As Intel CEO and President Craig Barrett argues, the processes of continuous improvement common in the business world also can promote successful education reforms. To advance the cause of quantitative literacy, such processes must ultimately incorporate all the action steps described above into what Barrett, quoting W. Edwards Deming, calls a "plan-do-check-act" cycle.[16]

Advocates for quantitative literacy must first *plan:* define and measure the problem and then formulate a plan for addressing it. Then they must *do:* implement the plan in both schools and workforce training programs. Next, they must *check:* monitor the plan's results according to preestablished criteria for success. Finally, they must *act:* on the basis of these results they must enact targeted changes to the original plan. Then the process begins again, at a higher level. By learning from their mistakes while capitalizing on their achievements, reformers can make incremental but significant progress toward the goal of quantitative literacy for all Americans.

Unless business leaders and educators work together to develop a road map for achieving this goal that is at once visionary and practical, the cause of quantitative literacy will not move forward with the speed and resolve required in a competitive global economy.

Conclusion

The jobs of the twenty-first century are more complex than ever before. Technologies such as computers, e-mail, faxes, and the Internet have created a world awash in data. To succeed in this data-drenched society, employees need to have tools to make sense of information in faster and cheaper ways than heretofore. The notion of quantitative literacy promises to offer a mechanism for making sense of this world.

The principles advanced in this essay cannot provide any immediate or easily implemented solutions to the shortage of quantitatively literate citizens. Rather, they call for a committed and sustained effort to specify emerging needs for new quantitative skills, and then to rally stakeholders around carefully targeted programs addressing these needs. Although such an effort presents great challenges, it promises even greater rewards. If they work together toward clearly articulated goals, the business and education communities will have an unprecedented opportunity to prepare every U.S. citizen for success in a constantly changing world.

Appendix

Business Coalition for Excellence in Education: Principles for K–12 Education Legislation

In a world of global competition and rapid technological advances, U.S. schools must prepare all students for the challenges and opportunities of the twenty-first century. *To achieve this goal, our school systems must adopt higher standards, use high-quality assessments aligned to these standards, and hold schools accountable for results, so that all students have the opportunity to succeed.* Federal investments must help each state implement a standards-based, performance-driven education system that is carefully aligned to the goal of higher student achievement. The Business Coalition for Excellence in Education* urges Congress to enact bipartisan legislation that embodies the following principles:

Achieving Systemic Reforms

- **Standards:** All states should have high-quality, rigorous academic standards that reflect the levels of student achievement necessary to succeed in society, higher education, and the workplace. The federal government should provide all states with the information and resources to develop, continuously improve, and benchmark rigorous academic standards that can be used to raise individual student performance to world-class levels.

- **Assessments:** All students should be tested annually with high-quality assessments aligned to state standards. The purpose must be to measure the progress of school, teacher, and student achievement against standards and to identify where additional support is needed for students to reach them.

- **Student Achievement:** Assessments should be used as diagnostic tools to ensure that all students, particularly those identified as under-performing, receive the assistance they need to succeed in reaching high academic standards. Similarly, federal leadership should ensure that preschool aid focuses on helping prepare children to enter school ready to learn.

- **Accountability:** States, districts, and principals should ensure that all students, including disadvantaged and under-performing students, meet high academic standards. States should have policies of rewards and sanctions to hold systems accountable for improving the performance of students, teachers, and principals. Such policies should be based on performance, including student achievement.

---

* An ad hoc coalition of leading U.S. corporations and business organizations that support these principles in the reauthorization of the Elementary and Secondary Education Act

- **Flexibility:** States, localities, and schools should have flexibility for their educational organization, innovation, and instruction while being held accountable for raising student achievement.

- **Alignment:** States must ensure that high-quality assessments, accountability systems, teacher preparation and training, and curriculum are aligned with high state standards so that students, teachers, parents, and administrators can measure progress against common expectations for student achievement.

- **Data, Research, and Best Practices:** Student achievement data should be collected regularly, and made public in formats that can guide the decision-making of teachers, parents, and students to improve performance. Research must be pertinent to standards-based education systems to enable teachers to apply proven findings in the classroom.

Areas of Special Focus

- **Math and Science Excellence:** Efforts must be undertaken to increase significantly the number of skilled math and science teachers in K–12 by substantially improving the quality of their preparation and professional development and by expanding recruitment incentives. Investments must focus on raising student achievement in math and science by encouraging the use of world-class educational materials and instructional practice.

- **Teacher Preparation and Training:** It should be a national priority to increase significantly the quality, professionalism, and career opportunities within teaching. States should ensure that teachers have the necessary skills and expertise in the content areas in which they teach. They should ensure that teacher preparation and professional development programs include training to integrate relevant technologies into the classroom. Professional development programs should include principals.

- **Technology:** Technology and the Internet must be integrated into all appropriate aspects of teaching and learning to improve students' twenty-first century skills as well as educational accountability and administrative effectiveness. Aid should be provided to states and districts to help identify, acquire, and utilize the best available technology and to help teachers integrate it into the curriculum.

Notes

1. Philip R. Day and Robert H. McCabe, "Remedial Education: A Social and Economic Imperative," American Association of Community Colleges (AACC) Issue Paper, Washington, DC: American Association of Community Colleges, 1997.

2. American Management Association. Retrieved at http://www.amanet.org/research/pdfs/bjp_2001.pdf.

3. *Training Magazine,* Annual Report, Minneapolis: Bil Communications, Vol. 36, No. 10 (1999). Retrieved at http://www.trainingsupersite.com.

4. Milton Goldberg and Susan L. Traiman, "Why Business Backs Education Standards," in *Brookings Papers on Education Policy,* Diane Ravitch, ed. (Washington, DC: Brookings Institution, 2001).

5. U.S. Department of Labor, "20 Million Jobs: January 1993–November 1999," A Report by the Council of Economic Advisors and the Chief Economist, U.S. Department of Labor, December 3, 1999. Retrieved from http://clinton4.nova.gov/media/pdf/20miljobs.pdf

6. To date, the CEOs from Boeing, Eastman Kodak, IBM, Intel, Proctor & Gamble, Prudential, State Farm, and Williams have served on Achieve. Other executives—from Bristol-Myers Squibb, Pfizer, Washington Mutual, to name a few—have attended the meetings as guests.

7. National Alliance of Business, *Investing in Teaching* (Washington, DC: National Alliance of Business, 2001).

8. *Skills and Competencies Needed by Arizona's Workforce: The Environmental Technologies Industry* (Prepared for the Arizona Department of Commerce by Advancing Employee Systems, Inc. 2001), 16.

9. Visit http://www.act.org/workkeys/.

10. Visit http://www.nssb.org/.

11. See http://www.pisa.oecd/pisa/math.htm. Although the United States scored near the international average in the mathematical literacy part of the 2000 PISA examination, students in eight countries—Japan, Korea, New Zealand, Finland, Australia, Canada, Switzerland, and the United Kingdom—significantly outperformed American students. Results such as these underscore the urgency of developing a more quantitatively literate citizenry as a means of preserving our long-term economic competitiveness.

12. Lynn Arthur Steen, ed., *Mathematics and Democracy: The Case for Quantitative Literacy* (Princeton, NJ: National Council on Education and the Disciplines, 2001), 16–17.

13. U.S. Department of Labor Bureau of Labor Statistics, *Occupational Outlook Handbook* 2000–01 Edition (January 2000), 4–5.

14. See The Work in Northeast Ohio Council, "The Impact of Basic Skills Training on Employee and Organizational Effectiveness (October 2000); American Society for Training and Development, "Training Investments Improve Financial Success" (September 2000); "U.S. Business Views on Workforce Training," Price Waterhouse, prepared for American Society for Training Development, National Retail Federation, National Association of Manufacturing, and Student Loan Marketing Association (April 1994), 7–10. Also visit www.nam.org/tertiary_print.asp?TrackID=&CategoryID=678&DocumentID=1419.

15. *Training Magazine,* "2000 Industry Report: A Comprehensive Analysis of Employer-Sponsored Training in the U.S."

16. Craig R. Barrett, speech delivered at the 33rd Annual Meeting of the National Alliance of Business in Arlington, VA (November 6, 2001).

Data, Shapes, Symbols: Achieving Balance in School Mathematics

LYNN ARTHUR STEEN

Mathematics is our "invisible culture" (Hammond 1978). Few people have any idea how much mathematics lies behind the artifacts and accoutrements of modern life. Nothing we use on a daily basis—houses, automobiles, bicycles, furniture, not to mention cell phones, computers, and Palm Pilots—would be possible without mathematics. Neither would our economy nor our democracy: national defense, Social Security, disaster relief, as well as political campaigns and voting, all depend on mathematical models and quantitative habits of mind.

Mathematics is certainly not invisible in education, however. Ten years of mathematics is required in every school and is part of every state graduation test. In the late 1980s, mathematics teachers led the national campaign for high, publicly visible standards in K-12 education. Nonetheless, mathematics is the subject that parents most often recall with anxiety and frustration from their own school experiences. Indeed, mathematics is the subject most often responsible for students' failure to attain their educational goals. Recently, mathematics curricula have become the subject of ferocious debates in school districts across the country.

My intention in writing this essay is to make visible to curious and uncommitted outsiders some of the forces that are currently shaping (and distorting) mathematics education. My focus is on the second half of the school curriculum, grades 6 to 12, where the major part of most students' mathematics education takes place. Although mathematics is an abstract science, mathematics education is very much a social endeavor. Improving mathematics education requires, among many other things, thorough understanding of the pressures that shape current educational practice. Thus I begin by unpacking some of the arguments and relevant literature on several issues—tracking, employment, technology, testing, algebra, data, and achievement—that are responsible for much of the discord in current public discussion about mathematics education.

Following discussion of these external forces, I examine the changing world of mathematics itself and its role in society. This leads to questions of context and setting, of purposes and goals, and quickly points in the direction of broader mathematical sciences such as statistics and numeracy. By blending the goals of mathematics, statistics, and numeracy, I suggest—in the final section of the essay—a structure for mathematics education in grades 6 to 12 that can help more students leave school equipped with the mathematical tools they will need for life and career.

External Forces

Beginning with *A Nation at Risk* (National Commission on Excellence in Education 1983) and continuing through *Before It's Too Late,* the report of the Glenn Commission (National Commission on Mathematics and Science Teaching for the 21st Century 2000), countless hand-wringing reports have documented deficiencies in mathematics education. Professional societies (American Mathe-

Lynn Arthur Steen is Professor of Mathematics at St. Olaf College, and an advisor to the Mathematics Achievement Partnership (MAP) of Achieve, Inc. Earlier, Steen served as executive director of the Mathematical Sciences Education Board and as president of the Mathematical Association of America. Steen is the editor or author of many books and articles, including *Mathematics and Democracy* (2001), *Why Numbers Count* (1997), *On the Shoulders of Giants* (1991), and *Everybody Counts* (1989).

matical Association of Two-Year Colleges 1995; National Council of Teachers of Mathematics 1989, 2000) have responded with reform-oriented recommendations while states (e.g., California, Virginia, Minnesota, Texas, and dozens of others) have created standards and frameworks suited to their local traditions. Analysis of these proposals, much of it critical, has come from a wide variety of sources (e.g., Cheney 1997; Kilpatrick 1997; Wu 1997; Raimi and Braden 1998; Gavosto, et al. 1999; Stotsky 2000). In some regions of the country, these debates have escalated into what the press calls "math wars" (Jackson 1997).

Nearly one-hundred years ago, Eliakim Hastings Moore, president of the young American Mathematical Society, argued that the momentum generated by a more practical education in school would better prepare students to proceed "rapidly and deeply" with theoretical studies in higher education (Moore 1903). In the century that followed, mathematics flowered in both its practical and theoretical aspects, but school mathematics bifurcated: one stream emphasized mental exercises with little obvious practical value; the other stream stressed manual skills with no theoretical value. Few schools ever seriously followed Moore's advice of using practical education as a stepping-stone to theoretical studies.

Now, following a century of steady growth based on rising demand and a relatively stable curricular foundation, a new president of the American Mathematical Society has warned his colleagues that the mathematical sciences are undergoing a "phase transition" from which some parts might emerge smaller and others dispersed (Bass 1997). The forces creating this transition are varied and powerful, rarely under much control from educators or academics. I have selected only a few to discuss here, but I believe these few will suffice to illustrate the nuances that too often are overlooked in simplistic analyses of editorials, op-ed columns, and school board debate. I begin with the contentious issue of tracking.

TRACKING

Until quite recently, mathematics was never seen as a subject to be studied by all students. For most of our nation's history, and in most other nations, the majority of students completed their school study of mathematics with advanced arithmetic—prices, interest, percentages, areas, and other topics needed for simple commerce. Only students exhibiting special academic interest studied elementary algebra and high school geometry; even fewer students, those exhibiting particular mathematical talent, took advanced algebra and trigonometry. For many generations, the majority of students studied only commercial or vocational mathematics, which contained little if any of what we now think of as high school mathematics.

In recent decades, as higher education became both more important and more available, the percentage of students electing the academic track increased substantially. In the 1970s, only about 40 percent of U.S. students took two years of mathematics (algebra and geometry) in secondary school; 25 years later that percentage has nearly doubled. The percentage of high school students taking three years of mathematics has climbed similarly, from approximately 30 percent to nearly 60 percent (National Science Board 1996; Dossey and Usiskin 2000).

This shift in the presumption of mathematics as a subject for an academic elite to mathematics as a core subject for all students represents the most radical transformation in the philosophy of mathematics education in the last century. In 1800, Harvard University expected of entering students only what was then called "vulgar" arithmetic. One century later, Harvard expected a year of Euclid; two centuries later—in 2000—Harvard expects that most entering students have studied calculus. In no other subject has the expected level of accomplishment of college-bound students increased so substantially. These changes signal a profound shift in public expectations for the mathematical performance of high school graduates, a change that is sweeping the globe as nations race to keep up with rapidly advancing information technology. Secondary school mathematics is no longer a subject for the few, but for everyone.

In response to the increasing need for mathematical competence in both higher education and the high-performance workplace, the National Council of Teachers of Mathematics (NCTM) initiated the 1990s movement for national standards by recommending that *all* students learn a common core of high-quality mathematics including algebra, geometry, and data analysis (NCTM 1989). Dividing students into academic and nonacademic tracks, NCTM argued, no longer makes the sense it once did when the United States was primarily an agrarian and assembly line economy. In this old system—remnants of which have not yet entirely disappeared—college-bound students were introduced to algebra and geometry while those in vocational tracks were expected only to master arithmetic. Because algebra was not needed in yesterday's world of work, it was not taught to students in the lower tracks. This vocational tradition of low expectations (and low prestige) is precisely what NCTM intended to remedy with its call for a single core curriculum for all students.

Yet even as "mathematics for all" has become the mantra of reform, schools still operate, especially in mathematics, with separate tracks as the primary strategy for delivery of curriculum. They are reinforced in this habit by teachers who find it easier to teach students with similar mathematical backgrounds and by parents who worry not that *all* children learn but that their *own* children learn. Indeed, parents' anxiety about ensuring their own children's success has rapidly transformed an academic debate about tracking into one of the more contentious issues in education (e.g., Oakes 1985; Oakes 1990; Sheffield 1999). Thus, the most common critique of the NCTM standards is that by advocating the same mathematics for all they fail to provide mathematically talented students with the stimulation they need and deserve (Jackson 1997; Wu 1996).

As the world of work has become increasingly quantitative, even the historic reasons for tracking have come under scrutiny. From advanced manufacturing to precision agriculture, from medical imaging to supermarket management, competitive industries now depend not just on arithmetic and percentages but also on such tools as quantitative models, statistical quality control, and computer-controlled machines. Effective vocational programs must now set demanding mathematics standards that reflect the same kinds of higher-order thinking heretofore found only in the academic track (Steen and Forman 1995). Although details of content differ, expectations for rigorous logical thinking are very similar.

Indeed, mathematics in the workplace offers students opportunities to grapple with authentic, open-ended problems that involve messy numbers, intricate chains of reasoning, and lengthy multistep solutions— opportunities that rarely are found in traditional college-preparatory mathematics curricula. By deploying elementary mathematics in sophisticated settings, modern work-based tasks can give students not only motivation and context but also a concrete foundation from which they can later abstract and generalize.

Both traditional tracks—academic and vocational—have been pushed by their clienteles to increase significantly the level of mathematical performance expected of students. To be sure, not every school or program has responded equally to these heightened expectations. There are still large numbers of students who complete a vocational program (and sometimes an academic program) without really mastering any significant part of secondary school mathematics. But the direction of change is clear and the movement to eliminate dead-end courses is gaining momentum.

EMPLOYMENT

During the last decade of the twentieth century, just as the movement for academic standards began, business and industry launched a parallel effort to articulate entry-level skill standards for a broad range of industries (NSSB 1998) as well as to suggest better means of linking academic preparation with the needs of employers (Bailey 1997; Forman and Steen 1998).

Although preparing students for work has always been one purpose of education, teachers generally adopt broader goals and more specifically academic purposes. Mathematics educators are

no exception. The canonical curriculum of school mathematics— arithmetic, algebra, geometry, trigonometry, calculus—is designed primarily to introduce students to the discipline of mathematics and only incidentally to provide tools useful for jobs and careers. Were schools to design mathematics programs expressly for work and careers, the selection of topics, the order in which they are taken up, and the kinds of examples employed would be substantially different.

The contrast between these two perspectives—mathematics in school versus mathematics at work—is especially striking (Forman and Steen 1999). Mathematics in the workplace makes sophisticated use of elementary mathematics rather than, as in the classroom, elementary use of sophisticated mathematics. Work-related mathematics is rich in data, interspersed with conjecture, dependent on technology, and tied to useful applications. Work contexts often require multistep solutions to open-ended problems, a high degree of accuracy, and proper regard for required tolerances. None of these features is found in typical classroom exercises.

Even core subjects within mathematics change when viewed from an employment perspective. Numbers in the workplace are embedded in context, used with appropriate units of measurement, and supported by computer graphics. They are used not just to represent quantities but also to calculate tolerances and limit errors. Algebra is used not so much to solve equations as to represent complex relationships in symbolic form. Geometry is used not so much to prove results as for modeling and measuring, especially in three dimensions.

It should come as no surprise, therefore, to discover that employers are distressed by the weak mathematical and quantitative skills of high school graduates. It is not uncommon for employers in high-performance industries such as Motorola, Siemens, and Michelin to find that only 1 in 20 job applicants has the skills necessary to join their training programs, and that only 1 in 50 can satisfactorily complete job training. (This employment situation is the industrial face of the immense remediation problem facing colleges and universities.)

It turns out that what current and prospective employees lack is not calculus or college algebra, but a plethora of more basic quantitative skills that could be taught in high school but are not (Murnane and Levy 1996; Packer 1997). Employees need statistics and three-dimensional geometry, systems thinking and estimation skills. Even more important, they need the disposition to think through problems that blend quantitative data with verbal, visual, and mechanical information; the capacity to interpret and present technical information; and the ability to deal with situations when something goes wrong (MSEB 1995). Although many jobs in the new economy require advanced training in mathematics, most do not. Nonetheless, all require a degree of numeracy unheard of a generation earlier as computers, data, and numbers intrude into the language of ordinary work.

This broader perspective of employers is well expressed in an influential government report entitled *What Work Requires of Schools* (Secretary's Commission on Achieving Necessary Skills 1991). Instead of calling for *subjects* such as mathematics, physics, and history, this so-called SCANS report asks for *competencies* built on a foundation of basic skills (reading, writing, listening, speaking, arithmetic), thinking skills (creative thinking, reasoning, problem solving, decision making, processing symbols, acquiring and applying new knowledge), and personal qualities (responsibility, self-esteem, sociability, self-management, integrity). These competencies, similar to what in other countries are sometimes called "key skills," are:

- *Resources:* Time, money, material, facilities, and human resources

- *Interpersonal:* Teamwork, teaching, service, leadership, negotiation, and diversity

- *Information:* Acquire, evaluate, organize, maintain, interpret, communicate, and transform

- *Systems:* Understand, monitor, and improve social, organizational, and technological systems

- *Technology:* Select, apply, and maintain technology

Mathematical thinking is embedded throughout these competencies, not just in the set of basic skills but as an essential component of virtually every competency. Reasoning, making decisions, solving problems, managing resources, interpreting information, understanding systems, applying technology — all these and more build on quantitative and mathematical acumen. But they do not necessarily require fluency in factoring polynomials, deriving trigonometric identities, or other arcana of school mathematics (Packer, see pp. 39–41).

TECHNOLOGY

The extraordinary ability of computers to generate and organize data has opened up an entire new world to mathematical analysis. Mathematics is the science of patterns (Steen 1988; Devlin 1994) and technology enables mathematicians (and students) to study patterns as they never could before. In so doing, technology offers mathematics what laboratories offer science: an endless source of evidence, ideas, and conjectures. Technology also offers both the arts and sciences a new entrée into the power of mathematics: fields as diverse as cinema, finance, and genetics now deploy computer-based mathematical tools to discover, create, and explore patterns.

Modern computers manipulate data in quantities that overwhelm traditional mathematical tools. Computer chips now finally have achieved sufficient speed and power to create visual displays that make sense to the human eye and mind. Already visualization has been used to create new mathematics (fractals), to develop new proofs (of minimal surfaces), to provide tools for new inferences (in statistics), and to improve instruction (geometer's sketchpad). Indeed, the computer-enhanced symbiosis of eye and image is fundamentally changing what it means to understand mathematics.

Computers also are changing profoundly how mathematics is practiced. The use of spreadsheets for storing, analyzing, and displaying data is ubiquitous in all trades and crafts. So too are computer tools of geometry that enable projection, rotation, inversions, and other fundamental operations to be carried out with a few keystrokes. Scientists and engineers report that, for students in these fields, facility with spreadsheets (as well as other mathematical software) is as important as conceptual understanding of mathematics and more valuable than fluency in manual computation (Barker 2000). With rare exceptions (primarily theoretical scientists and mathematicians) mathematics in practice means mathematics mediated by a computer.

As the forces unleashed by the revolution in technology change the character of mathematics, so they also impact mathematics education. It has been clear for many years that technology alters priorities for mathematics education (e.g., MSEB 1990). Much of traditional mathematics (from long division to integration by parts) was created not to enhance understanding but to provide a means of calculating results. This mathematics is now embedded in silicon, so training people to implement these methods with facility and accuracy is no longer as important as it once was. At the same time, technology has increased significantly the importance of other parts of mathematics (e.g., statistics, number theory, discrete mathematics) that are widely used in information-based industries.

Calculators and computers also have had enormous—and controversial—impact on mathematics pedagogy. Wisely used, they can help students explore patterns and learn mathematics by direct experience (Hembree and Dessart 1992; Askew and William 1995; Waits and Demana 2000), processes heretofore only possible through tedious and error-prone manual methods. Unwisely used, they become an impediment to students' mastery of basic skills or, even worse, a device that misleads students about the true nature of mathematics. Students who rely inappropriately on calculators often confuse approximations with exact answers, thereby depriving themselves of any possibility of recognizing or appreciating the unique certainty of mathematical deduction.

In the long run, technology's impact on mathematics education may be much broader than merely influencing changes in content or pedagogy. The rapid growth of a technology-driven economy that creates wealth as much from information and ideas as from labor and capital magnifies enormously the importance of intellectual skills such as mathematics. It also increases the social costs of differential accomplishment in school mathematics. Because of technology, it matters much more now than previously if a student leaves school with weak mathematical skills.

At the same time, computers and calculators are increasing dramatically the number of people who use mathematics, many of whom are not well educated in mathematics. Previously, only those who learned mathematics used it. Today many people use mathematical tools for routine work with spreadsheets, calculators, and financial systems, tools that are built on mathematics they have never studied and do not understand. This is a new experience in human history, with problematic consequences that we are only gradually discovering.

Finally, as the technology-driven uses of mathematics multiply, pressure will mount on schools to teach both information technology and more and different mathematics (ITEA 2000; NRC 1999). At the same time, and for the same reasons, increasing pressure will be applied on teachers and schools to ensure that no child is left behind. Alarms about the "digital divide" already have sounded and will continue to ring loudly in the body politic (Compaigne 2001; Norris 2001; Pearlman 2002). The pressure on mathematics to form a bipartisan alliance with technology in the school curriculum will be enormous. This easily could lead to a new type of tracking—one track offering the minimal skills needed to operate the new technology with little if any understanding, the other offering mathematical understanding as the surest route to control of technology. Evidence of the emergence of these two new cultures is not hard to find.

TESTING

Largely because of its strong tradition of dispersed authority and local control, the United States has no system to ensure smooth articulation between high school and college mathematics programs. Instead, students encounter a chaotic mixture of traditional and standards-based high school curricula; Advanced Placement (AP) examinations in Calculus, Statistics, and Computer Science; very different SAT and ACT college entrance examinations; diverse university admissions policies; skills-based mathematics placement examinations; and widely diverse first-year curricula in college, including several levels of high school algebra

(elementary, intermediate, and "college") and of calculus ("hard" (mainstream), "soft," and "reformed").

This cacophony of tests and courses is not only confusing and inefficient but also devastating for students who lack the support of experienced adult advocates. Following the rules and passing the tests does not necessarily prepare students either for employment or for continuing education. As a consequence, many new graduates find that they "can't get there from here." For some students, mathematics education turns out to be a "hoax" (Education Trust 1999).

The negative consequences of this incoherent transition have been magnified greatly in recent years as states began, for the first time, to institute meaningful (high-stakes) exit examinations that students must pass to receive a high school diploma (Gardner 1999; Sacks 2000; Shrag 2000). Many states have been shocked by the low passing rates on such examinations, and have had to retrench on their graduation requirements (Groves 2000). At the same time, parents and politicians have increased their emphasis on tests such as the SAT, ACT, and AP that have significant influence in college admissions even as university officials (led by University of California President Richard Atkinson) have called into question the appropriateness of these tests as a gateway to college (Atkinson 2001).

Despite all this testing, once students arrive in college, hundreds of thousands find themselves placed in remedial courses such as intermediate algebra in which they are required to master arcane skills that rarely are encountered in adult life. As more students pursue postsecondary study—both before and while working—and as these students bring to their studies increasingly diverse backgrounds and career intentions, incoherent and arbitrary testing in the transition from school to college becomes increasingly untenable.

A rational system of mathematics education should provide clear and consistent messages about what knowledge and skills are expected at each educational level. Ideally, graduation examinations from secondary school also would certify, based on different scores, admission to college without remediation. Such a system would require that everyone involved in the transition from high school to college concur on the expected outcomes of high school mathematics and that these goals be reflected in the tests. To be politically acceptable, transition tests must be within reach of most students graduating from today's high schools, yet to be educationally useful, they must ensure levels of performance appropriate to life, work, and study after high school. No state has yet figured out how to meet both these objectives.

ALGEBRA

In the Middle Ages, algebra meant calculating by rules (algorithms). During the Renaissance, it came to mean calculation with signs and symbols—using x's and y's instead of numbers. (Even today, laypersons tend to judge algebra books by the symbols they contain: they believe that more symbols mean more algebra, more words, less.) In subsequent centuries, algebra came to be primarily about solving equations and determining unknowns. School algebra still focuses on these three aspects: following procedures, employing letters, and solving equations.

In the twentieth century, algebra moved rapidly and powerfully beyond its historical roots. First it became what we might call the science of arithmetic—the abstract study of the operations of arithmetic. As the power of this "abstract algebra" became evident in such diverse fields as economics and quantum mechanics, algebra evolved into the study of *all* operations, not just the four found in arithmetic. Thus did it become truly the language of mathematics and, for that reason, the key to access in our technological society (Usiskin 1995).

Indeed, algebra is now, in Robert Moses' apt phrase, "the new civil right" (Moses 1995). In today's society, algebra means access. It unlocks doors to productive careers and democratizes access to big ideas. As an alternative to dead-end courses in general and commercial mathematics, algebra serves as an invaluable engine of equity. The notion that by identifying relationships we can discover things that are unknown—"that we can find out what *we* want to know"—is a very powerful and liberating idea (Malcolm 1997).

Not so long ago, high school algebra served as the primary filter to separate college-bound students from their work-bound classmates. Advocates for educational standards then began demanding "algebra for all," a significant challenge for a nation accustomed to the notion that only some could learn algebra (Steen 1992; Chambers 1994; Lacampagne et al. 1995; Silver 1997; NCTM and MSEB 1998). More recently, this clamor has escalated to a demand that every student complete algebra by the end of eighth grade (Steen 1999; Achieve 2001).

The recent emphasis on eighth-grade algebra for all has had the unfortunate side effect of intensifying distortions that algebra already imposes on school mathematics. One key distortion is an overemphasis on algebraic formulas and manipulations. Students quickly get the impression from algebra class that mathematics *is* manipulating formulas. Few students make much progress toward the broad goals of mathematics in the face of a curriculum dominated by the need to become fluent in algebraic manipulation. Indeed, overemphasis on algebra drives many students away from mathematics: most students who leave mathematics do so because they cannot see any value in manipulating strings of meaningless symbols.

What is worse, the focus on formulas as the preferred methodology of school mathematics distorts the treatment of other important parts of mathematics. For example, despite the complexity of its algebraic formula, the bell-shaped normal distribution is as ubiquitous in daily life as are linear and exponential functions and far more common than quadratic equations. As citizens, it is very helpful to understand that repeated measurements of the same thing (length of a table) as well as multiple measurements of different although similar things (heights of students) tend to follow the normal distribution. Knowing why some distributions (e.g., salaries, sizes of cities) do not follow this pattern is equally important, as is understanding something about the tails of the normal distribution—which can be very helpful in thinking about risks (or SAT scores).

Yet despite its obvious value to society, the normal distribution is all but ignored in high school mathematics, whereas quadratic and periodic functions are studied extensively. Many reasons can be advanced to explain this imbalance, e.g., that mathematicians favor models of the physical over the behavioral sciences. But surely one of the most important is that the algebraic formula for the normal distribution is quite complex and cannot be fully understood without techniques of calculus. The bias in favor of algebraic formulas as the preferred style of understanding mathematics—instead of graphs, tables, computers, or verbal descriptions—causes mathematics teachers to omit from the high school curriculum what is surely one of the most important and most widely used tools of modern mathematics.

That a subject that for many amounts to little more than rote fluency in manipulating meaningless symbols came to occupy such a privileged place in the school curriculum is something of a mystery, especially since so many parents, when they were students, found it unbearable. Perhaps more surprising is algebra's strong support among those many successful professionals who, having mastered algebra in school, found no use for it in their adult lives. Why is it that we insist on visiting on eighth graders a subject that, more than any other, has created generations of math-anxious and math-avoiding adults?

Many argue on the simple, pragmatic "civil right" ground that algebra is, wisely or unwisely, of central importance to the current system of tests that govern the school-to-college transition (not to mention providing essential preparation for calculus, which itself has taken on exaggerated significance in this same transition). But this is just a circular argument. We need to study algebra to pass tests that focus on algebra. And why do the tests focus on algebra? Because it is the part of mathematics that virtually all students study.

Others may cite, as grounds for emphasizing algebra, the widespread use of formulas in many different fields of work; however, this use is only a tiny part of what makes up the school subject of algebra. Moreover, most business people give much higher priority to statistics than to algebra. Some mathematicians and scientists assert that algebra is *the* gateway to higher mathematics, but this is so only because our curriculum makes it so. Much of mathematics can be learned and understood via geometry, or data, or spreadsheets, or software packages. Which subjects we emphasize early and which later is a choice, not an inevitability.

Lurking behind the resurgent emphasis on algebra is a two-edged argument concerning students who are most likely to be poorly educated in mathematics—poor, urban, first generation, and minority. Many believe that such students, whose only route to upward mobility is through school, are disproportionately disadvantaged if they are denied the benefits that in our current system only early mastery of algebra can confer. Others worry that emphasis on mastering a subject that is difficult to learn and not well taught in many schools will only exacerbate existing class differences by establishing algebra as a filter that will block anyone who does not have access to a very strong educational environment. Paradoxically, and unfortunately, both sides in this argument appear to be correct.

Data

Although algebra and calculus may be the dominant goals of school mathematics, in the real world mathematical activity usually begins not with formulas but with data. Measurements taken at regular intervals—be they monthly sales records, hourly atmospheric pressure readings, or millisecond samples of musical tones—form the source data for mathematical practice. Rarely if ever does nature present us with an algebraic formula to be factored or differentiated. Although the continuous model of reality encapsulated by algebra and calculus is a powerful tool for developing theoretical models, real work yielding real results must begin and end in real data.

In past eras, mathematics relied on continuous models because working with real data was too cumbersome. An algebraic or differential equation with three or four parameters could describe reasonably well the behavior of phenomena with millions of potential data points, but now computers have brought digital data into the heart of mathematics. They enable practitioners of mathematics to work directly with data rather than with the simplified continuous approximations that functions provide. Moreover, they have stimulated whole new fields of mathematics going under names such as combinatorics, discrete mathematics, and exploratory data analysis.

Thus as school mathematics has become increasingly preoccupied with the role of algebra, many users of mathematics have discovered that combinatorial and computer methods are of far greater utility. Whereas school algebra deals primarily with models and continuous functions, combinatorics and data analysis deal with measurements and discrete data. The one reflects a Platonic world of ideal objects, the other the realism of measured quantities. In the Platonic world, theorems are eternal; in the real world, computations are contingent. This contrast between the ideal and the utilitarian can be seen from many different perspectives ranging from philosophical to pedagogical.

One such domain is education. The competition for curricular time between functions and data reflects fundamental disagreements about the nature of mathematics as a discipline and as a school subject. Traditionally, and philosophically, mathematics has been thought of as a science of ideal objects—numbers, quantities, and shapes that are precisely defined and thus amenable to logically precise relations known as theorems. In practice, mathematics presents a more rough-and-ready image: it is about solving problems in the real world that involve measured quantities that are never perfectly precise. Tension between these two views of mathematics has a long history. But now, with the advent of computers, this tension has resurfaced with even greater force and significance. At its core, the debate is about the definition of mathematics as a discipline.

Achievement

Strained by a growing number of forces and pressures (only some of which are discussed here), U.S. mathematics educators have found it very difficult to improve student achievement—education's bottom line. For at least the last half-century, graduates of U.S. secondary schools have lagged behind their peers in other nations, especially those of the industrial world and the former Communist bloc. Documentation of this deficiency has been most consistent in mathematics and science, subjects that are relatively common in the curricula of other nations and that are examined internationally at regular intervals. Some U.S. analysts seek to explain (or excuse) poor U.S. performance by hypothesizing a negative impact of our relatively heterogeneous population, or conjecturing that a larger percentage of U.S. students complete secondary school, or arguing that other nations (or the United States) did not test a truly random sample. But despite these exculpatory claims, a central stubborn fact remains: on international tests administered over several decades to similarly educated students, the mathematics performance of U.S. eighth- and twelfth-grade students has always been well below international norms.

The most recent headlines came from TIMSS, the Third International Mathematics and Science Study, and its repeat, TIMSS-R.

The TIMSS results, confirmed by TIMSS-R, document a decline in the performance of U.S. students, as compared with their peers in other nations, as they progress through school (IEA 2000). Fourth graders in the United States have command of basic arithmetic on a par with students in most other nations, but the longer U.S. students study mathematics, the worse they become at it, comparatively speaking (Beaton et al. 1996; Schmidt et al. 1996). Middle school mathematics, especially, exhibits "a pervasive and intolerable mediocrity" (Silver 1998) that sends students into a downward glide that leaves them in twelfth grade with a mathematical performance that is virtually at the bottom of all industrialized nations. Even the best U.S. twelfth-grade students who are enrolled in advanced mathematics courses perform substantially below the average twelfth-grade students in most other nations (National Center for Education Statistics 1998).

The TIMSS findings are consistent with other analyses of U.S. student achievement from an international perspective (McKnight et al. 1987; Lapointe et al. 1989). They document the consequences of a leisurely curriculum in the last half of elementary school when textbooks fail to introduce much that has not already been covered (Flanders 1987). What makes matters even worse is the long-standing performance differences among white, black, and Hispanic students at all grade levels (Campbell et al. 1996; National Center for Education Statistics 2000). Although this performance gap has been narrowing on tasks that assess procedural knowledge and skills, substantial differences remain on tasks that assess conceptual understanding, mathematical reasoning, and problem solving (Secada 1992; Kenney and Silver 1996). Thus at a time of increasing integration of a global economy, large numbers of U.S. students, disproportionately minority, leave school significantly behind world norms in the language of the information age—mathematics.

Not surprisingly, more detailed examination of the TIMSS results reveals that U.S. students perform relatively better on some mathematical topics and worse on others. For example, relative to their international peers, our eighth-grade students are especially weak in geometry, measurement, and proportional reasoning, although closer to average in arithmetic and algebra. A similar profile emerged from the Second International Mathematics Study (SIMS) conducted in 1981–82 (Crosswhite et al. 1986; McKnight et al. 1987). Interestingly, the topics on which our students lag behind international norms (for example, measurement, geometry, and proportional thinking) are precisely the areas cited by noneducators as most important for adult life.

Quantitative Practices

The forces created by differential tracking, needs of employment, impacts of technology, misaligned testing, overemphasis on algebra, underemphasis on data, and student underachievement exert profound influence on schools, teachers, and students. These forces shape and often distort the educational process, constraining teachers and enticing students in directions that are rarely well aligned with sound educational goals. To have a significant and lasting effect, changes proposed for school mathematics must take these external forces into account, seeking wherever possible to use them for advantageous leverage.

School mathematics also needs to be responsive to changes in mathematics itself—its scope, practice, methods, and roles in society. Most people think of mathematics as unchanging, as a collection of formulas and facts passed down like ancient texts from earlier generations. Nothing could be further from the truth. Mathematical discovery has grown at an amazing rate throughout the past century, accelerating in recent decades as computers provide both new problems to solve and new tools with which to solve old problems (Odom 1998). At the same time, and for much the same reason, the roles played by mathematics in society have expanded at a phenomenal rate. No longer confined to specialized fields such as engineering or accounting, mathematical methods permeate work and life in the information age.

As mathematics has expanded rapidly to provide models for computer-based applications, so too has statistics, the science of data. Statistics is a hybrid discipline with some roots in mathematics but even more in social science, agriculture, government records, economic policy, and medical research. Especially since 1989, when NCTM called for greater emphasis on statistics and data analysis in the school curriculum, statistics has become part of the agenda for school mathematics. Arguably, for most students it may be the most important part.

As mathematical ideas increasingly permeate public policy, those concerned with citizenship and democracy have begun to see a real need for quantitative practices not readily subsumed by either mathematics or statistics. These practices, called "numeracy" elsewhere, are relatively new in the U.S. educational context. Indeed, the explicit parallels between numeracy and literacy as marks of an educated person are really no more than 10 or 15 years old (Paulos 1988; Steen 1990). As the disciplines of mathematics and statistics have expanded in scope and influence, their impact on public life has created a rising demand for the interdisciplinary (or crosscutting) capacity we call numeracy. Mathematics and numeracy are two sides of the same coin—the one Platonic, the other pragmatic, the one abstract, the other contextual.

As all three forms of quantitative practice—mathematics, statistics, and numeracy— evolve under the selective pressures of information technology and a global economy, schools must find ways to teach all three. Before exploring how this might be done, we first elaborate on the nature of these three domains of quantitative practice.

MATHEMATICS

During the last half-century, as mathematics in school grew from an elite to a mass subject, mathematics expanded into a portfolio of mathematical sciences that now includes, in addition to traditional pure and applied mathematics, subjects such as statistics, financial mathematics, theoretical computer science, operations research (the science of optimization) and, more recently, financial mathematics and bioinformatics. (It is a little-appreciated fact that most of the advances—and fortunes—being made in investments, genetics, and technology all derive from clever applications of sophisticated mathematics.) Although each of these specialties has its own distinctive character, methodologies, standards, and accomplishments, they all build on the same foundation of school and college mathematics.

Mathematics is far more than just a tool for research. In fact, its most common uses—and the reason for its prominent place in school curricula—are routine applications that are now part of all kinds of jobs. Examples include:

- Testing products without destroying them

- Managing investments to minimize risks while maximizing returns

- Creating terrain maps for farmers that reflect soil chemistry and moisture levels

- Processing photographic images to transform, clarify, and combine

- Detecting disease by monitoring changes in medical images and data

- Creating special cinematic effects such as moving clouds and rushing water

- Anticipating changes in production processes

- Controlling risks by managing distribution of hazardous materials

- Designing products to minimize costs of construction, maintenance, and operation

- Interpreting vital signs displayed as dynamic graphs of biological data

- Minimizing total costs of materials, inventory, time, shipments, and waste

If we look at these common uses of mathematics from the perspective of the school curriculum, we see that mathematics at work is very different from mathematics in school:

- Arithmetic is not just about adding, subtracting, multiplying, and dividing but about units and conversions, measurements and tolerances, spreadsheets and calculators, and estimates and accuracy.

- Numbers are not just about place value and digits but about notation and coding, index numbers and stock market averages, and employment indexes and SAT scores.

- Geometry is not just about the properties of circles, triangles, areas, and volumes but about shapes and measurements in three dimensions, reading maps and calculating latitude and longitude, using dimensions to organize data, and modern tools such as global positioning systems (GPS) and geographic information systems (GIS).

- Statistics is not just about means, medians, and standard deviations but about visual displays of quantitative ideas (for example, scatter plots and quality control charts) as well as random trials and confidence intervals.

- Logic is not just about mathematical rigor and deductive proof but about hypotheses and conjectures, causality and correlation, and random trials and inference in the face of incomplete information.

- Probability is not just about calculating combinations but about estimating and comparing risks (for example, of accidents, diseases, or lotteries) as well as about chance and randomness (in coincidences or analyses of bias claims).

- Applications are not just about solving word problems but about collecting, organizing, and interpreting data; allocating resources and negotiating differences; and understanding annuities and balancing investments.

- Proof is not just about logical deduction but about conjectures and counterexamples, scientific reasoning and statistical inference, and legal standards such as preponderance of evidence or beyond reasonable doubt.

- Technology is not just about doing arithmetic, performing algebra, or creating graphs but about facility with spreadsheets, statistical packages, presentation software, and Internet resources.

Mathematics in practice is far subtler than mathematics in school. Elementary mathematical ideas applied in sophisticated settings are amazingly powerful but rarely appreciated. An important conclusion from this examination of mathematics in practice is that topics common to school mathematics have surprising depth and power in their own right, quite apart from their role in providing prerequisites for college mathematics. Indeed, one could productively pursue applications of school topics for several years without ever taking up the more abstract concepts of calculus (or even so-called "college" algebra). But no one does this, preferring instead to rush students as quickly as possible to the abstractions of calculus.

STATISTICS

The age of information is an age of numbers. We are surrounded by data that both enrich and confuse our lives. Numbers provide descriptions of daily events, from medical reports to political trends and social policy. News reports are filled with charts and graphs, while politicians debate quantitatively based proposals that shape public policy in education, health, and government.

The study of numbers is usually associated with statistics. In schools, the term "quantitative literacy" is often employed as an informal synonym for "elementary statistics." Although statistics is today a science of numbers and data, historically (and etymologically) it is the science of the state that developed in the Napoleonic era when central governments used data about population, trade, and taxes to assert control over distant territory. The value of systematic interpretation of data quickly spread to agriculture, medicine, economics, and politics. Statistics now underlies not only every economic report and census but also every clinical trial and opinion survey in modern society.

However valuable statistics may be, it seems never to have shared the curricular privilege accorded to mathematics. Indeed, high school mathematics devotes relatively little emphasis to topics designed to build a numbers-based bridge from the arithmetic of the elementary grades to the subtle and fascinating world of data and statistics. Computers have significantly transformed the potential, power, and pedagogy of statistics (Hoaglin and Moore 1992) and this evolution has profoundly changed the relation between mathematics, statistics, and their many client disciplines (Moore and Cobb 2000). It is past time for statistics to claim its proper place in the school mathematics curriculum.

One impediment statistics faces is a public perception that it is not as rigorous as calculus. This perception is no doubt due to its association with the "soft" sciences of psychology and economics, in contrast with the "hard" calculus-based disciplines of physics and engineering. Evidence from the new and rapidly growing AP Statistics course, however, confirms what many teachers have long

known—that the subtle reasoning involved in data-based statistical inference is harder for students to grasp and explain than the comparable symbol-based problems and proofs in a typical calculus course. Properly taught, statistics is probably a better vehicle than algebra and calculus for developing students' capacity to reason logically and express complex arguments clearly.

Statistics is also very practical; far more so than any part of the algebra-trigonometry-calculus sequence that dominates school mathematics. Every issue in the daily newspaper, every debate that citizens encounter in their local communities, every exhortation from advertisers invites analysis from a statistical perspective. Statistical reasoning is subtle and strewn with counterintuitive paradoxes. It takes a lot of experience to make statistical reasoning a natural habit of mind (Nisbett et al. 1987; Hoffrage et al. 2000). That is why it is important to start early and to reinforce at every opportunity.

NUMERACY

The special skills required to interpret numbers—what we call numeracy or quantitative literacy—are rarely mentioned in national education standards or state frameworks. Nonetheless, these skills nourish the entire school curriculum, including not only the natural, social, and applied sciences but also language, history, and fine arts (Steen 1990). They parallel and enhance the skills of literacy—of reading and writing—by adding to words the power of numbers.

Numeracy lies at the intersection of statistics, mathematics, and democracy. Like statistics, numeracy is centered on interpretation of data; like mathematics, numeracy builds on arithmetic and logic. But the unique niche filled by numeracy is to support citizens in making decisions informed by evidence. Virtually every major public issue—from health care to Social Security, from international economics to welfare reform—depends on data, projections, inferences, and the kind of systematic thinking that is at the heart of quantitative literacy. So too do many aspects of daily life, from selecting telephone services to buying a car, from managing household expenses to planning for retirement. For centuries, verbal literacy has been recognized as a free citizen's best insurance against ignorance and society's best bulwark against demagoguery. Today, in the age of data, numeracy joins literacy as the guarantor of liberty, both individual and societal (Steen 1998, 2000).

Numeracy is largely an approach to thinking about issues that employs and enhances both statistics (the science of data) and mathematics (the science of patterns). Yet unlike statistics, which is primarily about uncertainty, numeracy is often about the logic of certainty. And unlike mathematics, which is primarily about a Platonic realm of abstract structures, numeracy often is anchored in data derived from and attached to the empirical world. Surprisingly to some, this inextricable link to reality makes quantitative reasoning every bit as challenging and rigorous as mathematical reasoning.

Mathematics teachers often resist emphasizing data because the subject they are trying to teach is about Platonic ideals—numbers and functions, circles and triangles, sets and relationships. Employers and parents, however, often are frustrated by this stance because school graduates so frequently seem inexperienced in dealing with data, and the real world presents itself more often in terms of data than in the Platonic idealizations of mathematics.

Although numeracy depends on familiar mathematical topics from arithmetic, algebra, and geometry, its natural framework is commonly described in broader terms (Steen 2001). Some are foundational, focused on learned skills and procedures:

- *Practical Skills:* Using elementary mathematics in a wide variety of common situations

- *Confidence with Mathematics:* Being comfortable with numbers and at ease in applying quantitative methods

- *Number Sense:* Estimating with confidence; employing common sense about numbers; exhibiting accurate intuition about measurements

- *Mathematics in Context:* Using mathematical tools in settings in which the context provides both meaning and performance expectations

- *Prerequisite Knowledge:* Using a wide range of algebraic, geometric, and statistical tools that are required for many fields of postsecondary education

Other elements of numeracy live on a higher cognitive plateau and represent capacities as useful and ingrained as reading and speaking:

- *Interpreting Data:* Reasoning with data, reading graphs, drawing inferences, and recognizing sources of error

- *Making Decisions:* Using logical and quantitative methods to solve problems and make decisions in everyday life

- *Symbol Sense:* Employing, reading, and interpreting mathematical symbols with ease; exhibiting good sense about their syntax and grammar

- *Thinking Logically:* Analyzing evidence, reasoning carefully, understanding arguments, questioning assumptions, detecting fallacies, and evaluating risks

- *Cultural Appreciation:* Understanding the nature and history of mathematics, its role in scientific inquiry and technological progress, and its importance for comprehending issues in the public realm

Whereas the mathematics curriculum historically has focused on school-based knowledge, numeracy involves mathematics acting in the world. Typical numeracy challenges involve real data and uncertain procedures but require primarily elementary mathematics. In contrast, typical school mathematics problems involve simplified numbers and straightforward procedures but require sophisticated abstract concepts. The test of numeracy, as of any literacy, is whether a person naturally uses appropriate skills in many different contexts.

School Mathematics

For various reasons having to do with a mixture of classical tradition and colonial influence, the school curriculum in mathematics is virtually the same all over the world. Fifteen years ago, the secretary of the International Commission on Mathematics Instruction reported that apart from local examples, there were few significant differences to be found in the mathematics textbooks used by different nations around the world (Howson and Wilson 1986). Even a country as culturally separate as Japan follows a canonical "western" curriculum with only minor variations (Nohda et al. 2000). Detailed review of U.S. practice in the mid-1980s showed little significant change from the practice of previous decades (Hirsch and Zweng 1985). At the end of the twentieth century, therefore, a bird's-eye view of school mathematics reveals little substantive variation in either time or space.

Not surprisingly, however, a more refined analysis prepared in advance of the TIMSS study reveals subtle differences in scope, sequence, and depth (Howson 1991). The TIMSS study itself included an extensive analysis of curricula (and of teaching practices) in participating nations. This analysis showed significant variation in the number of topics covered at different grade levels, a variation that appears to be inversely correlated with student performance (Schmidt et al. 1997). In the case of mathematics education, it seems, more really is less: too many topics covered superficially lead to less student learning. The consensus of experts who have studied both domestic and international assessments is that neither the mathematics curriculum nor the classroom instruction is as challenging in the United States as it is in many other countries (e.g., Stevenson 1998).

This tradition of mathematics programs that are a "mile wide and an inch deep" is not easy to change. In contrast with most nations whose central ministries of education prescribe the goals and curriculum of school mathematics, the United States has no legally binding national standards. That is not to say, however, that we do not have a national curriculum. Textbooks, traditions, and standardized tests do as much to constrain mathematics teaching in the United States as national curricula do in other nations. All too often, these constraints produce what analysts of SIMS called an "underachieving" curriculum (McKnight et al. 1987).

In response to SIMS, NCTM prepared an innovative set of standards for school mathematics—a "banner" for teachers to rally behind in a national crusade to raise classroom expectations and student performance (NCTM 1989). Ten years later, NCTM revised these standards, producing a more tightly focused set of goals to guide states and districts as they developed their own frameworks and curriculum guides (NCTM 2000). This revised document, entitled *Principles and Standards for School Mathematics* (PSSM), is organized around five so-called "content" standards (number and operations, algebra, geometry, measurement, and data analysis and probability) and five "process" standards (problem solving, reasoning and proof, communication, connections, and representation).

The first five PSSM standards (see Appendix I) correspond to topics and chapter titles found in most mathematics textbooks. They represent the traditional content of mathematics: numbers, symbols, functions, shapes, measurements, probability, and the like. The second five, interestingly, fit better with the skills employers seek or the numeracy that citizenship requires—e.g., evaluating arguments, communicating quantitative ideas, interpreting real-world phenomena in mathematical terms. This distinction resonates with what we often hear from users of mathematics: it is not so much the specific content of mathematics that is valuable as the process of thinking that this content represents. Only mathematicians and mathematics teachers really worry much about the specifics of content.

Were all ten NCTM standards stressed equally in each grade from 6 to 12, and enriched with significant real-world examples, many more students would emerge from high school well prepared in mathematics, statistics, and numeracy. But this is far from true of today's curricula. As assessment data show, the content goals of arithmetic and algebra are stressed at the expense of geometry, measurement, data analysis, and probability. In terms of the process goals, only problem solving is consistently stressed; the others—reasoning and proof, communication, connections, and representation—are barely visible in the curriculum and totally absent from common standardized tests. Some of this imbalance reflects differences in the cost of assessment: we test not what is most important but what is easiest and cheapest to test. The pre-

occupation with algebraic symbol manipulation is one result of this approach, because scoring mindless exercises is so much cheaper than judging thoughtful and unpredictable responses.

CHALLENGES

Fixing school mathematics requires attention to many significant (and overwhelming) issues such as teacher competence, recruitment, salaries, and performance; class size and classroom conditions; alignment of standards with textbooks and tests; and consistent support by parents, professionals, and politicians. Here I merely acknowledge these issues but do not deal with any of them.

Instead, my primary purpose in this essay is to think through the goals of mathematics in grades 6 to 12 in light of the significant forces that are shaping the environment of school mathematics. These include:

- Underperformance of U.S. students, especially in areas of mathematics that are seriously neglected in school instruction;

- Continued support for tracking in an environment in which all students need high-quality mathematical experiences;

- Employers' demand for performance competencies that cut across academic areas;

- Changes in curricular priorities, pedagogical strategies, and career options due to the increasing mathematical power of technology;

- Inconsistent expectations and misaligned tests that confront students as they finish high school and move on to postsecondary education;

- Unprecedented increases in routine uses of mathematics and in the types of mathematics being used;

- Extraordinary expansion in sophisticated applications of elementary mathematics;

- Increasing reliance on inferences from numerical evidence in business decisions, analyses, and political debates;

- Rapid growth in the use of computer-generated data, graphs, charts, and tables to present information; and

- Confusion about the relative importance of algebra as one among many mathematical subjects that students must learn.

These environmental forces are not hidden. Everyone who is concerned about the quality of mathematics education is aware of them. Nonetheless, school mathematics continues to serve primarily as a conveyor belt to calculus that educates well only a minority of students. Many individuals and organizations have developed proposals for change (e.g., California Academic Standards Commission 1997; MSEB 1998; NCTM 2000; Achieve 2001; Steen 2001), but these proposals represent contrasting rather than consensus visions of school mathematics.

The traditional curriculum in grades 6 to 12 is organized like a nine-layer cake: advanced arithmetic, percentages and ratios, elementary algebra, geometry, intermediate algebra, trigonometry, advanced algebra, pre-calculus, and (finally) calculus. Each subject builds on topics that precede it, and each topic serves as a foundation for something that follows. Although this sequence has the benefit of ensuring (at least on paper) that students are prepared for each topic by virtue of what has come before, the sequence does this at the expense of conveying a biased view of mathematics (because topics are stressed or ignored primarily on the basis of their utility as a tool in calculus) and creating a fragile educational environment (because each topic depends on mastery of most preceding material). The inevitable result can be seen all around us: most students drop out of mathematics after they encounter a first or second roadblock, while many of those who survive emerge with a distorted (and often negative) view of the subject.

The intense verticality of the current mathematics curriculum not only encourages marginal students to drop out but also creates significant dissonance as states begin to introduce high-stakes graduation tests. Inevitably, student performance spreads out as students move through a vertical curriculum because any weakness generates a cascading series of problems in subsequent courses. The result is an enormous gap between curricular goals and a politically acceptable minimum requirement for high school graduation. Consequently, in most states, the only enforced mathematics performance level for high school graduation is an eighth- or ninth-grade standard. This large discrepancy between goals and achievement discredits mathematics education in the eyes of both parents and students.

BREADTH AND CONNECTEDNESS

I suggest that the way to resolve these conflicts—and to address many of the environmental factors mentioned above—is to structure mathematics in grades 6 to 12 to stress breadth and connectedness rather than depth and dependency. Instead of selecting topics for their future utility, as prerequisites for something to follow that most students will never see, select topics for their current value in building linkages both within mathematics and between mathematics and the outside world. Instead of selecting

topics for their contribution to the foundation of calculus, only one among many important parts of advanced mathematics, select topics for their contribution to a balanced repertoire of all the mathematical sciences. And in each grade, but especially in middle school, stress topics that contribute simultaneously to mathematics, statistics, and numeracy.

A good place to start is with the revised NCTM standards (Appendix I). These ten standards, if treated with equal seriousness and supplemented with significant connections to the real world, would provide a very strong framework for mathematics in grades 6 to 12. Unfortunately, "equal seriousness" is rare. Geometry, measurement, data analysis, and probability need as strong a presence in the curriculum as algebra and number. Similarly, reasoning, communication, and connections need as much emphasis as problem solving and representation.

There is an ever-present danger that these NCTM goals will be viewed as mere rhetoric and that not much will change in the actual priorities of teachers or in the tests that districts and states use to monitor student performance. Taking all the standards seriously means that students need to work with data as much as with equations, with measurements and units as much as with abstract numbers. To learn to communicate quantitatively, students need as much experience reading texts that use quantitative or logical arguments as they have with literary or historical texts. And they need experience not only with the self-contained exercises in mathematics textbooks but also with realistic problems that require a combination of estimation, assumption, and analysis.

To some, these broad goals may seem to move well beyond the security zone of objective, Platonic mathematics in which proof and precision matter most and transformation of symbols replaces narrative explanations as a means of expressing thought. They do indeed move well beyond this protected arena, into the pragmatic world of mathematical practice broadly conceived. Yet it is only in this broad domain, not in the more restricted sphere of symbolic thinking, that mathematics can assert its warrant to special status in the school curriculum. (If it makes purists feel better, perhaps this curriculum should be identified, as the profession is, by the term "mathematical sciences.")

To accomplish such a transformation, mathematics teachers must become diplomats, recruiting allies from teachers in other fields who will stress the role of mathematics in the subjects they teach. Mathematics can be seen both as a service subject (Howson et al. 1988) and as a subject served. Art abounds with geometry; history with data and probability; music with ratios and series; science with measurement and algebra; economics with data and graphs. Every subject relies on, and teaches, the NCTM process standards such as reasoning, communication, and problem solving. To build breadth and secure connections, the mathematical sciences must be taught both in the mathematics classroom and in classrooms across the entire curriculum (Steen 1997; Wallace 1999).

MIDDLE GRADES

For several reasons, it is helpful to think of the seven years of grades 6 to 12 in three parts: the middle grades 6 to 8; the core high school grades 9 to 11; and the transition grade 12. To oversimplify (but not by much), the goal for grades 6 to 8 would be numeracy, for grades 9 to 11, mathematical sciences, and for grade 12, options. Data analysis, geometry, and algebra would constitute three equal content components in grades 6 to 8 and in grades 9 to 11. (In this simplified synopsis, measurement and probability can be viewed as part of data analysis, while number and operations can be viewed as part of algebra; discrete mathematics and combinatorics are embedded in every topic.) The five NCTM process standards cut across all topics and grade levels, but rather than being left to chance, they do need to be covered intentionally and systematically.

Careful planning can ensure that the foundational parts of school mathematics are covered in grades 6 to 8, without tracking but with multiple points of entry and many opportunities for mutual reinforcement. There are many different ways to do this, one of which is being developed by a dozen or so states belonging to the Mathematics Achievement Partnership (Achieve 2001). In a curriculum designed for breadth and connections, anything not learned the first time will appear again in a different context in which it may be easier to learn. For example, graphing data gathered through measurement activities provides review of, or introduction to, algebra and geometry; finding lengths and angles via indirect measurements involves solving equations; and virtually every task in data analysis as well as many in algebra and geometry reinforces and extends skills involving number and calculation.

Used this way, with intention and planning, linkages among parts of mathematics can be reinforcing rather than life-threatening. Instead of leading to frustration and withdrawal, a missing link can lead to exploration of alternative routes through different parts of mathematics. If middle school teachers give priority to topics and applications that form the core of quantitative literacy, students will encounter early in their school careers those parts of mathematics that are most widely used, most important for most people, and most likely to be of interest. More specialized topics can and should be postponed to grades 9 to 11.

SECONDARY SCHOOL

In high school, all students should take three additional years of mathematics in grades 9 to 11, equally divided between data analysis, geometry, and algebra but not sequentially organized. Parallel development is essential to build interconnections both within the

mathematical sciences and with the many other subjects that students are studying at the same time. Parallel does not necessarily mean integrated, although there certainly could be integration in particular curricula. It does mean that in each grade, students advance significantly in their understanding of each component of the triad of data analysis, geometry, and algebra. Parallel development reduces the many disadvantages of the intense and unnecessary verticality.

The content of this curriculum would not differ very much from the recommendations in the NCTM standards. The core of mathematics—data analysis, geometry, and algebra—is what it is and can be neither significantly changed nor totally avoided. There is, however, considerable room for variation in the implementation of specific curricula, notably in the examples that are used to motivate and illuminate the core. Appendix II, adapted from a report of the National Center for Research in Vocational Education (Forman and Steen 1999), offers some examples of important but neglected topics that can simultaneously reinforce mathematical concepts in the core and connect mathematics to ideas and topics in the world in which students live. Some recent textbooks (e.g., Pierce et al. 1997) build on similar ideas.

But perhaps even more important than an enriched variety of examples and topics would be a powerful emphasis on aspects of what NCTM calls process standards. As the practice of medicine involves far more than just diagnosing and prescribing, so the practice of mathematics involves far more than just deducing theorems or solving problems. It involves wide-ranging expertise that brings number and inference to bear on problems of everyday life. Part of learning mathematics is to experience the wide scope of its practice, which is what the process standards are all about.

Some aspects of mathematical practice are entirely pragmatic, dealing with real systems and situations of considerable complexity. A mathematics education should prepare students to deal with the kinds of common situations in which a mathematical perspective is most helpful. Common examples include scheduling, modeling, allocating resources, and preparing budgets. In this computer age, students also need to learn to use the tools of modern technology (e.g., spreadsheets, statistical packages, Internet resources) to collect and organize data, to represent data visually, and to convert data from one form and system to another. Performance standards for mathematics in the age of computers means performance *with* computer tools.

Other aspects of mathematics are anchored more in logic than in practice, in drawing inferences rather than working with data. Ever since Euclid, mathematics has been defined by its reliance on deductive reasoning, but there are many other kinds of reasoning in which mathematical thinking plays an important role. Students finishing high school should have enough experience with different kinds of reasoning to understand the differences between them and the appropriate role for each. Some examples include:

- *Scientific Inference:* Gathering data; detecting patterns, making conjectures; testing conjectures; drawing inferences; verifying versus falsifying theories

- *Legal Inference:* Levels of convincing argument; persuasion and counterexamples; informal inference (suspicion, experience, likelihood); legal standards (beyond reasonable doubt versus preponderance of evidence); logical trees in court decisions

- *Mathematical Inference:* Logical reasoning and deduction; assumptions and conclusions; axiomatic systems; theorems and proofs; proof by direct deduction, by indirect argument, and by "mathematical induction"; classical proofs (e.g., isosceles triangle, infinitude of primes, Pythagorean theorem)

- *Statistical Inference:* Rationale for random samples; double-blind experiments; surveys and polls; confidence intervals; causality versus correlation; multiple and hidden factors, interaction effects; judging validity of statistical claims in media reports.

Both in practical situations of planning and modeling and in the more intellectual sphere of reasoning and inference, these aspects of high school mathematics are well suited to reinforcement in other subjects. As previously noted, to build mathematical breadth and ensure lasting connections, mathematics must be taught, to some degree, in every subject and every classroom.

I have argued for parallel development of the three legs of the mathematical stool—data analysis, geometry, and algebra—to maximize interconnections that are essential for long-term learning. But in grades 9 to 11 there is yet another very practical reason: the increasing number of state-mandated tests that are often set at the tenth-grade level. These tests, if they are aligned with the goals of instruction, should treat all standards in a balanced manner. In particular, data analysis, geometry, and algebra should be equally present on tenth-grade tests; they therefore must be equally present in ninth- and tenth-grade courses. If high school courses remain layered as they are now, state examinations will continue to concentrate only on algebra and geometry, leaving data analysis out of the picture.

OPTIONS

Ideally, every student should study the same mathematics through grade 8, with only minor variation in examples to support different student interests and abilities. Accommodation to student differences in middle school should reflect student needs, not variations in anticipated career plans or college requirements. More instruction should be provided for students who need more support, more extensions for students who need greater challenges. Most students who are able to move rapidly through the core curriculum would be much better served with extensions that provide additional depth and variety than with acceleration, especially with examples that open their minds to the many connections among mathematical topics and with diverse applications. (Acceleration may be appropriate for a very few exceptionally talented students—fewer than one in a hundred—but only if they are able to pursue the entire curriculum at its deepest level. Acceleration of the core curriculum alone, without extensions, is pointless.)

In high school, student interests emerge with greater strength and legitimacy and both students and parents expect schools to provide some options. Historically, schools have tried to do this by a combination of two strategies: tracking and filtering. Both strategies amount to an abdication of educational responsibility. Weaker students were placed in commercial or general tracks that avoided algebra, thus barring them from further work in any quantitatively based field. Stronger students were immersed in a form of algebra that was designed to filter out students who did not appear capable of later success in calculus. The consequences of this strategy are well known: large numbers of students leave school both ignorant of and anxious about mathematics.

It is possible to offer options without foreclosing students' futures. Three types of very successful programs can be found in today's schools: career, academic, and scientific. The first provides rigorous preparation for the high-performance workplace, the second offers thorough preparation for college, the third offers advanced preparation for scientific careers. These programs vary in mathematical intensity and depth, but all provide students with substantial experience in data analysis, geometry, and algebra. Each leaves students prepared for work and postsecondary education but at different mathematical levels, separated by approximately one year of mathematical study.

Many educators argue vehemently against any tracks on the ground that they magnify inequities in educational advantage at a time when all students need to be equally prepared (rather than unequally prepared) for postsecondary education. Others argue that mathematically able students need a separate track to enable them to maintain their interest and fulfill their potential (Gavosto et al. 1999; Sheffield 1999). Still others argue, for similar reasons, that many students will thrive better in a career-oriented track—especially one that stresses skills required for new high-performance, technologically intensive industries (Bottoms 1993; Hoachlander 1997).

Research and practice show definitively that students learn better when they can fit new ideas into meaningful contexts (Askew and William 1995; Bransford et al. 1999). Because high school students have quite different interests, it makes sense to provide some choices in the context and setting of their mathematics courses. Moreover, given the variety of programs in higher education—ranging from technical certificates offered by community colleges to bachelor's degrees offered by liberal arts colleges, from majors in philosophy or art to hotel management and hazardous waste disposal—it is clear that student preparation can legitimately be varied.

Thus we can imagine different settings for mathematics in grades 9 to 11, each achieving the same general goals but with rather different details. If rigorously delivered, a variety of substantive programs can prepare students for postsecondary education without remediation—an important practical and political point. Whether the equations studied in algebra come from physics or automobile mechanics, or the data from economics or computer repair, what students learn about handling equations and data would be approximately the same. Differences among programs become weaknesses only if some programs leave students ill prepared for their future—either for work or for study. But options that differ primarily in specifics rather than in broad goals can serve all students well.

Providing options in grades 9 to 11 does mean that students will finish the eleventh grade at different mathematical levels—some much more advanced than others. Especially in a subject like mathematics, wide variation in achievement is inevitable. By encouraging students to relate mathematics to their personal interests, all students' learning will be enhanced, but so will variability. Success in mathematics education is not determined by the quantity of mathematics learned but by the ability and disposition to use a variety of mathematical tools in further work or study. It is far better for students to finish the required core of school mathematics willing and eager to learn more than to have mastered skills that they hope never to have to use again.

Student options become fully realized in grade 12 when mathematics itself becomes optional. Ideally, schools should offer a wide choice of further mathematics—for example, calculus-readiness, computer graphics, mathematical modeling, computer science, statistics, or biomathematics—in part to show students how pervasive mathematics really is and how many options there are for continued study. These elective courses need not be offered every year because none is uniquely necessary for students' further study and none is likely to be part of the testing associated with the school-college transition. Calculus itself can easily be left for college (except for the few students who can legitimately cover this entire program one year ahead of the others). One measure of success of a school's mathematics program would be the percentage of students who elect mathematics in twelfth grade.

SYNOPSIS

To summarize, all middle school students (grades 6 to 8) would study a three-year, non-tracked curriculum that provides equal and tightly linked introductions to data analysis, geometry, and algebra. When students enter high school, they would move into a second three-year mathematics curriculum that may provide some options based on student interests. No matter the emphasis, however, each high school program would advance equally the three main themes (data analysis, geometry, algebra) without letting any lag behind. Different programs may emphasize different contexts, different tools, and different depths, but each would leave students prepared both for the world of work and for postsecondary education.

In this plan, minimum high school graduation requirements (certified, for example, by high-stakes state tests that are typically set at tenth-grade competence) would represent citizen-level quantitative literacy, one year behind mathematics preparation for college admission (eleventh grade), which would be one year behind qualification for mathematically intensive college programs. Aiming for this three-step outcome of high school mathematics is more logical and more achievable than the imagined (but never achieved) ideal of having every student leave high school equally educated in mathematics and equally prepared for college admission.

By studying a balanced curriculum, students would leave school better prepared for employment, more competitive with their international peers, and well positioned for a variety of postsecondary programs. By experiencing breadth and connectedness rather than depth and verticality, students would have repeated opportunities to engage mathematics afresh as their own interests and attitudes evolve. By focusing on the symbiosis of computers and mathematics, students would experience how mathematics is practiced. And by studying a blend of mathematics, statistics, and numeracy, students would be flexibly prepared for life and work in the twenty-first century.

Appendix I: Standards for School Mathematics

(Adapted from *Principles and Standards for School Mathematics,* National Council of Teachers of Mathematics 2000)

Content Standards:

Instructional programs should enable all students,

in number and operations, to

- understand numbers, ways of representing numbers, relationships among numbers, and number systems;

- understand meanings of operations and how they relate to one another;

- compute fluently and make reasonable estimates;

in algebra, to

- understand patterns, relations, and functions;

- represent and analyze mathematical situations and structures using algebraic symbols;

- use mathematical models to represent and understand quantitative relationships;

- analyze change in various contexts;

in geometry, to

- analyze characteristics and properties of two- and three-dimensional geometric shapes and develop mathematical arguments about geometric relationships;

- specify locations and describe spatial relationships using coordinate geometry and other representational systems;

- apply transformations and use symmetry to analyze mathematical situations;

- use visualization, spatial reasoning, and geometric modeling to solve problems;

in measurement, to

- understand measurable attributes of objects and the units, systems, and processes of measurement;

- apply appropriate techniques, tools, and formulas to determine measurements;

in data analysis and probability, to

- formulate questions that can be addressed with data and collect, organize, and display relevant data to answer them;

- select and use appropriate statistical methods to analyze data;

- develop and evaluate inferences and predictions that are based on data;

- understand and apply basic concepts of probability.

Process Standards:

Instructional programs should enable all students,

in problem solving, to

- build new mathematical knowledge through problem solving;

- solve problems that arise in mathematics and in other contexts;

- apply and adapt a variety of appropriate strategies to solve problems;

- monitor and reflect on the process of mathematical problem solving;

in reasoning and proof, to

- recognize reasoning and proof as fundamental aspects of mathematics;

- make and investigate mathematical conjectures;

- develop and evaluate mathematical arguments and proofs;

- select and use various types of reasoning and methods of proof;

in communication, to

- organize and consolidate their mathematical thinking through communication;

- communicate their mathematical thinking coherently and clearly to peers, teachers, and others;

- analyze and evaluate the mathematical thinking and strategies of others;

- use the language of mathematics to express mathematical ideas precisely;

in connections, to

- recognize and use connections among mathematical ideas;

- understand how mathematical ideas interconnect and build on one another to produce a coherent whole;

- recognize and apply mathematics in contexts outside of mathematics;

in representation, to

- create and use representations to organize, record, and communicate mathematical ideas;

- select, apply, and translate among mathematical representations to solve problems;

- use representations to model and interpret physical, social, and mathematical phenomena.

Appendix II: Selected Topics for School Mathematics

(Adapted from *Beyond Eighth Grade: Functional Mathematics for Life and Work*, published by the National Center for Research in Vocational Education 1999)

Geometry: In addition to standard topics (e.g., measurement of figures in two- and three-dimensions, congruence and similarity, reflections and rotations, triangle trigonometry, classical proofs and constructions), students should be introduced to:

- *Dimensions:* Coordinate notation; dimension as factor in multivariable phenomena. Geometric dimensions (linear, square, and cubic) versus coordinate dimensions in multivariable phenomena. Proper versus improper analogies. Discrete versus continuous dimensions.

- *Dimensional Scaling:* Linear, square, and cubic growth of length, area, and volume; physical and biological consequences. Fractal dimensions.

- *Spatial Geometry:* Calculating angles in three dimensions (e.g., meeting of roof trusses); building three-dimensional objects and drawing two-dimensional diagrams. Interpreting construction diagrams; nominal versus true dimensions (e.g., of 2 x 4s); tolerances and perturbations in constructing three-dimensional objects.

- *Global Positioning:* Map projections, latitude and longitude, global positioning systems (GPS); local, regional, and global coordinate systems.

Data: In addition to standard topics (e.g., ratios, percentages, averages, probabilities) students should be introduced to:

- *Measurement:* Estimating weights, lengths, and areas. Direct and indirect measurement. Use of appropriate instruments (rulers, tapes, micrometers, pacing, electronic gauges, plumb lines). Squaring corners in construction. Estimating tolerances. Detecting and correcting misalignments.

- *Calculation:* Accurate paper-and-pencil methods for simple arithmetic and percentage calculations; calculator use for complex calculations; spreadsheet methods for problems with a lot of data. Use of mixed methods (mental, pencil, calculator). Strategies for checking reasonableness and accuracy. Significant digits; interval arithmetic; errors and tolerances. Accuracy of calculated measurements.

- *Mental Estimation:* Quick, routine mental estimates of costs, distances, times. Estimating orders of magnitude. Reasoning with ratios and proportions. Mental checking of calculator and computer results. Estimating unknown quantities (e.g., number of high school students in a state or number of gas stations in a city).

- *Numbers:* Whole numbers (integers), fractions (rational numbers), and irrational numbers (π, $\sqrt{2}$). Number line; mixed numbers; decimals; percentages. Prime numbers, factors; simple number theory; fundamental theorem of arithmetic. Binary numbers and simple binary arithmetic. Scientific notation; units and conversions. Number sense, including intuition about extreme numbers (lottery chances, national debt, astronomical distances).

- *Coding:* Number representations (decimal, binary, octal, and hex coding). ASCII coding; check digits. Patterns in credit card, Social Security, telephone, license plate numbers. Passwords and PINS.

- *Index Numbers:* Weighted averages. Definitions and abuses. Examples in the news: stock market averages; consumer price index; unemployment rate; SAT scores; college rankings.

- *Data Analysis:* Measures of central tendency (average, median, mode) and of spread (range, standard deviation, mid-range, quartiles, percentiles). Visual displays of data (pie charts, scatter plots, bar graphs, box and whisker charts). Quality control charts. Recognizing and dealing with outliers.

- *Probability:* Chance and randomness. Calculating odds in common situations (dice, coin tosses, card games); expected value. Random numbers; hot streaks. Binomial probability; binomial approximation of normal distribution. Computer simulations; estimating area by Monte Carlo methods. Two-way contingency tables; bias paradoxes.

- *Risk Analysis:* Estimates of common risks (e.g., accidents, diseases, causes of death, lotteries). Confounding factors. Communicating and interpreting risk.

Algebra: In addition to standard topics (e.g., variables, symbols, equations, relations, graphs, functions, slope, inequalities), students should be introduced to:

- *Algorithms:* Alternative arithmetic algorithms; flow charts; loops; constructing algorithms; maximum time versus average time comparisons.

- *Graphs:* Sketching and interpreting graphs; translating between words and graphs (and vice versa) without intervening formulas.

- *Growth and Variation:* Linear, exponential, quadratic, harmonic, and normal curve patterns. Examples of situations that fit these patterns (bacterial growth, length of day) and of those that do not (e.g., height versus weight; income distribution).

- *Financial Mathematics:* Personal finance; loans, annuities, insurance. Investment instruments (stocks, mortgages, bonds).

- *Exponential Growth:* Examples (population growth, radioactivity, compound interest) in which rate of change is proportional to size; doubling time and half-life as characteristics of exponential phenomena; ordinary and log-scaled graphs.

- *Normal Curve:* Examples (e.g., distribution of heights, repeated measurements, production tolerances) of phenomena that distribute in a bell-shaped curve and examples that do not (e.g., income, grades, typographical errors, life spans). Area as measure of probability. Meaning of 1-, 2-, and 3σ.

- *Parabolic Patterns:* Examples (falling bodies, optimization, acceleration) that generate quadratic phenomena; relation to parabolic curves.

- *Cyclic functions:* Examples (time of sunrise, sound waves, biological rhythms) that exhibit cyclic behavior. Graphs of sin and cos; consequences of $\sin^2 \theta + \cos^2 \theta = 1$.

References

Achieve Mathematics Achievement Partnership (Achieve). 2001. *Mathematics Expectations for the End of Eighth Grade.* Washington, DC: Achieve Mathematics Achievement Partnership.

American Mathematical Association of Two-Year Colleges. 1995. *Crossroads in Mathematics: Standards for Introductory College Mathematics Before Calculus.* Memphis, TN: American Mathematical Association of Two-Year Colleges. Retrieved 04/10/02, at www.richland.cc.il.us/imacc/standards/.

Askew, Mike, and Dylan William. 1995. *Recent Research in Mathematics Education 5–16.* London: Her Majesty's Stationery Office.

Atkinson, Richard C. 2001. "Standardized Tests and Access to American Universities." Robert H. Atwell Distinguished Lecture. Washington, DC: American Council on Education. Retrieved 04/10/02, at www.ucop.edu/ucophome/commserv/sat/speech.html.

Bailey, Thomas R. 1997. *Integrating Academic and Industry Skill Standards.* Berkeley, CA: National Center for Research in Vocational Education, University of California.

Barker, William H. 2000. *Curriculum Foundations.* Working papers for the Committee on the Undergraduate Program in Mathematics (CUPM). Washington, DC: Mathematical Association of America. Retrieved 04/10/02, at academic.bowdoin.edu/faculty/B/barker/dissemination/Curriculum_Foundations/.

Bass, Hyman. 1997. "Mathematicians as Educators." *Notices of American Mathematical Society.* 44:1 (January): 18–21. Reprinted in *Contemporary Issues in Mathematics Education,* edited by Estela A. Gavosto, Steven G. Krantz, and William McCallum, 1–6. New York, NY: Cambridge University Press, 1999.

Beaton, A. E., et al. 1996. *Mathematics Achievement in the Middle School Years: IEA's Third International Mathematics and Science Study.* Chestnut Hill, MA: Center for the Study of Testing, Evaluation, and Educational Policy, Boston College.

Bottoms, Gene. 1993. *Redesigning and Refocusing High School Vocational Studies.* Atlanta, GA: Southern Regional Education Board.

Bransford, John D., Ann L. Brown, and Rodney R. Cocking, eds. 1999. *How People Learn: Brain, Mind, Experience, and School.* National Research Council. Washington, DC: National Academy Press.

California Academic Standards Commission. 1997. *Mathematics Content Standards for California Public Schools.* Sacramento, CA: State Board of Education. Retrieved 04/10/02, at www.cde.ca.gov/standards/math/.

Campbell, J. R., et al. 1996. *NAEP 1994 Trends in Academic Progress.* Washington, DC: National Center for Education Statistics, U.S. Department of Education.

Chambers, Donald L. 1994. "The right algebra for all." *Educational Leadership,* 51:6, pp. 85–86.

Cheney, Lynne. 1997. "Creative Math or Just 'Fuzzy Math'? Once Again, Basic Skills Fall Prey to a Fad." *New York Times,* 11 August 1997: A13.

Compaine, Benjamin M., ed. 2001. *The Digital Divide.* Cambridge, MA: Massachusetts Institute of Technology Press.

Crosswhite, F. Joe, et al. 1986. *Second International Mathematics Study: Report for the United States* (2 vols.). International Association for the Evaluation of Educational Achievement. Champaign, IL: Stipes.

Devlin, Keith. 1994. *Mathematics: The Science of Patterns.* New York, NY: Scientific American Library.

Dossey, John, and Zalman Usiskin. 2000. *Mathematics Education in the United States—2000: A Capsule Summary.* Washington, DC: United States National Commission on Mathematics Instruction.

Education Trust. 1999. *You Can't Get There from Here: A Study of Tests from High School through Postsecondary Admission and Placement.* Washington DC: Education Trust.

Flanders, James. 1987. "How Much of the Content in Mathematics Textbooks Is New?" *Arithmetic Teacher* 35(1): 18-23.

Forman, Susan L., and Lynn Arthur Steen. 1998. *Beyond Eighth Grade: Report of a Workshop on Mathematical and Occupational Skill Standards*. Berkeley, CA: National Center for Research in Vocational Education.

Forman, Susan L., and Lynn Arthur Steen. 1999. *Beyond Eighth Grade: Functional Mathematics for Life and Work*. Berkeley, CA: National Center for Research in Vocational Education. Reprinted in *Learning Mathematics for a New Century,* edited by Maurice Burke, 127–57. Reston, VA: National Council of Teachers of Mathematics, 2000. Retrieved 04/10/02, at ncrve.berkeley.edu/abstracts/MDS-1241/.

Gardner, Howard. 1999. "With Pencils Sharpened: Taking Tests to Task in America." *Harvard Magazine* (November–December): 29–35.

Gavosto, Estela A., Steven G. Krantz, and William McCallum. 1999. *Contemporary Issues in Mathematics Education*. MSRI Publications, vol. 36. New York, NY: Cambridge University Press.

Groves, Martha. "Exit-Exam Retreats Reflect Fears That Students Lack Skills." *Los Angeles Times* 17 December 2000.

Hammond, Allen. 1978. "Mathematics—Our Invisible Culture." In *Mathematics Today: Twelve Informal Essays,* edited by Lynn Arthur Steen, 15–34. New York, NY: Springer-Verlag.

Hembree, Ray, and Donald J. Dessart. 1992. "Research on Calculators in Mathematics Education." In *Calculators in Mathematics Education,* edited by James T. Fey, 23–32. Reston, VA: National Council of Teachers of Mathematics.

Hirsch, Christian R., and Marilyn J. Zweng, eds. 1985. *The Secondary School Mathematics Curriculum*. Reston, VA: National Council of Teachers of Mathematics.

Hoachlander, Gary. 1997. "Organizing Mathematics Education Around Work." In *Why Numbers Count: Quantitative Literacy for Tomorrow's America,* edited by Lynn Arthur Steen, 122–36. New York, NY: College Entrance Examination Board.

Hoaglin, David C., and Davis S. Moore, eds. 1992. *Perspectives on Contemporary Statistics*. Washington, DC: Mathematical Association of America.

Hoffrage, Ulrich, Samuel Lindsey, Ralph Hartwig, and Gerd Gigerenzer. 2000. "Communicating Statistical Information." *Science* 290 (11 December): 2261–62.

Howson, A. Geoffrey and Bryan Wilson, eds. 1986. *School Mathematics in the 1990s*. ICMI Study Series. Cambridge, UK: Cambridge University Press.

Howson, A. Geoffrey, Jean-Pierre Kahane, P. Lauginie, E. de Turckheim., eds. 1988. *Mathematics as a Service Subject*. ICMI Study Series. Cambridge, UK: Cambridge University Press.

Howson, Geoffrey. 1991. *National Curricula in Mathematics*. Leister, UK: The Mathematical Association.

International Association for the Evaluation of Educational Achievement (IEA). 2000. *TIMSS 1999: Trends in Mathematics and Science Achievement Around the World*. Boston, MA: Boston College International Study Center. Retrieved 04/10/02, at timss.bc.edu/timss1999.html.

International Association for the Evaluation of Educational Achievement (IEA). 2001. *TIMSS 1999 Benchmarking Report*. Boston, MA: Boston College International Study Center. www.timss.org/timss1999b/mathbench_report/t99b_math_report.html.

International Technology Education Association (ITEA). 2000. *Standards for Technological Literacy: Content for the Study of Technology*. Reston, VA: International Technology Education Association.

Jackson, Allyn. 1997. "The Math Wars," Parts I and II. *Notices of American Mathematical Society*. 44 (June/July, August): 619–702; 817–27.

Kenney, P. A., and Edward A. Silver, eds. 1996. *Results from the Sixth Mathematics Assessment of the National Assessment of Educational Progress*. Reston, VA: National Council of Teachers of Mathematics.

Kilpatrick, Jeremy. 1997. "Confronting Reform." *The American Mathematical Monthly* 104(10) (December): 955–62.

Lacampagne, Carole B. William Blair, and Jim Kaput., eds. 1995. *The Algebra Initiative Colloquium* (2 vols.). Washington, DC: Office of Educational Research and Improvement, U.S. Department of Education.

Lapointe, A. E., N. A. Mead, and G. W. Phillips. 1989. *A World of Differences: An International Assessment of Mathematics and Science*. Princeton, NJ: Educational Testing Service.

Malcom, Shirley. 1997. "Making Mathematics the Great Equalizer." In *Why Numbers Count: Quantitative Literacy for Tomorrow's America,* edited by Lynn Arthur Steen, 30–35. New York, NY: College Entrance Examination Board.

Mathematical Sciences Education Board (MSEB). 1990. *Reshaping School Mathematics: A Philosophy and Framework for Curriculum*. Washington, DC: National Research Council.

Mathematical Sciences Education Board (MSEB). 1995. *Mathematical Preparation of the Technical Work Force*. Washington, DC: National Research Council.

Mathematical Sciences Education Board (MSEB). 1998. *High School Mathematics at Work: Essays and Examples for the Education of all Students*. Washington, DC: National Academy Press.

McKnight, Curtis C., F. Joe Crosswhite, John A Dossey, Edward Kifer, Jane O. Swafford, Kenneth J. Travers, and Thomas J. Cooney. 1987. *The Underachieving Curriculum: Assessing U.S. School Mathematics from an International Perspective*. Champaign, IL: Stipes.

Moore, David S., and George W. Cobb. 2000. "Statistics and Mathematics: Tension and Cooperation." *The American Mathematical Monthly* 107(7) 615–30.

Moore, Eliakim Hastings. 1903. "On the Foundations of Mathematics." *Science* 217: 401–16.

Moses, Robert. 1995. "Algebra, The New Civil Right." In *The Algebra Initiative Colloquium,* vol. II edited by Carol Lacampagne, et al., 53–67. Washington, DC: Office of Educational Research and Improvement, U.S. Department of Education.

Murnane, Richard, and Frank Levy. 1996. *Teaching the New Basic Skills: Principles for Educating Children to Thrive in a Changing Economy.* New York, NY: Free Press.

National Center for Education Statistics. 1998. *Pursuing Excellence: A Study of U.S. Twelfth-Grade Mathematics and Science Achievement in International Context.* Washington, DC: Office of Educational Research and Improvement, U.S. Department of Education. Retrieved 04/10/02, at nces.ed.gov/pubsearch/pubsinfo.asp?pubid=98049.

National Center for Education Statistics. 2000. *NAEP 1999 Trends in Academic Progress: Three Decades of Student Performance.* Washington, DC: Office of Educational Research and Improvement, U.S. Department of Education. Retrieved 04/10/02, at nces.ed.gov/pubsearch/pubsinfo.asp?pubid=2000469.

National Commission on Excellence in Education. 1983. *A Nation at Risk: The Imperative for Educational Reform.* Washington, DC: U.S. Government Printing Office. Retrieved 04/10/02, at www.ed.gov/pubs/NatAtRisk/.

National Commission on Mathematics and Science Teaching for the 21st Century. 2000. *Before It's too Late.* Washington, DC: U.S. Department of Education.

National Council of Teachers of Mathematics. 1989. *Curriculum and Evaluation Standards for School Mathematics.* Reston, VA: National Council of Teachers of Mathematics. Retrieved 04/10/02, at standards.nctm.org/Previous/CurrEvStds/index.htm.

National Council of Teachers of Mathematics. 2000. *Principles and Standards for School Mathematics.* Reston, VA: National Council of Teachers of Mathematics. Retrieved 04/10/02, at standards.nctm.org/document/index.htm.

National Council of Teachers of Mathematics and Mathematical Sciences Education Board (MSEB). 1998. *The Nature and Role of Algebra in the K–14 Curriculum.* Washington, DC: National Research Council.

National Research Council (NRC). 1999. *Being Fluent with Information Technology.* Washington, DC: National Academy Press.

National Science Board. 1996. *Science and Engineering Indicators 1996.* Washington, DC: National Science Foundation.

National Skills Standards Board (NSSB). 1998. *Skills Standards and Initiatives.* Washington, DC: National Skills Standards Board. Retrieved 04/10/02, at www.nssb.org.

Nisbett, Richard E., et al. 1987. "Teaching Reasoning." *Science* 238 (30 October): 625–31.

Nohda, Nobuhiko, Shizumi Shimizu, Kohzoh Tsubota, Akira Suzuki, and Kazuhiko Murooka. 2000. *School Mathematics in Japan.* Makuhari, Japan: Japan Society of Mathematical Education.

Norris, Pippa. 2001. *Digital Divide: Civic Engagement, Information Poverty, and the Internet Worldwide.* New York, NY: Cambridge University Press.

Oakes, Jeannie. 1985. *Keeping Track: How Schools Structure Inequality.* New Haven, CT: Yale University Press.

Oakes, Jeannie. 1990. *Multiplying Inequalities: The Effects of Race, Social Class, and Tracking on Opportunities to Learn Mathematics and Science.* Santa Monica, CA: Rand Corporation.

Odom, William E. 1998. *Report of the Senior Assessment Panel for the International Assessment of the U.S. Mathematical Sciences.* Washington, DC: National Science Foundation. Retrieved 04/10/02, at www.nsf.gov/cgi-bin/getpub?nsf9895.

Packer, Arnold. 1997. "Mathematical Competencies that Employers Expect." In *Why Numbers Count: Quantitative Literacy for Tomorrow's America,* edited by Lynn Arthur Steen, 137–54. New York, NY: College Entrance Examination Board.

Paulos, John Allen. 1988. *Innumeracy: Mathematical Illiteracy and Its Consequences.* New York, NY: Hill and Wang.

Pearlman, Robert. 2001. "Inside the Digital Divide: Connecting Youth to Opportunities in the New Economy." Digital Divide Network. Retrieved 04/10/02, at www.digitaldividenetwork.org/content/stories/index.cfm?key=224.

Pierce, Don, Ed Wright, and Leon Roland. 1997. *Mathematics for Life: A Foundation Course for Quantitative Literacy.* Upper Saddle River, NJ: Prentice Hall.

Raimi, Ralph A., and Lawrence S. Braden. 1998. *State Mathematics Standards.* Washington, DC: Thomas B. Fordham Foundation. Retrieved 04/10/02, at www.edexcellence.net/standards/math.html.

Sacks, Peter. 2000. *Standardized Minds: The High Price of America's Testing Culture and What We Can Do to Change It.* Cambridge, MA: Perseus.

Schmidt, William H., Curtis C. McKnight, and Senta A. Raizen. 1996. *A Splintered Vision: An Investigation of U.S. Science and Mathematics Education.* Dordrecht: Kluwer.

Schmidt, William H., et al. 1997. *Many Visions, Many Aims, Volume 1. A Cross National Investigation of Curricular Intentions in School Mathematics.* Dordrecht: Kluwer.

Secada, Walter G. 1992. "Race, Ethnicity, Social Class, Language, and Achievement in Mathematics." In *Handbook of Research on Mathematics Teaching and Learning,* edited by D. A. Grouws, 623–60. New York, NY: Macmillan.

Secretary's Commission on Achieving Necessary Skills (SCANS). 1991. *What Work Requires of Schools: A SCANS Report for America 2000.* Washington, DC: U.S. Department of Labor.

Sheffield, Linda Jensen. 1999. *Developing Mathematically Promising Students.* Reston, VA: National Council of Teachers of Mathematics.

Shrag, Peter. 2000. "High Stakes Are for Tomatoes." *Atlantic Monthly* 286(2) (August): 19–21. Retrieved 04/10/02, at www.theatlantic.com/issues/2000/08/schrag.htm.

Silver, Edward A. 1997. "Algebra for All: Increasing Student Access to Algebraic Ideas, Not Just Algebra Courses." *Mathematics Teaching in the Middle School* 2(4): 204–207.

Silver, Edward A. 1998. *Improving Mathematics in Middle School: Lessons from TIMSS and Related Research.* Washington, DC: Office of Educational Research and Improvement, U.S. Department of Education.

Steen, Lynn Arthur. 1988. "The Science of Patterns." *Science* 240 (29 April): 611–16.

Steen, Lynn Arthur. 1990. "Numeracy." *Daedalus* 119(2) (Spring): 211–31.

Steen, Lynn Arthur. 1992. "Does Everybody Need to Study Algebra?" *Mathematics Teacher* 85 (4) (April): 258–60. Also printed in *Basic Education* 37 (January 1992): 9–13.

Steen, Lynn Arthur, and Susan L. Forman. 1995. "Mathematics for Work and Life." In *Seventy-Five Years of Progress: Prospects for School Mathematics,* edited by Iris Carl, 219–41. Reston, VA: National Council of Teachers of Mathematics.

Steen, Lynn Arthur, ed. 1997. *Why Numbers Count: Quantitative Literacy for Tomorrow's America.* New York, NY: College Entrance Examination Board.

Steen, Lynn Arthur. 1998. "Numeracy: The New Literacy for a Data-Drenched Society." *Educational Leadership* 47(2) (October): 8–13.

Steen, Lynn Arthur. 1999. "What's the Rush: Algebra for All in Eighth Grade?" *Middle Matters* 8(1) (Fall): 1–6, 7.

Steen, Lynn Arthur. "Reading, Writing, and Numeracy." 2000. *Liberal Education* 86(2) (Spring): 26–37.

Steen, Lynn Arthur, ed. 2001. *Mathematics and Democracy: The Case for Quantitative Literacy.* Princeton, NJ: National Council on Education and the Disciplines. Retrieved 04/10/02, at www.woodrow.org/nced/mathematics___democracy.html.

Stevenson, Harold W. 1998. *A TIMSS Primer: Lessons and Implications for U.S. Education.* Washington, DC: Thomas R. Fordham Foundation. Retrieved 04/10/02, at www.edexcellence.net/library/timss.html.

Stotsky, Sandra, ed. 2000. *What's at Stake in the K–12 Standards Wars: A Primer for Educational Policy Makers.* New York, NY: Peter Lang.

Usiskin, Zalman. 1995. "Why Is Algebra Important to Learn?" *American Educator* (Spring): 30–37.

Waits, Bert, and Franklin Demana. 2000. "Calculators in Mathematics Teaching and Learning: Past, Present, and Future." In *Learning Mathematics for a New Century,* edited by Maurice Burke, 51–66. Reston, VA: National Council of Teachers of Mathematics.

Wallace, Dorothy. 1999. "If I Could Talk to the Animals." In *Contemporary Issues in Mathematics Education,* edited by Estela A. Gavosto, Steven G. Krantz, and William McCallum, 39–43. New York, NY: Cambridge University Press.

Wu, Hung-Hsi. 1996. "The Mathematician and the Mathematics Education Reform." *Notices of American Mathematical Society* 43(12) (December): 1531–37.

Wu, Hung-Hsi. 1997. "The Mathematics Education Reform: Why You Should Be Concerned and What You Can Do." *The American Mathematical Monthly* 104(10) (December): 946–54.

Mathematics for Literacy

JAN DE LANGE

(In)numeracy

In 1990, a newspaper reported:

> Yesterday, Monday October 9, AVRO Television paid attention to analphabetism in The Netherlands. From data collected for the transmission, it appeared that no fewer than 1 out of 25 people cannot read or write, that is, cannot read or write a shopping list, cannot follow subtitles on TV, cannot read newspapers, cannot write a letter.
>
> Just imagine, 1 out of 25 people, in a country that sends helpers to developing countries in order to teach their folks reading and writing! 1 out of 25, which means 25% of our citizens.
>
> How many citizens does The Netherlands have? 14 million? That means that in our highly developed country no less than three and a half million cannot read or write.
>
> Aren't you speechless?

Speechless, indeed. Errors such as the one above often are not noticed by our literate, educated citizens. Innumeracy, or the inability to handle numbers and data correctly and to evaluate statements regarding problems and situations that invite mental processing and estimating, is a greater problem than our society generally recognizes. According to Treffers (1991), this level of innumeracy might not be the result of content taught (or not taught) but rather the result, at least in part, of the structural design of teaching practices. "Fixing" this problem, however, requires dealing with several issues: From a mathematical perspective, how do we define literacy? Does literacy relate to mathematics (and what kind of mathematics)? What kind of competencies are we looking for? Are these competencies teachable?

Introduction

Before trying to answer the question "What knowledge of mathematics is important?", it seems wise first to look at a "comfortable" definition of quantitative literacy (QL). Lynn Arthur Steen (2001) pointed out that there are small but important differences in the several existing definitions and, although he did not suggest the phrase as a definition, referred to QL as the "capacity to deal effectively with the quantitative aspects of life." Indeed, most existing definitions Steen mentioned give explicit attention to number, arithmetic, and quantitative situations, either in a rather narrow way as in the National Adult Literacy Survey (NCES 1993):

> The knowledge and skills required in applying arithmetic operations, either alone or sequentially, using numbers embedded in printed material (e.g., balancing a checkbook, completing an order form).

Jan de Lange is Director of the Freudenthal Institute at Utrecht University in The Netherlands. A member of the Mathematical Sciences Education Board (MSEB), de Lange's work focuses on modeling and applications in mathematics education, implementation of mathematics curriculum reform, and assessing student learning in mathematics. De Lange is chair of the Expert Group for Mathematics of OECD's new Program for International Student Assessment (PISA).

or more broadly as in the International Life Skills Survey (ILSS 2000):

> An aggregate of skills, knowledge, beliefs, dispositions, habits of mind, communication capabilities, and problem solving skills that people need in order to engage effectively in quantitative situations arising in life and work.

The problem we have with these definitions is their apparent emphasis on *quantity*. Mathematical literacy is not restricted to the ability to apply quantitative aspects of mathematics but involves knowledge of mathematics in the broadest sense. As an example, being a foreigner who travels a great deal in the United States, I often ask directions of total strangers. What strikes me in their replies is that people are generally very poor in what I call navigation skills: a realization of where you are, both in a relative and absolute sense. Such skills include map reading and interpretation, spatial awareness, "grasping space" (Freudenthal 1973), understanding great circle routes, understanding plans of a new house, and so on. All kinds of visualization belong as well to the literacy aspect of mathematics and constitute an absolutely essential component for literacy, as the three books of Tufte (1983, 1990, 1997) have shown in a very convincing way.

We believe that describing what constitutes mathematical literacy necessitates not only this broader definition but also attention to changes within other school disciplines. The Organization for Economic Cooperation and Development (OECD) publication *Measuring Student Knowledge and Skills* (OECD 1999) presents as part of reading literacy a list of types of texts, the understanding of which in part determines what constitutes literacy. This list comes close, in the narrower sense, to describing many aspects of quantitative literacy. The publication mentions, as examples, texts in various formats:

- Forms: tax forms, immigration forms, visa forms, application forms, questionnaires

- Information sheets: timetables, price lists, catalogues, programs

- Vouchers: tickets, invoices, etc.

- Certificates: diplomas, contracts, etc.

- Calls and advertisements

- Charts and graphs; iconic representations of data

- Diagrams

- Tables and matrices

- Lists

- Maps

The definition Steen used in *Mathematics and Democracy: The Case for Quantitative Literacy* (2001) refers to these as "document literacy," following a definition adopted by the National Center for Education Statistics (NCES).

Against this background of varying perspectives, I chose for "mathematical literacy" a definition that is broad but also rather "mathematical":

> Mathematical literacy is an individual's capacity to identify and understand the role that mathematics plays in the world, to make well-founded judgments, and to engage in mathematics in ways that meet the needs of that individual's current and future life as a constructive, concerned and reflective citizen (OECD 1999).

This definition was developed by the Expert Group for Mathematics of the Programme for International Student Assessment (PISA), of which I am chair. (I will refer to this document repeatedly below.) Later in this essay I further discriminate between the concepts of numeracy, spatial literacy (SL), quantitative literacy (QL), and mathematical literacy (ML). I also try to build an argument that there is a need for consensus on what constitutes *basic* mathematical literacy as distinct from *advanced* mathematical literacy.

"What Mathematics?" Not Yet the Right Question

In an interview in *Mathematics and Democracy,* Peter T. Ewell (2001) was asked: "'The Case for Quantitative Literacy' argues that quantitative literacy (QL) is not merely a euphemism for mathematics but is something significantly different—less formal and more intuitive, less abstract and more contextual, less symbolic and more concrete. Is this a legitimate and helpful distinction?" Ewell answered that indeed this distinction is meaningful and powerful.

The answer to this question depends in large part on the interpretation of what constitutes good mathematics. We can guess that in Ewell's perception, mathematics is formal, abstract, and symbolic—a picture of mathematics still widely held. Ewell continued to say that literacy implies an integrated ability to function seamlessly within a given community of practice. Functionality is surely a key point, both in itself and in relation to a community of practice, which includes the community of mathematicians. Focusing on functionality gives us better opportunity to bridge gaps or identify overlaps. In the same volume, Alan H. Schoenfeld (2001) observed that in the past, literacy and what is learned in mathematics classes were largely disjointed. Now, however, they should be thought of as largely overlapping and taught as largely overlapping. In this approach, which takes into consideration the changing perception of what constitutes mathematics, mathematics and mathematical literacy are positively not disjointed.

For Schoenfeld, the distinction most likely lies in the fact that as a student he never encountered problem-solving situations, that he studied only "pure" mathematics and, finally, that he never saw or worked with real data. Each of these is absolutely essential for literate citizenship, but none even hints at defining what mathematics is needed for ML, at least not in the traditional school mathematics curricula descriptions of arithmetic, algebra, geometry, and so on.

Again, in *Mathematics and Democracy*, Wade Ellis, Jr. (2001) observes that many algebra teachers provide instruction that constricts rather than expands student thinking. He discovered that students leaving an elementary algebra course could solve fewer real-world problems after the course than before it: after completing the course, they thought that they had to use symbols to solve problems they had previously solved using only simple reasoning and arithmetic. It may come as no surprise that Ellis promotes a new kind of common sense—a quantitative common sense based on mathematical concepts, skills, and know-how. Despite their differences, however, Schoenfeld and Ellis seem to share Treffers' observation that innumeracy might be caused by a flaw in the structural design of instruction.

These several observers seem to agree that in comparison with traditional school mathematics, ML is less formal and more intuitive, less abstract and more contextual, less symbolic and more concrete. ML also focuses more attention and emphasis on reasoning, thinking, and interpreting as well as on other very mathematical competencies. To get a better picture of what is involved in this distinction, we first need to describe what Steen (2001) called the "elements" needed for ML. With a working definition of ML and an understanding of the elements (or "competencies," as they are described in the PISA framework) needed for ML, we might come closer to answering our original question—what mathematics is important?—or formulating a better one.

Competencies Needed for ML

The competencies that form the heart of the ML description in PISA seem, for the most part, well in line with the elements in Steen (2001). The competencies rely on the work of Niss (1999) and his Danish colleagues, but similar formulations can be found in the work of many others representing many countries (as indicated by Neubrand et al. 2001):

1. *Mathematical thinking and reasoning.* Posing questions characteristic of mathematics; knowing the kind of answers that mathematics offers, distinguishing among different kinds of statements; understanding and handling the extent and limits of mathematical concepts.

2. *Mathematical argumentation.* Knowing what proofs are; knowing how proofs differ from other forms of mathematical reasoning; following and assessing chains of arguments; having a feel for heuristics; creating and expressing mathematical arguments.

3. *Mathematical communication.* Expressing oneself in a variety of ways in oral, written, and other visual form; understanding someone else's work.

4. *Modeling.* Structuring the field to be modeled; translating reality into mathematical structures; interpreting mathematical models in terms of context or reality; working with models; validating models; reflecting, analyzing, and offering critiques of models or solutions; reflecting on the modeling process.

5. *Problem posing and solving.* Posing, formulating, defining, and solving problems in a variety of ways.

6. *Representation.* Decoding, encoding, translating, distinguishing between, and interpreting different forms of representations of mathematical objects and situations as well as understanding the relationship among different representations.

7. *Symbols.* Using symbolic, formal, and technical language and operations.

8. *Tools and technology.* Using aids and tools, including technology when appropriate.

To be mathematically literate, individuals need all these competencies to varying degrees, but they also need confidence in their own ability to use mathematics and comfort with quantitative ideas. An appreciation of mathematics from historical, philosophical, and societal points of view is also desirable.

It should be clear from this description why we have included functionality within the mathematician's practice. We also note that to function well as a mathematician, a person needs to be literate. It is not uncommon that someone familiar with a mathematical tool fails to recognize its usefulness in a real-life situation (Steen 2001, 17). Neither is it uncommon for a mathematician to be unable to use common-sense reasoning (as distinct from the reasoning involved in a mathematical proof).

As Deborah Hughes Hallett (2001) made clear in her contribution to *Mathematics and Democracy,* one of the reasons that ML is hard to acquire and hard to teach is that it involves insight as well as algorithms. Some algorithms are of course necessary: it is difficult to do much analysis without knowing arithmetic, for example. But learning (or memorizing) algorithms is not enough: insight is an essential component of mathematical understanding. Such insight, Hughes Hallett noted, connotes an understanding of quantitative relationships and the ability to identify those relationships in an unfamiliar context; its acquisition involves reflection, judgment, and above all, experience. Yet current school curricula seldom emphasize insight and do little to actively support its development at any level. This is very unfortunate. The development of insight into mathematics should be actively supported, starting before children enter school.

Many countries have begun to take quite seriously the problems associated with overemphasizing algorithms and neglecting insight. For example, the Netherlands has had some limited success in trying to reform how mathematics is taught. To outsiders, the relatively high scores on the Third International Mathematics and Science Study (TIMSS) and TIMSS-R by students in the Netherlands appear to prove this, but the results of the Netherlands in the PISA study should provide even more proof.

The Netherlands has been helped in moving away from the strictly algorithmic way of teaching mathematics by the recognition that mathematical abilities or competencies can be clustered: one cluster includes reproduction, algorithms, definitions, and so on; another cluster encompasses the ability to make connections among different aspects or concepts in mathematics to solve simple problems; and a third cluster includes insight, reasoning, reflection, and generalization as key components (de Lange 1992, 1995). In designing curricula and assessments as well as items for international examinations, this clustering approach became a mirror reflecting back to us what we thought constituted good mathematics in the sense of competencies. To a large extent, this approach also prevented the very present danger of viewing the National Council of Teachers of Mathematics (NCTM) goals—reasoning, communication, and connections—as merely rhetoric (Steen 2001). Eventually, this clustering of mathematical competencies found its way into the present OECD PISA study (1999) as well as into a classroom mathematics assessment framework (de Lange 1999) and an electronic assessment tool (Cappo and de Lange 1999).

Finally, we want to make the observation that the competencies needed for ML are actually the competencies needed for mathematics *as it should be taught.* Were that the case (with curricula

following the suggestions made by Schoenfeld and Hughes Hallett and extrapolating from experiences in the Netherlands and other countries), the gap between mathematics and mathematical literacy would be much smaller than some people suggest it is at present (Steen 2001). It must be noted, however, that in most countries this gap is quite large and the need to start thinking and working toward an understanding of what makes up ML is barely recognized. As Neubrand et al. (2001) noted in talking about the situation in Germany: "In actual practice of German mathematics education, there is no correspondence between the teaching of mathematics as a discipline and practical applications within a context" (free translation by author).

What Is Mathematics?

To provide a clearer picture of literacy in mathematics, it seems wise to reflect for a moment on what constitutes mathematics. Not that we intend to offer a deep philosophical treatment—there are many good publications around—but it is not unlikely that many readers might think of school mathematics as representing mathematics as a science. Several authors in *Mathematics and Democracy* (Steen 2001) clearly pointed this out, quite often based on their own experiences (Schoenfeld, Schneider, Kennedy, and Ellis, among others). Steen (1990) observed in *On the Shoulders of Giants: New Approaches to Numeracy* that traditional school mathematics picks a very few strands (e.g., arithmetic, algebra, and geometry) and arranges them horizontally to form the curriculum: first arithmetic, then simple algebra, then geometry, then more algebra and, finally, as if it were the epitome of mathematical knowledge, calculus. Each course seems designed primarily to prepare for the next. These courses give a distorted view of mathematics as a science, do not seem to be related to the educational experience of children, and bear no relevance for society. A result of this is that the informal development of intuition along the multiple roots of mathematics, a key characteristic in the development of ML, is effectively prevented. To overcome this misimpression about the nature of mathematics left by such courses, we will try to sketch how we see mathematics and, subsequently, what the consequences can be for mathematics education.

Mathematical concepts, structures, and ideas have been invented as tools to organize phenomena in the natural, social, and mental worlds. In the real world, the phenomena that lend themselves to mathematical treatment do not come organized as they are in school curriculum structures. Rarely do real-life problems arise in ways and contexts that allow their understanding and solutions to be achieved through an application of knowledge from a single content strand. If we look at mathematics as a science that helps us solve real problems, it makes sense to use a phenomenological approach to describe mathematical concepts, structures, and ideas. This approach has been followed by Freudenthal (1973) and by others such as Steen (1990), who state that if mathematics curricula featured multiple parallel strands, each grounded in appropriate childhood experiences, the collective effect would be to develop among children diverse mathematical insight into the many different roots of mathematics. Steen then suggested that we should seek inspiration in the developmental power of five deep mathematical ideas: dimension, quantity, uncertainty, shape, and change. The OECD PISA mathematics expert group has adapted these, creating four phenomenological categories to describe what constitutes mathematics: *quantity*, *space* and *shape*, *change* and *relationships*, and *uncertainty*.

Using these four categories, mathematics content can be organized into a sufficient number of areas to help ensure a spread of items across the curriculum, but also a small enough number to avoid an excessively fine division—which would work against a focus on problems based in real-life situations. Each phenomenological category is an encompassing set of phenomena and concepts that make sense together and may be encountered within and across a multitude of quite different situations. By their very nature, each idea can be perceived as a general notion dealing with a generalized content dimension. This implies that the categories or ideas cannot be sharply delineated vis-à-vis one another. Rather, each represents a certain perspective, or point of view, which can be thought of as possessing a core, a center of gravity, and a somewhat blurred penumbra that allow intersection with other ideas. In principle, any idea can intersect with any other idea. (For a more detailed description of these four categories or ideas, please refer to the PISA framework (OECD 2002).)

Quantity. This overarching idea focuses on the need for quantification to organize the world. Important aspects include an understanding of relative size, recognition of numerical patterns, and the ability to use numbers to represent quantifiable attributes of real-world objects (measures). Furthermore, quantity deals with the processing and understanding of numbers that are represented to us in various ways. An important aspect of dealing with quantity is quantitative reasoning, whose essential components are developing and using number sense, representing numbers in various ways, understanding the meaning of operations, having a feel for the magnitude of numbers, writing and understanding mathematically elegant computations, doing mental arithmetic, and estimating.

Space and Shape. Patterns are encountered everywhere around us: in spoken words, music, video, traffic, architecture, and art. Shapes can be regarded as patterns: houses, office buildings, bridges, starfish, snowflakes, town plans, cloverleaves, crystals, and shadows. Geometric patterns can serve as relatively simple models of many kinds of phenomena, and their study is desirable at all levels (Grünbaum 1985). In the study of shapes and constructions, we look for similarities and differences as we analyze the components of form and recognize shapes in different representations and different dimensions. The study of shapes is closely connected to the concept of "grasping space" (Freudenthal 1973)—learning to know, explore, and conquer, in order to live, breathe, and move with more understanding in the space in which we live. To achieve this, we must be able to understand the properties of objects and the relative positions of objects; we must be aware of how we see things and why we see them as we do; and we must learn to navigate through space and through constructions and shapes. This requires understanding the relationship between shapes and images (or visual representations) such as that between a real city and photographs and maps of the same city. It also includes understanding how three-dimensional objects can be represented in two dimensions, how shadows are formed and interpreted, and what perspective is and how it functions.

Change and Relationships. Every natural phenomenon is a manifestation of change, and in the world around us a multitude of temporary and permanent relationships among phenomena are observed: organisms changing as they grow, the cycle of seasons, the ebb and flow of tides, cycles of unemployment, weather changes, stock exchange fluctuations. Some of these change processes can be modeled by straightforward mathematical functions: linear, exponential, periodic or logistic, discrete or continuous. But many relationships fall into different categories, and data analysis is often essential to determine the kind of relationship present. Mathematical relationships often take the shape of equations or inequalities, but relations of a more general nature (e.g., equivalence, divisibility) may appear as well. Functional thinking—that is, thinking in terms of and about relationships—is one of the fundamental disciplinary aims of the teaching of mathematics. Relationships can take a variety of different representations, including symbolic, algebraic, graphic, tabular, and geometric. As a result, translation between representations is often of key importance in dealing with mathematical situations.

Uncertainty. Our information-driven society offers an abundance of data, often presented as accurate and scientific and with a degree of certainty. But in daily life we are confronted with uncertain election results, collapsing bridges, stock market crashes, unreliable weather forecasts, poor predictions of population growth, economic models that do not align, and many other demonstrations of the uncertainty of our world. Uncertainty is intended to suggest two related topics: data and chance, phenomena that are the subject of mathematical study in statistics and probability, respectively. Recent recommendations concerning school curricula are unanimous in suggesting that statistics and probability should occupy a much more prominent place than they have in the past (Cockroft 1982; LOGSE 1990; MSEB 1993; NCTM 1989, 2000). Specific mathematical concepts and activities that are important in this area include collecting data, data analysis, data display and visualization, probability, and inference.

The Real World

Although we now have "answers" to what constitutes ML, what the needed skills or competencies are, and what mathematics is, we still are not in a position to give an answer to what mathematics is needed for ML. The reason is simple: mathematics curricula have focused on school-based knowledge whereas mathematical literacy involves mathematics as it is used in the real world.

An important part of mathematical literacy is using, doing, and recognizing mathematics in a variety of situations. In dealing with issues that lend themselves to a mathematical treatment, the choice of mathematical methods and representations often depends on the situations in which the problems are presented. Teachers of mathematics often complain that students have difficulty applying the mathematics they have learned in different contexts. As Hughes Hallett (2001) correctly observed, nonscience students often dislike contexts involving physics applications in mathematics because they do not understand the physics. Building from this, I think we need to examine the wisdom of confronting nonscience students with mathematics applications that need specific science literacy at a nonbasic level. As has been pointed out before, to effectively transfer their knowledge from one area of application to another, students need experience solving problems in many different situations and contexts (de Lange 1987). Making competencies a central emphasis facilitates this process: competencies are independent of the area of application. Students should be offered real-world situations relevant to them, either real-world situations that will help them to function as informed and intelligent citizens or real-world situations that are relevant to their areas of interest, either professionally or educationally.

By *situation,* we mean the part of the student's world in which a certain problem is embedded. It is very convenient and relevant to the art of teaching for ML to see situations as having certain distances in relation to the student (de Lange 1995; OECD 1999, 2002). The closest distance is the student's personal life; next is school (educational) life, then work (occupational) and leisure, followed by the local community and society as encountered in daily life. Furthest away are scientific situations. It might be desirable to enlarge the distance domain as the age of the students increases, but not in a strict way.

Steen (2001, 9–15) itemized an impressive list of expressions of numeracy, most of which can be seen as having a certain "distance" from "citizens." Under personal life we include, depending on age, games, daily scheduling, sports, shopping, saving, interpersonal relations, finances, voting, reading maps, reading tables, health, insurance, and so on. School life relates to understanding the role of mathematics in society, school events (e.g., sports,

teams, scheduling), understanding data, computers, and so on. Work and leisure involves reasoning, understanding data and statistics, finances, taxes, risks, rates, samples, scheduling, geometric patterns, two- and three-dimensional representations, budgets, visualizations, and so on. In the local community, we see the intelligent citizen making appropriate judgments, making decisions, evaluating conclusions, gathering data and making inferences, and in general adopting a critical attitude—seeing the reasoning behind decisions.

Last, we come to science situations. To function as an intelligent citizen, individuals need to be literate in many fields, not only in mathematics. The use of scientific situations or contexts in mathematics classes should not be avoided per se, but some care must be taken. If we try to teach students the right competencies but use the wrong context, we are creating a problem, not solving it. A good but rather unscientific example concerns work with middle-school students in the United States. The designed lesson sequence had archeology as a context. Archeologists sometimes use rather straightforward but quite unexpected and rather "subjective" mathematical methods in their research—just the kind of mathematics middle school students can handle. The question, therefore, was not whether the students could do the mathematics but whether the context was engaging enough in this short-attention-span society. The students were highly engaged because of the unexpectedness of what they were learning and the relevance of the methods used. As we learned in this instance, connecting to the students' real world can be a complex but highly rewarding journey.

What has become clear in dealing with mathematics in context over the past 25 years is that making mathematics relevant by teaching it in context is quite possible and very rewarding, despite the many pitfalls. We note that much more experience and research is needed, but based on previous experiences we also note that teaching for both mathematical literacy and relevant mathematics at almost the same time might very well prove feasible.

A Matter of Definitions

Having set the context, it seems appropriate now to make clear distinctions among types of literacies so that, at least in this essay, we do not declare things equal that are not equal. For instance, some equate numeracy with quantitative literacy; others equate quantitative and mathematical literacy. To make our definitions functional, we connect them to our phenomenological categories.

Spatial Literacy (SL). We start with the simplest and most neglected, spatial literacy. SL supports our understanding of the (three-dimensional) world in which we live and move. To deal with what surrounds us, we must understand properties of objects, the relative positions of objects and the effect thereof on our visual perception, the creation of all kinds of two- and three-dimensional paths and routes, navigational practices, shadows—even the art of Escher.

Numeracy (N). The next obvious literacy is numeracy (N), fitting as it does directly into quantity. We can follow, for instance, Treffers' (1991) definition, which stresses the ability to handle numbers and data and to evaluate statements regarding problems and situations that invite mental processing and estimating in real-world contexts.

Quantitative Literacy (QL). When we look at quantitative literacy, we are actually looking at literacy dealing with a cluster of phenomenological categories: quantity, change and relationships, and uncertainty. These categories stress understanding of, and mathematical abilities concerned with, certainties (quantity), uncertainties (quantity as well as uncertainty), and relations (types of, recognition of, changes in, and reasons for those changes).

Mathematical Literacy (ML). We think of mathematical literacy as the overarching literacy comprising all others. Thus we can make a visual representation as follows:

Advanced Mathematical Literacy and Basic Mathematical Literacy. Another possibly fruitful way to make distinctions within the field of mathematical literacy is to think about the "community of practitioners" in somewhat more detail. Being mathematically literate means different things according to the needs of the community, both as a group and as individuals. It may be a good idea, although well beyond the comfort zone for many, to speak of *basic mathematical literacy* (BML), a level expected of all students up to age 15 or so, independent of their role in society. Individual countries or communities should be able to define in some detail what this actually means in the local culture. After age 15, however, as students begin to think of their future careers, they should, accordingly, acquire *advanced mathematical literacy* (AML), defined by their need to fit into their community of practice. Because of the many different communities of practice in a given society, defining the general content for career-related AML may be unwise, if not impossible. But defining an early career-entry AML for high school students and undergraduates might be appropriate, as might defining a general AML for adult life in society, linking its development, support, and enhancement to continuing education for adults.

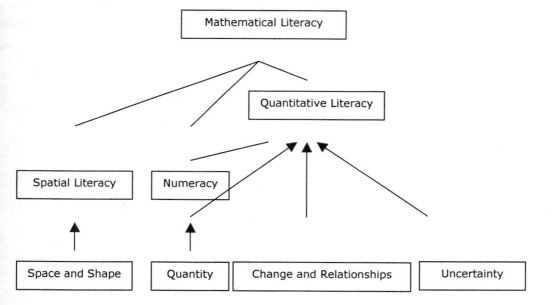

Examples: The Mathematics Necessary for Development of ML

Examples from real curricula offer the best illustrations of mathematics that meet at least some of the requirements of ML. It will come as no surprise, perhaps, that the examples offered here, andour frame of reference, will be the Netherlands, but with an eye to the U.S. situation.

In the 1970s, it became increasingly clear that there was a serious mismatch in the Netherlands between what many students needed and what was offered to them in mathematics curricula, a mismatch still present in many curricula. Traditional curricula, for example, include calculus taught in a way that seldom leads to any understanding of its power or usefulness and seldom either develops students' ability to reason with it as a tool or develops it with an eye to mathematical or scientific proof. Few mathematics educators see any merit in this approach (see de Lange 1994). Yet despite the fact that calculus has few easily accessible applications outside the exact sciences, it has survived "for all," albeit in very different shapes, in upper secondary curricula.

This mismatch is particularly acute for the majority of students who do not want to pursue university study in the exact sciences but who need mathematics for economics, biological sciences, language, arts, social sciences, and so on. More generally, this mismatch affects all future members of our society, which depends so heavily on mathematics and technology. In the early 1980s, a specific curriculum was developed in the Netherlands to meet the need for more general, socially relevant mathematical knowledge (ML). The political reasons were simple and clear: all students needed mathematics, but what they needed to study was the mathematics required to function well in society and the concepts and areas relevant to their future work and study. As part of this change, curricula differing in mathematical content, level of formality, context, and even (to a certain extent) pedagogy were created to fit the needs of different clusters of students beyond the age of 14. To convey the nature of this change, we give below some concrete examples of this mathematics, presented in the order of our phenomenological categories.

QUANTITY

The Defense Budget. In a certain country, the defense budget was $30 million for 1980. The total budget for that year was $500 million. The following year, the defense budget was $35 million, whereas the total budget was $605 million. Inflation during the period between the two budgets was 10 percent.

(a) You are invited to hold a lecture for a pacifist society. You want to explain that the defense budget has decreased this year. Explain how to do this.

(b) You are invited to lecture to a military academy. You want to claim that the defense budget has increased this year. Explain how to do this (de Lange 1987).

This problem has been thoroughly researched with 16-year-old students. It illustrates very well the third cluster on reflection and insight. Students recognized the literacy aspect immediately and quite often were able to make some kind of generalization; the heart of the solution lies in recognizing that the key mathematical concepts here are absolute and relative growth. Inflation can of course be left out to make the problem accessible to somewhat younger students without losing the key conceptual ideas behind the problem, but doing so reduces the complexity and thus the required mathematization. Another way to make the item simpler is to present the data in a table or schema. In this case, students have no preliminary work to carry out before they get to the heart of the matter.

SPACE AND SHAPE

Casting Shadows. We first show an example of basic spatial literacy that reflects a well-known daily experience, but one in which people seldom realize what they see. The variety of shadows cast by the sun (or a light bulb) is an interesting starting point for a wide array of mathematical questions that have a much wider impact than people initially realize. Students first are introduced to a picture of an outdoor lamp surrounded by posts (Feijs 1998):

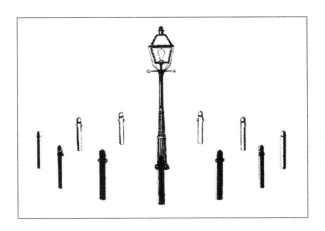

They then are asked to draw the shadows created by the lamp (Top View A) and also the shadows cast by the sun (Top View B):

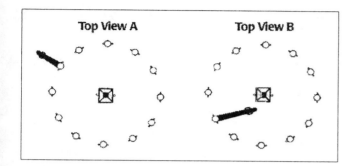

The answers to both questions are rather straightforward:

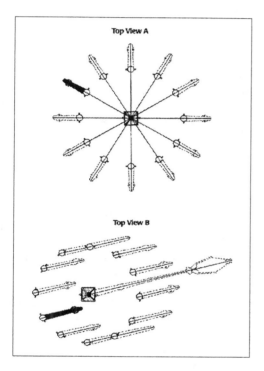

They are based on understanding the path of light rays in relation to the objects that are casting shadows:

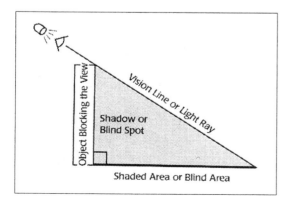

This example not only illustrates aspects of mathematical literacy as it deals with the world in which we live but also can stimulate thinking about deeper mathematical ideas that are not immediately evident, for example, parallel and central projection, vision lines, blind spots, and ratios.

The second example dealing with space and shape is taken from the curriculum for students preparing for study in the exact sciences.

Equal Distances. The economies of some countries depend on their fishing industries. Other countries are interested in the ocean for reasons of oil drilling rights. How do we establish "fair" rules about who gets what and for what reasons? If we are considering a straight canal with two different countries on both sides, it seems obvious: the line through the middle of the canal forms the boundary because it is the line with equal distances to both countries. The political and societal relevance of this and similar questions is immediately clear. But how many people understand the logic and common sense behind the rules?

The part of geometry that deals with equal distances is sometimes called Voronoi geometry. It is an area of mathematics that has relevance to practical (and very often political) problems and also offers experience in useful mathematical reasoning. Unlike the previous example, which illustrated Basic ML, this one is for senior high school students, taken from students' materials at a Dutch high school.

The illustration shows the Netherlands portioned by use of a Voronoi diagram: all cities (city centers) are equidistant to the borders.

(a) What do you know about the distances from A to Middelburg, from A to Den Haag and from A to Den Bosch?

(b) Explain why a Voronoi diagram with three points can never look like the following diagram (Goddijn 1997, taken out of context and order).

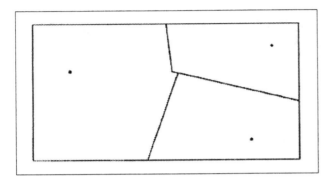

These examples form the starting point for a sequence of very interesting space and shape mathematics that is very relevant from a societal point of view (e.g., fishing rights, oil-drilling rights). But Voronoi diagrams have much more to offer in the mathematical sense. For example, although the last question above is not of immediate relevance to fishing or oil-drilling rights, it requires coherent, competent, and consistent reasoning, which is at least as important as the first questions for intelligent citizens to function in their societies.

CHANGE AND RELATIONSHIPS

Cheetahs and Horses. Some animals that dwell on grassy plains are safeguarded against attacks by their large size; others are so small that they can protect themselves by burrowing into the ground. Still others must count on speed to escape their enemies.

An animal's speed depends on its size and the frequency of its strides. The tarsal (foot) bone of animals of the horse family is lengthened, with each foot having been reduced to only one toe. One thick bone is stronger than a number of thin ones. This single toe is surrounded by a solid hoof, which protects the bone against jolts when the animal is galloping over hard ground. The powerful leg muscles are joined together at the top of the leg so that just a slight muscle movement at that point can freely move the slim lower leg.

The fastest sprinter in the world is the cheetah. Its legs are shorter than those of a horse, but it can reach a speed of more than 110 km/h in 17 seconds and maintain that speed for more than 450 meters. The cheetah tires easily, however, whereas a horse, whose top speed is 70 km/h, can maintain a speed of 50 km/h for more than 6 km.

A cheetah is awakened from its afternoon nap by a horse's hooves. At the moment the cheetah decides to give chase, the horse has a lead of 200 meters. The horse, traveling at its top speed, still has plenty of energy. Taking into consideration the above data on the running powers of the cheetah and the horse, can the cheetah catch the horse? Assume that the cheetah will need around 300 meters to reach its top speed. Solve this problem by using graphs. Let the vertical axis represent distance and the horizontal axis time (Kindt 1979, in de Lange 1987).

As Freudenthal (1979) lamented:

> This story of the cheetah seems rather complex. There is an abundance of numbers . . . and nowhere an indication of which operation to perform on which numbers. Indeed, is there anything like a solution? The only question to be answered is, "Does the cheetah catch up with the horse?" It is "yes" or "no"—no numbers, no kilometers, no seconds. Is that a solution in the usual sense? (free translation by author).

According to Freudenthal, this is what mathematics is all about, especially mathematics for ML. This example also shows how we can introduce students to calculus. Calculus needs to be perceived as "the science that keeps track of changes," as a student once characterized it. A qualitative discussion about rates of change can be very illuminating for students and at the same time enable mathematics to contribute to ML. It prevents students from perceiving calculus as that part of mathematics in which "you take the exponent, put it in front, and the new exponent is one less than the original one." Another student in the course in a nonmathematics-related major, who was not very successful in traditional mathematics, answered: "Differentiation is about how to keep check on rates of change." Part of the importance of ML can be seen in the gap between these two answers.

Tides. Natural phenomena should play a vital role in mathematics for ML. For a country like the Netherlands, with 40 percent of its area below sea level, the tides are very important. The following protocol is taken from a classroom of 16-year-olds (de Lange 2000):

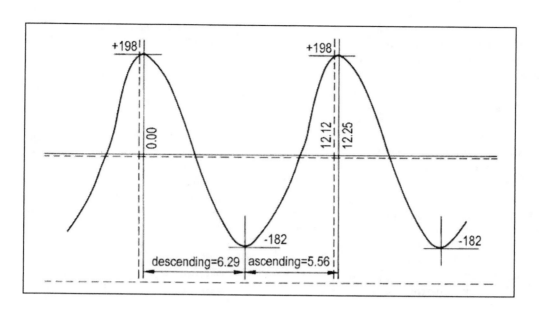

Teacher: Let's look at the mean tidal graph of Flushing. What are the essentials?

Student A: High water is 198 cm, and low is −182 cm.

Teacher: And? [pause]

Student A: So it takes longer to go down than up.

Teacher: What do you mean?

Student A: Going down takes 6 hours 29 minutes, up only 5 hours 56 minutes.

Teacher: OK. And how about the period?

Student A: 6 hours 29 and 5 hours 56 makes 12 hours 25 minutes.

Teacher: Now, can we find a simple mathematical model?

Student B: [pause] Maybe 2 sin x.

Teacher: What is the period, then?

Student B: 2 pi, that means around 6.28 hours [pause] 6 hours 18 minutes [pause] oh, I see that it must be 2x, or, no, x/2.

Teacher: So?

Student C: 2 sin (x/2) will do.

Teacher: Explain.

Student C: Well, that's simple: the maximum is 2 meters, the low is −2 meters, and the period is around 12 hours 33 minutes or so. That's pretty close, isn't it?

Teacher: [to the class] Isn't it?

Student D: No, I don't agree. I think the model needs to show exactly how high the water can rise. I propose 190 sin (x/2) + 8. In that case, the maximum is exactly 198 cm, and the minimum exactly −182 cm. Not bad.

Teacher: Any comments, anyone? [some whispering, some discussion]

Student E: I think it is more important to be precise about the period. 12 hours 33 minutes is too far off to make predictions in the future about when it will be high water. We should be more precise. I think 190 sin [(pi/6.2)x] is much better.

Teacher: What's the period in that case?

Student F: 12.4 hours, or 12 hours 24 minutes, only 1 minute off.

Teacher: Perfect. What model do we prefer? [discussion]

Student G: 190 sin [(pi/6.2)x] + 8.

The discussion continued with "What happens if we go to a different city that has smaller amplitudes and where high tides come two hours later? How does this affect the formula? "Why is the rate of change so important?"

Why do we consider this a good example of mathematics for ML? Given the community in which this problem is part of the curriculum, the relevance for society is immediately clear—and the relevance is rising with global temperatures. The relevance also becomes clear at a different level, however. The mathematical method of trial and error illustrated here not only is interesting by itself, but the combination of the method with the most relevant variables also is interesting: in one problem setting we are interested in the exact time of high water, in another we are interested in the exact height of the water at high tide. Intelligent citizens need insight into the possibilities and limitations of models. This problem worked very well for these students, age 16, and the fact that the "real" model used 40 different sine functions did not really make that much difference with respect to students' perceptions.

Uncertainty

Challenger. If we fail to pose problems properly or fail to seek essential data and represent them in a meaningful way, we can very easily drown in data. One dramatic example concerns the advice of the producer of solid rocket motors (SRM) to NASA concerning the launch of the space shuttle Challenger in 1986. The recommendation issued the day before the launch was *not* to launch if the temperature was less than 53 degrees Fahrenheit; the low temperature (29 degrees) that was predicted for the day of the launch might produce risks. As beautifully laid out by Tufte (1997), the fax supporting the recommendation was an excellent example of failed mathematical and common-sense reasoning. Instead of looking at the data on all 24 previous launches, the fax related to only two actual launches (giving temperatures, with ensuing damage to rubber O-rings). NASA, of course, refused to cancel the launch based on the arguments found in the fax. Simple mathematics could have saved the lives of the seven astronauts.

The scientists at Morton Thiokol, producer of the O-rings, were right in their conclusion but were unable to find a correlation between O-ring damage and temperature. Let us look at the problem systematically. The first thing to do if we suspect a correlation is to look at all the data available, in this case, the temperatures at the time of launch for all 24 launches and the ensuing damage to the O-rings. At that point, we then order the entries by possible cause: temperature at launch, from coolest to warmest. Next, for each launch, we calculate the damage to the O-rings and then draw a scatter plot showing the findings from all 24 launches prior to the Challenger.

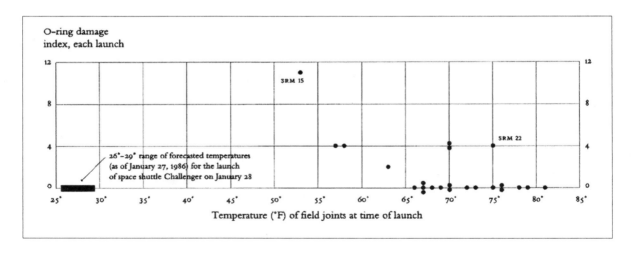

In this graph, the temperature scale extends down to 29 degrees, visually expressing the extraordinary extrapolation (beyond all previous experience) that had to be made to "see" the launch at 29 degrees. The coolest flight without any O-ring damage was at 66 degrees, some 37 degrees warmer than that predicted for the Challenger; the forecast of 29 degrees was 5.7 standard deviations distant from the average temperature on previous launches. This launch was completely outside the engineering database accumulated in 24 previous flights. The result: the O-rings had already failed before the rocket was launched.

What Mathematics Education Supports the Development of ML?

These examples, taken from the classroom, show what kinds of problems students need to work with to learn good mathematics while at the same time becoming mathematically literate. In a general sense, we agree with Steen (2001) that deploying mathematics in sophisticated settings such as modern work-based tasks gives students not only motivation and context but also a concrete foundation from which they can later abstract and generalize. As these examples show, however, it is not necessary to restrict ourselves to work-based settings. Not every setting lends itself equally to the successful development of mathematical concepts. The importance of choosing appropriate contexts is well documented (e.g., de Lange 1987; Feijs in press), and the issues involved in selecting situations to develop mathematical concepts are quite different from those involved in choosing contexts "just" for application. This is a very tricky area, and much more research is needed before we can make general statements, but the view expressed here is not innovative in any sense. For example, in 1962, some 75 well-known U.S. mathematicians produced a memorandum, "On the Mathematics Curriculum of the High School," published in the *American Mathematical Monthly*:

> To know mathematics means to be able to do mathematics: to use mathematical language with some fluency, to do problems, to criticize arguments, to find proofs, and, what may be the most important activity, to recognize a mathematical concept in, or to extract it from, a given concrete situation (Ahlfors et al. 1962).

It is precisely this "most important activity" that is the essence of the philosophy of mathematics education in the Netherlands, mainly because of the influence of Hans Freudenthal, who in 1968 observed that the goals of teaching mathematics as a socially useful tool could only be reached by having students start from situations that needed to be mathematized. Many mathematics educators and researchers have since supported this view, among them Lesh and Landau (1986), who argued that applications should not be reserved for consideration only after learning has

occurred; they can and should be used as a context within which the learning of mathematical concepts takes place.

Our first observation about the mathematics needed to support ML is that *mathematical concepts should be learned through solving problems in appropriate settings,* with opportunities for progressive mathematization and generalization. It should be noted that certain areas in mathematics lend themselves better than others to these purposes. For instance, matrices and graphs, introduced into curricula in the Netherlands in the 1980s, lend themselves very nicely to modeling and representation without the burden of too much specialized language or too many formulas.

A desirable consequence of starting with real settings is the bonus of connected and integrated mathematics. The same problem, but especially the more complex ones, often can be solved in many different ways. Sometimes students choose a more algebraic method, sometimes a more geometric one; sometimes they integrate these, or produce something completely unexpected. Our second observation, then, is that *the mathematics that is taught not only should be connected to other mathematics but also should be embedded in the real world of the student.*

Our third observation is that *the goals of education should not be formulated exclusively in subject areas but should also include competencies.* This holds as well for areas within mathematics: we should not think along the subject lines of arithmetic, algebra, geometry, among others, but about mathematical competencies. This point of view forms the backbone of the PISA Framework for Mathematics, supported by more than 30 countries, including the United States.

The fourth observation is a trivial but important one: *mathematics literacy will lead to different curricula in different cultures.* ML will need to be culturally attuned and defined by the needs of the particular country. This should be kept in mind as we attempt to further determine what mathematics is needed for ML. (We also note that the technology gap will have a serious impact on the type of mathematics competencies that define being mathematically literate in a given country.)

The fifth observation is that, given the goals of ML, *the content of curricula will have to be modernized at least every five to 10 years.* Mathematics is a very dynamic discipline. The culture, and thus the relation between mathematics and society, changes very quickly as well. (In the Netherlands, the curricula for mathematics have a life span of about seven years.)

The sixth observation is that *we might be able to reach some degree of consensus about the meaning of basic mathematical literacy.* A good starting point, as Steen, Schoenfeld, and many others have pointed out, could be the revised NCTM standards (NCTM

2000). The standards, however, stick relatively close to tradition and clearly reflect the difficult process of trying to please everyone. As a result, they can serve only as a starting point, not as a definitive framework for ML.

The seventh observation is that *I can neither describe a curriculum for ML nor even identify the relevant mathematics in any detail.* Some things are clear: from kindergarten on, we should focus on competencies; right from the start we should pay attention not just to arithmetic but to all four phenomenological categories; we should rethink completely the role of algebra; we should design the longitudinal development of mathematical concepts in a very coherent way (at least for students from 4 to 15 years of age); and we should formulate in some detail what it means to be mathematically literate in the basic sense. In this, the results from PISA might help us in a modest way. I also suggest that we should not shy away from new mathematical developments (e.g., discrete dynamic modeling).

The examples I have presented, if properly interpreted and extrapolated, together with these several observations, give the interested reader an impression of the mathematics needed for ML. But designing such a curriculum, let alone teaching it, is a completely different story.

Reflections

I have not answered the question I was asked to address, namely, what mathematics is important for ML? But I have attempted to offer some directions: the desired competencies, not the mathematical content, are the main criteria, and these are different at different ages and for different populations. From a competencies perspective, mathematics for ML can coexist with calculus—or even better, should coexist with a calculus track—but with opportunities to develop intuition, to explore real-world settings, to learn reasoning, and so on. It goes without saying that the line of reasoning I have tried to follow holds for all ages, including university students. We also need mathematicians to become mathematically literate—as such, they are much better prepared to participate in society at large and, even more important, can contribute in a constructive and critical way to the discussion about mathematics education. We all need to understand how important, how essential, ML is for every student, and mathematicians in particular need to understand that ML will contribute to a better perception about what constitutes mathematics and how important that field is to our lives.

We have not addressed several other questions. One of the most important is: How do we teach mathematics for ML? What are the pedagogical arguments and didactics of mathematics for ML? But

that question needs an article by itself, as in fact do most of the issues I have discussed here.

But let me end positively. If the experiences in my own country, the experiments we carried out in the United States, and the observations we made worldwide are any indication, there is a good chance that we can achieve ML. The issue is very complex, however, and we have a long and challenging way to go.

References

Ahlfors, L. V. et al. 1962. "On the Mathematics Curriculum of the High School." *Mathematics Teacher* 55(3): 191–95.

Cappo, M., and de Lange, J. 1999. "AssessMath!," Santa Cruz, CA: Learning in Motion.

Cockroft, W. H. 1982. *Mathematics Counts*. Report of the Committee of Inquiry into the Teaching of Mathematics in Schools. London: Her Majesty's Stationery Office.

De Lange, J. 1987. *Mathematics, Insight, and Meaning. Teaching, Learning, and Testing of Mathematics for the Life and Social Sciences.* Utrecht: Vakgroep Onderzoek Wiskundeonderwijs en Onderwijscomputercentrum (OW&OC).

De Lange, J. 1992. "Higher Order (Un-)Teaching." In *Developments in School Mathematics Education around the World,* edited by I. Wirszup and R. Streit, vol. 3, 49–72. Reston, VA: National Council of Teachers of Mathematics (NCTM).

De Lange, J., ed. 1994. *Rapport Studiecommissie Wiskunde B-VWO.* Utrecht: Onderzoek Wiskundeonderwijs en Onderwijscomputercentrum (OW&OC).

De Lange, J. 1995. "Assessment: No Change Without Problems." In *Reform in School Mathematics and Authentic Assessment,* edited by T. A. Romberg, 87–172. New York, NY: State University of New York Press.

De Lange, J. 1999. *Framework for Assessment in Mathematics.* Madison, WI: National Center for Improving Student Learning and Achievement in Mathematics and Science (NCISLA).

De Lange, J. 2000. "The Tides They are A-Changing." *UMAP-Journal* 21(1): 15–36.

Ellis, Wade Jr. 2001. "Numerical Common Sense for All." In *Mathematics and Democracy: The Case for Quantitative Literacy,* edited by Lynn Arthur Steen, 61–66. Princeton, NJ: National Council on Education and the Disciplines.

Ewell, Peter T. 2001. "Numeracy, Mathematics, and General Education." In *Mathematics and Democracy: The Case for Quantitative Literacy,* edited by Lynn Arthur Steen, 37–48. Princeton, NJ: National Council on Education and the Disciplines.

Feijs, E. et al. 1998. "Looking at an Angle." In *Mathematics in Context.* Chicago, IL: Encyclopedia Britannica.

Feijs, E. Forthcoming. *Constructing a Learning Environment that Promotes Understanding.* Madison, WI: National Center for Improving Student Learning and Achievement in Mathematics and Science (NCISLA).

Freudenthal, H. 1973. *Mathematics as an Educational Task.* Dordrecht: Reidel.

Freudenthal, H. 1979. "Een manier om veranderingen bij te houden." *Wiskrant* 18: 6–7.

Goddijn, A. 1997. *Afstanden, Grenzen en Gebieden.* Utrecht: Freudenthal Instituut.

Grünbaum, B. 1985. "Geometry Strikes Again." *Mathematics Magazine* 58:1, pp. 12–18.

Hughes-Hallett, Deborah. 2001. "Achieving Numeracy: The Challenge of Implementation." In *Mathematics and Democracy: The Case for Quantitative Literacy,* edited by Lynn Arthur Steen, 93–98. Princeton, NJ: National Council on Education and the Disciplines.

International Life Skills Survey (ILSS). 2000. Policy Research Initiative. Statistics Canada.

Kennedy, Dan. 2001. "The Emperor's Vanishing Clothes." In *Mathematics and Democracy: The Case for Quantitative Literacy,* edited by Lynn Arthur Steen, 55–60. Princeton, NJ: National Council on Education and the Disciplines.

Kindt, M. 1979. "Differentiëren, een manier om veranderingen bij te houden." *Wiskrant* 17: 12–15.

Lesh, R. et al. 1986. "Conceptual Models and Applied Mathematical Problem-Solving Research." In *Acquisition of Mathematics Concepts and Process,* edited by R. Lesh and M. Landau. New York, NY: Academic Press.

LOGSE 1990. *Ley de Ordenación General del Sistema Educativo.* Madrid.

Mathematical Sciences Education Board (MSEB). 1993. *Measuring What Counts: A Conceptual Guide for Mathematical Assessment.* Washington, DC: National Academy Press.

National Center for Education Statistics. 1993. *National Adult Literacy Survey.* Washington D.C.: National Center for Education Statistics (NCES).

National Council of Teachers of Mathematics. 1989. *Curriculum and Evaluation Standards for School Mathematics.* Reston, VA: National Council of Teachers of Mathematics (NCTM).

National Council of Teachers of Mathematics. 2000. *Principles and Standards for School Mathematics.* Reston, VA: National Council of Teachers of Mathematics (NCTM).

Neubrand, N. et al. 2001. "Grundlager der Ergänzung des Internationalen PISA-Mathematik-Tests in der Deutschen Zusatzerhebung." *ZDM* 33(2): 45–59.

Niss, M. 1999. "Kompetencer og Uddannelsesbeskrivelse" (Competencies and Subject-Description). *Uddanneise* 9: 21–29.

Organization for Economic Cooperation and Development. 1999. *Measuring Student Knowledge and Skills. A New Framework for Assessment.* Paris: OECD.

Organization for Economic Cooperation and Development. 2002. *Framework for Mathematics Assessment.* Paris: Organization for Economic Cooperation and Development (OECD).

Schneider, Carol Geary. 2001. "Setting Greater Expectations for Quantitative Learning." In *Mathematics and Democracy: The Case for Quantitative Literacy,* edited by Lynn Arthur Steen, 99–106. Princeton, NJ: National Council on Education and the Disciplines.

Schoenfeld, Alan H. 2001. "Reflections on an Impoverished Education." In *Mathematics and Democracy: The Case for Quantitative Literacy,* edited by Lynn Arthur Steen, 49–54. Princeton, NJ: National Council on Education and the Disciplines.

Steen, Lynn Arthur. 1990. *On the Shoulders of Giants: New Approaches to Numeracy.* Washington, DC: National Academy Press.

Steen, Lynn Arthur, ed. 2001. *Mathematics and Democracy: The Case for Quantitative Literacy.* Princeton, NJ: National Council on Education and the Disciplines.

Treffers, A. 1991. "Meeting Innumeracy at Primary School." *Educational Studies in Mathematics* 22: 333–52.

Tufte, E. R. 1983. *The Visual Display of Quantitative Information.* Cheshire, CT: Graphic Press.

Tufte, E. R. 1990. *Envisioning Information.* Cheshire, CT: Graphic Press.

Tufte, E. R. 1997. *Visual Explanations—Images and Quantities, Evidence and Narrative.* Cheshire, CT: Graphic Press.

The Role of Mathematics Courses in the Development of Quantitative Literacy

DEBORAH HUGHES HALLETT

Conventional wisdom holds that quantitative literacy is developed by taking mathematics courses. Although this is often true, mathematics courses are no panacea. The views of mathematics acquired by many students during their education often hamper the development of quantitative literacy and therefore have profound implications for the strategies that we should adopt to promote it. This essay analyzes the ways in which the curriculum and pedagogy of mathematics courses could better enhance quantitative literacy.

Quantitative Literacy: A Habit of Mind

Quantitative literacy is the ability to identify, understand, and use quantitative arguments in everyday contexts. An essential component is the ability to adapt a quantitative argument from a familiar context to an unfamiliar context. Just as verbal literacy describes fluency with new passages, so quantitative literacy describes fluency in applying quantitative arguments to new contexts.

Quantitative literacy describes a habit of mind rather than a set of topics or a list of skills. It depends on the capacity to identify mathematical structure in context; it requires a mind searching for patterns rather than following instructions. A quantitatively literate person needs to know some mathematics, but literacy is not defined by the mathematics known. For example, a person who knows calculus is not necessarily any more literate than one who knows only arithmetic. The person who knows calculus formally but cannot see the quantitative aspects of the surrounding world is probably not quantitatively literate, whereas the person who knows only arithmetic but sees quantitative arguments everywhere may be.

Adopting this definition, those who know mathematics purely as algorithms to be memorized are clearly not quantitatively literate. Quantitative literacy insists on understanding. This understanding must be flexible enough to enable its owner to apply quantitative ideas in new contexts as well as in familiar contexts. Quantitative literacy is not about how much mathematics a person knows but about how well it can be used.

Mathematical Underpinnings of Quantitative Literacy

An alarming number of U.S. students do not become quantitatively literate on their journey through school and college. Indeed, the general level of quantitative literacy is currently sufficiently limited that it threatens the ability of citizens to make wise decisions at work and in public and private life. To rectify this, changes are needed in many areas: educational policy, pedagogy, and curriculum. Unfortunately, one of the more plausible vehicles for improvement—mathematics courses—will require significant alteration before they are helpful.

Deborah Hughes Hallett is Professor of Mathematics at the University of Arizona and Adjunct Professor at the Kennedy School of Government, Harvard. Hughes Hallett is an author of several college mathematics textbooks, including those created by the Calculus Consortium based at Harvard. Hughes Hallett served as a member of the National Research Council's Committee on Advanced Study in American High Schools and was elected a Fellow of the American Association for the Advancement of Science (AAAS) for contributions to mathematics education.

To be able to recognize mathematical structure in context, it is of course necessary to know some mathematics. Although the knowledge of basic mathematical algorithms such as how to multiply decimals does not guarantee literacy, the absence of this knowledge makes literacy unlikely, if not impossible. It would be helpful to agree on which mathematical algorithms are necessary underpinning of quantitative literacy, but this is a matter on which reasonable people differ. The answer also may differ from country to country and from era to era; however, the fundamental description of quantitative literacy as a habit of mind is not affected by the mathematical underpinnings chosen.

In this essay, we take the mathematical underpinnings of quantitative literacy to be the topics in a strong U.S. middle school curriculum, in addition to some topics traditionally taught later, such as probability and statistics. For us, quantitative literacy includes the use of basic spreadsheets and formulas (but not, for example, the spreadsheet's built-in statistical functions). Quantitative literacy, therefore, includes some aspects of algebra, but not all. The ability to create and interpret formulas is required; their symbolic manipulation is not. Reading simple graphs is necessary; the ability to construct them is not.

Our interpretation of quantitative literacy does not involve most of traditional algebra and geometry (for example, factoring polynomials, simplifying algebraic fractions, knowing the geometric properties of circles, chords, and tangents). The reason for this choice is that most adults do not use such algebra and geometry at work, or in their private lives, or as voting citizens. This is not to deny that some traditional algebra and geometry should have a central role in the high school curriculum. The development of manipulative skill, in particular, is important in any field that makes frequent use of symbols; however, the understanding of formulas required for our definition of quantitative literacy is hardly touched on in an algebra class that focuses on the rules for symbolic manipulation.

Let us see what this definition of quantitative literacy means in practice. It includes being able to make a mental estimate of the tip in a restaurant; it includes realizing that if Dunkin' Donuts is selling donuts for 69¢ each and $3.29 a half-dozen, and if you want five, you might as well buy six. It includes reading graphs of the unemployment rate against time; it includes knowing what is meant by a report that housing starts are down by 0.2 percent over the same month last year. It includes an understanding of the implications of repeated addition (linear growth to a mathematician) and repeated percentage growth (exponential growth). Quantitative literacy does not expect, however, and in fact may not benefit from, the algebraic manipulation usually associated with these topics in a mathematics course.

To probe the boundary of quantitative literacy suggested by this definition, observe that it would not include understanding all the graphs in *The Economist* or *Scientific American* because both sometimes use logarithmic scales; however, understanding all the graphs in *USA Today* is included by this definition.

Mathematical Literacy and Quantitative Literacy

It may surprise some readers that advanced training in mathematics does not necessarily ensure high levels of quantitative literacy. The reason is that mathematics courses focus on teaching mathematical concepts and algorithms, but often without attention to context. The word "literacy" implies the ability to use quantitative arguments in everyday contexts that are more varied and more complicated than most mathematics textbook examples. Thus, although mathematics courses teach the mathematical tools that underpin quantitative literacy, they do not necessarily develop the skill and flexibility with context required for quantitative literacy.

There is, therefore, an important distinction between mathematical and quantitative literacy. A mathematically literate person grasps a large number of mathematical concepts and can use them in mathematical contexts, but may or may not be able to apply them in a wide range of everyday contexts. A quantitatively literate person may know many fewer mathematical concepts, but can apply them widely.

Quantitative Literacy: Who Is Responsible?

High school and college faculty may be tempted to think that because the underpinnings of quantitative literacy are middle school mathematics, they are not responsible for teaching it. Nothing could be further from the truth. Although the mathematical foundation of quantitative literacy is laid in middle school, literacy can be developed only by a continued, coordinated effort throughout high school and college.

The skill needed to apply mathematical ideas in a wide variety of contexts is not always acquired at the same time as the mathematics. Instructors in middle school, high school, and college need to join forces to deepen students' understanding of basic mathematics and to provide opportunities for students to become comfortable analyzing quantitative arguments in context.

Also key to improving quantitative literacy is the participation of many disciplines. Quantitative reasoning must be seen as playing a useful role in a wide variety of fields. The development of quantitative literacy is the responsibility of individuals throughout the education system.

Impediments to Quantitative Literacy: Pedagogy and Testing

We start by considering the common practices in mathematical pedagogy and testing that hinder the development of quantitative literacy. Here we are concerned with the ways in which topics are taught and assessed rather than with the topics themselves. What students learn about a topic is influenced more by the activities they do than by what the instructor says. In particular, tests often determine what is learned. Teachers "teach to the test" and students "study for the test." Thus, the types of problems assigned in courses have a large effect on what is learned.

The cornerstone of quantitative literacy is the ability to apply quantitative ideas in new or unfamiliar contexts. This is very different from most students' experience of mathematics courses, in which the vast majority of problems are of types that they have seen before. Mastering a mathematics course is, for them, a matter of keeping straight how to solve each type of problem that the teacher has demonstrated. A few students, faced with the dizzying task of memorizing all these types, make sense out of the general principles instead. But a surprisingly large number of students find it easier to memorize problem types than to think in general principles. Ursula Wagener described how teaching may encourage such memorization:

> A graduate student teacher in a freshman calculus class stands at the lectern and talks with enthusiasm about how to solve a problem: "Step one is to translate the problem into mathematical terms; step two is . . ." Then she gives examples. Across the room, undergraduates memorize a set of steps. Plugging and chugging—teaching students how to put numbers in an equation and solve it—elbows out theory and understanding.[1]

In my own classroom, I have had calculus students[2] who could not imagine how to create a formula from a graph because they did not "do their graphs in that order." For these otherwise strong students from the pre-graphing-calculator era, graphs were produced by a somewhat painful memorized algorithm that started with a formula and ended with a picture. Imagining the algorithm run backward to produce a possible formula struck them as impossible. These students could not identify which features of the graph corresponded to which features of the formula. Although they had a solid mathematical background for their age, these students were not quantitatively literate.

Calculus provides other examples of how easy it is to learn procedures without being able to recognize their meaning in context. Formulas, although a small part of quantitative literacy, are central to calculus. We expect literacy in calculus to include fluency with formulas for basic concepts. Problems such as "If $f(t)$ represents the population of the United States in millions at time t in years, what is the meaning of the statements $f(2000) = 281$ and $f'(2000) = 2.5$?" look as though calculus students should find them easy—there are no computations to be done, only symbols to read.[3] Yet such problems cause great difficulty to some students who are adept at calculations.

As another example, in 1996, a problem on the Advanced Placement (AP) Calculus Exam[4] gave students the rate of consumption of cola over some time interval and asked them to calculate and interpret the definite integral of the rate. All the students had learned the fundamental theorem of calculus, but many who could compute the integral did not know that it represented the total quantity of cola consumed.

These examples suggest how teaching practices in mathematics may differ from those required to develop quantitative literacy. Mathematics courses that concentrate on teaching algorithms, but not on varied applications in context, are unlikely to develop quantitative literacy. To improve quantitative literacy, we have to wrestle with the difficult task of getting students to analyze novel situations. This is seldom done in high school or in large introductory college mathematics courses. It is much, much harder than teaching a new algorithm. It is the difference between teaching a procedure and teaching insight.

Because learning to apply mathematics in unfamiliar situations is hard, both students and teachers are prone to take shortcuts. Students clamor to be shown "the method," and teachers often comply, sometimes because it is easier and sometimes out of a desire to be helpful. Learning the method may be effective in the short run—it may bring higher results on the next examination—but it is disastrous in the long run. Most students do not develop skills that are not required of them on examinations.[5] Thus if a course simply requires memorization, that is what the students do. Unfortunately, such students are not quantitatively literate.

Another obstacle to the development of quantitative literacy is the fact that U.S. mathematics texts often have worked examples of each type of problem. Most U.S. students expect to be shown how to do every type of problem that could be on an examination. They would agree with the Harvard undergraduate who praised a calculus instructor for teaching in a "cookbook fashion."[6] Both college and school teachers are rewarded for teaching practices that purposefully avoid the use of new contexts.

College mathematics faculty frequently fail to realize how carefully a course must be structured if students are to deepen their understanding. Many, many students make their way through introductory college courses without progressing beyond the memorization of problem types. Faculty and teaching assistants are not trying to encourage this, but are often blissfully unaware of the extent to which it is happening. This, of course, reinforces the students' sense that this is the way things are supposed to be, thereby making it harder for the next faculty member to challenge that belief.

K–12 teachers are more likely than college faculty to be aware of the way in which their students think. They are, however, under more pressure from students, parents, and administrators to ensure high scores on the next examination by illustrating one of every problem type. So K-12 teachers also often reinforce students' tendency to memorize.

There are strong pressures on college and K–12 mathematics instructors to use teaching practices that are diametrically opposed to those that promote quantitative literacy, and indeed much effective learning. Efforts to improve quantitative literacy must take these pressures into account.

Teaching Mathematics in Context

One of the reasons that the level of quantitative literacy is low in the U.S. is that it is difficult to teach students to identify mathematics in context, and most mathematics teachers have no experience with this. It is much easier to teach an algorithm than the insight needed to identify quantitative structure. Most U.S. students have trouble applying the mathematics they know in "word problems" and this difficulty is greatly magnified if the context is novel. Teaching in context thus poses a tremendous challenge.

The work of Erik De Corte, in Belgium, throws some light on what helps students to think in context. De Corte investigated the circumstances under which students give unrealistic answers to mathematical questions. For example, consider the problem that asks for the number of buses needed to transport a given number of people; researchers find that a substantial number of students give a fractional answer, such 33 2/3 buses. De Corte reported that if the context was made sufficiently realistic, for example, asking the students to write a letter to the bus company to order buses, many more students gave reasonable (non-fractional) answers.[7]

De Corte's work suggests that many U.S. students think the word problems in mathematics courses are not realistic. (It is hard to disagree.) Mathematicians have a lot of work to do to convince students that they are teaching something useful. Having faculty outside mathematics include quantitative problems in their own

courses is extremely important. These problems are much more likely to be considered realistic.

As another example, many calculus students are unaware that the derivative represents a rate of change, even if they know the definition.[8] Asked to find a rate, these students do not know they are being asked for a derivative; yet, this interpretation of the derivative is key to its use in a scientific context. The practical issue, then, is how to develop the intuitive understanding necessary to apply calculus in context.

Mathematicians have a natural tendency to try to help students who do not understand that the derivative is a rate by re-explaining the definition; however, the theoretical underpinning, although helping mathematicians understand a subject, often does not have the same illuminating effect for students. When students ask for "an explanation, not a proof,"[9] they are asking for an intuitive understanding of a topic. Mathematicians often become mathematicians because they find proofs illuminating. Other people, however, often develop intuitive understanding separately from proofs and formal arguments. My own experience teaching calculus suggests that the realization that a derivative is a rate comes not from the definition but by talking through the interpretation of the derivative in a wide range of concrete examples.

It is important to realize that any novel problem or context can be made "old" if students are taught a procedure to analyze it. Students' success then depends on memorizing the procedure rather than on developing their ability to apply the central mathematical idea. There is a difficult balance to be maintained between providing experience with new contexts and overwhelming students by too many new contexts. Familiar contexts should be included—they are essential for developing confidence—but if the course stops there, quantitative literacy will not be enhanced.

There is tremendous pressure on U.S. teachers to make unfamiliar contexts familiar and hence to make problems easy to do by applying memorized algorithms. Changing this will take a coordinated effort: both school and college teachers will need to be rewarded for breaking out of this mold.

Impediments to Quantitative Literacy: Attitudes Toward Mathematics

In the course of their education, many students develop attitudes about mathematics that inhibit the development of quantitative literacy. Particularly pernicious is the belief that mathematics is memorized procedures and that mere mortals do not figure things out for themselves. Students who subscribe to this view look at an unfamiliar context and immediately give up, saying that they never were "good at math."

Because this belief concerns the nature of mathematics, rather than the most efficient way to learn the subject, it often is held with surprising tenacity. Just how sure students can be that mathematics is to be memorized was brought home to me by the student whom I asked to explain why $\sqrt{xy} = \sqrt{x} \cdot \sqrt{y}$. He looked puzzled that I should ask such a question, and replied confidently "It's a rule." I tried again; he looked slightly exasperated and said emphatically "It's a law." For him, mathematics involved remembering what rules were true, not figuring out why they were true.

To further my understanding of students' attitudes toward mathematics, a few years ago I gave a questionnaire to all the students enrolled in Harvard's pre-calculus and first-semester calculus courses. Responses were collected from all of the several hundred students involved. Two of the questions were as follows:

> A well-written problem makes it clear what method should be used to solve it.

> If you can't do a homework problem, you should be able to find a worked example in the text to show you how.

On a scale of 1 to 5, on which 5 represented strong agreement, the pre-calculus students gave the first question 4.6 and the second question 4.7; the calculus students gave both 4.1. The numbers suggest that these students—who are among the country's brightest—still think of mathematics largely as procedures.

In teaching mathematics, we should of course give some problems that suggest the method to be used and some that should be similar to worked examples; however, if all or most of the problems we assign are of this type—as is true in many U.S. classrooms—it is not surprising that our students find it difficult to apply mathematics in novel contexts. It is equally understandable that they find it "unfair" that they should be asked to use quantitative ideas in other fields, in which the context is seldom one they have seen before. Although their indignation is understandable, it is also a clear signal that we have a problem.

Reports from students of Mercedes McGowen, who teaches at William Rainey Harper College, demonstrated similar beliefs about mathematics. For example, a pre-service elementary teacher wrote:[10]

> All throughout school, we have been taught that mathematics is simply just plugging numbers into a learned equation. The teacher would just show us the equation dealing with what we were studying and we would complete the equation given different numbers because we were shown how to do it.

Another elaborated:[11]

> When I began learning mathematics everything was so simple. As I got older there were many more rules taught to me. The more rules I learned, the easier it became to forget some of the older rules.

Unfortunately, the attitudes toward mathematics displayed in these responses are diametrically opposed to the attitudes required for quantitative literacy. In attempting to improve quantitative literacy, we ignore these attitudes at our peril.

The Mathematics Curriculum and Quantitative Literacy

Although quantitative literacy does not require the use of many mathematical tools, two curriculum areas are sufficiently important that they should receive much more emphasis. These are estimation, and probability and statistics.

ESTIMATION

The ability to estimate is of great importance for many applications of mathematics. This is especially true of any application to the real world and, therefore, of quantitative literacy. Unfortunately, however, estimation is a skill that falls between the cracks. Mathematics often does not see estimation as its responsibility; teachers in other fields do not teach it because they think it is part of mathematics. Many students therefore find estimation difficult. The solution is for all of us to teach it.

Worse still, because of mathematics' emphasis on precision, students often think that estimation is dangerous, even improper. In their minds, an estimate is a wrong answer much like any other wrong answer. The skill and the willingness to estimate should be included explicitly throughout the curriculum.

Given the current concern about calculator dependence, some people claim that students would be better at estimation if they were not allowed to use calculators. It is certainly true that proficiency with a slide rule required estimation; however, even in pre-calculator days, many students could not estimate. Instead of grabbing a calculator to do their arithmetic, past students launched into a memorized algorithm. For example, some years ago I watched a student use long division to divide 0.6 by 1, then 0.06 by 1, and then 0.006 by 1, before he observed the pattern.[12] Even then, he did not recognize the general principle. He never thought to make an estimate or to see if the answer was reasonable. Because this was a graduate student, we might reasonably conclude that his education had failed to develop his quantitative literacy skills.

PROBABILITY AND STATISTICS

One area of quantitative reasoning that is strikingly absent from the education of many students is probability and statistics. This gap is remarkable because probabilistic and statistical ideas are so extensively used in public and private life. Like quantitative literacy, probabilistic thinking is embedded in an enormous variety of contexts. For example, probabilities are used to quantify risk ("there is a 30 percent chance of recovery from this medical procedure") and in many news reports ("DNA tests . . . showed that it [the body] was 1.9 million times more likely to be the driver than anyone else." [13]) Familiarity with statistics is essential for anyone who plans to interpret opinion polls, monitor the development of a political campaign, or understand the results of a drug test. Statistical arguments are used as evidence in court and to analyze charges of racial profiling.

Let us look at an example in which public understanding of probability is crucial. Over the next generation, the effect of AIDS will be felt worldwide. How can people in the United States understand the impact of the epidemic without understanding the data? This is not to invalidate the need to understand the human suffering that the epidemic will cause; however, understanding the data is essential to constructing, voting for, and implementing policies that will mitigate the suffering. How many people die of AIDS? (In 2000, 3 million people died worldwide, and 5.3 million were infected.[14]) How many AIDS orphans will there be? (Millions.)[15] What will be the effect on the teaching profession? (In some countries, there are more AIDS deaths than retirements, which has significant implications for teacher availability.) Do these statistics describe the United States? Not now, but it would be risky to assume that they never could.

Avoiding similar statistics in the United States depends on sound educational policies aimed at prevention. These policies must be based on a solid understanding of infection rates. What does this mean for AIDS testing? The Center for Disease Control (CDC) in Atlanta spends tax dollars to track the disease and provide rapid, accurate testing.[16] In 1996, the American Medical Association approved a recommendation mandating HIV testing for pregnant women.[17] Yet Health Education AIDS Liaison (HEAL) in Toronto provided a passionate and well-argued warning about the dangers of widespread testing.[18] Using the following two-way table, HEAL argued that, with the current infection rate of 0.05 percent, even for a test which is 99 percent accurate, "of every three women testing HIV-positive, two are certain to be false positives." (False positives are people who test positive for HIV although they are not infected.)

As things stand now, many college students could not follow these discussions. Many might wrongly conclude that the accuracy of the test is at fault.[19] The public's lack of clarity on this issue could skew efforts to rationalize policies on mandatory testing.[20]

	Positive HIV	Negative HIV	Totals
Test Positive	495	995	1,490
Test Negative	5	98,505	98,510
Totals	500	99,500	100,000

Obstacles to Including Probability and Statistics in the Curriculum

The fact that universities teach probability and statistics in many departments (economics, business, medicine, psychology, sociology, and engineering, as well as mathematics and statistics) is evidence for their pervasive use. Yet many students pass through both school and college with no substantial exposure to these subjects. For example, applicants to medical school are more likely to be admitted without statistics than without calculus.[21] Even many mathematics and science majors are not required to take statistics.

Like estimation, the teaching of probability and statistics suffers from the fact that no one can agree on when or by whom these topics should be introduced. Each group thinks it is someone else's responsibility. Should it be in middle school? In high school? In college? It is all too reminiscent of the White Queen's proposal to Alice for "jam tomorrow and jam yesterday—but never jam today."[22]

In addition to timing, the other obstacle to the introduction of probability and statistics in the school curriculum is the question of what topics should be dropped to make room. Traditional middle school and high school curricula do not contain probability and statistics. Every topic in the traditional curriculum has its advocates, with the effect that the status quo often prevails. There are a number of notable counterexamples, such as some state's high-stakes tests[23] and the AP Statistics Examination. Many of the new school curricular materials do contain these topics, but they are usually the first to be skipped. Because probability and statistics are not required for college entrance, these topics are often considered a luxury that can be omitted if time is tight.

Many college faculty thus agree that probability and statistics are vitally important but cannot agree on what should be done about teaching them. This is a failure of leadership. The result is that most people in the United States see probabilistic and statistical arguments every day yet have no training in making sense of them.

Relationship Between Mathematics and the Public

Mathematicians sometimes feel that the general public does not appreciate their field, and may blame this phenomenon for the low level of quantitative literacy in the United States. There is some truth to this view; the question is what to do about it. Because the media is often the interface between academics and the general public, increasing the general level of quantitative literacy will require a better relationship with the media.

Many adults' last memory of mathematics still stings many years later. Whether their last course was in school or college, some remember a teacher whom they perceived as not caring. Some blame themselves for not being able to understand. Many remember a course they perceived as having no relevance or a jungle of symbols with little meaning. Their teachers may not have realized how little their students understood, or they may have felt that it was the students' problem.[24] But now it is mathematics' problem. Whether these memories are accurate is immaterial; they make a poor base on which to build collaboration.

To alter these perceptions, mathematics courses are needed that are meaningful—to everyone—and that do not sting in memory. Notice that what does and does not sting varies greatly from culture to culture. In some societies, the threat of humiliation is used as a spur to study; however, most U.S. students do not study harder if they are humiliated. Indeed, many will drop mathematics rather than subject themselves to such treatment. To be effective, each faculty member must know which techniques inspire students to learn in his or her particular culture, and use those techniques.

As a guide as to whether we have succeeded in teaching courses that are meaningful and that do not sting, we should ask ourselves the following question: Are we comfortable having the future of mathematics and quantitative literacy determined by those to whom we gave a "C" in mathematics and who took no further courses in the subject? This is not far from the truth at the present time. If not, we may be widening the split between mathematics and the general public.

Teaching Quantitative Literacy

Quantitative literacy requires students to have a gut feeling for mathematics. Because we desire widespread quantitative literacy, not just for those who find mathematics easy, mathematics teachers will need to diversify their teaching techniques. For example, I recently had two students who came to office hours together. One learned approximately the way I do, so writing a symbolic explanation usually worked. The second, who listened earnestly, was usually looking blank at the end of my discussion with the first student. I then had to start again and explain everything over in pictures if I wanted both students to understand. This happened numerous times throughout the semester, so it was not a function of the particular topic but of their different learning styles. To teach both of them, more than one approach was necessary.

For most students, an effective technique for improving their quantitative literacy is to be introduced to varied examples of the use of the same mathematical idea with the common theme highlighted. A student's ability to recognize quantitative structure is enhanced if faculty in many disciplines use the same techniques. The assistance ("a conspiracy," according to some students) of faculty outside mathematics is important because it sends the message that quantitative analysis is valued outside mathematics. If students see quantitative reasoning widely used, they are more likely to regard it as important.

The need to develop quantitative literacy will only be taken seriously when it is a prerequisite for college. Students and parents are rightfully skeptical that colleges think probability and statistics are important when they are not required for entrance. Making quantitative reasoning a factor in college admissions would give quantitative literacy a significant boost.

Conclusion

Achieving a substantial improvement in quantitative literacy will require a broad-based coalition dedicated to this purpose. Higher education should lead, involving faculty in mathematics and a wide variety of fields as well as people from industry and government. Classroom teachers from across grade levels and across institutions—middle schools, high schools, and colleges—must play a significant role. The cooperation of educational administrators and policymakers is essential. To make cooperation on this scale a realistic possibility, public understanding of the need for quantitative literacy must be vastly improved. Because the media informs the public's views, success will require a new relationship with the media.

Notes

1. Paper on "Pedagogy and the Disciplines," 1990. Written for the University of Pennsylvania.

2. For example, Harvard students who had already had some calculus in high school.

3. These statements tell us that in the year 2000, the U.S. population was 281 million and growing at a rate of 2.5 million per year.

4. AP Calculus Examination, Questions AB3 and BC3, 1996.

5. A few students will independently develop the skill to apply mathematics beyond what is asked of them in courses and on examinations.

These students are rare, however; they are the students who can learn without a teacher. If we want to increase the number of people who are quantitatively literate, we should not base our decisions about teaching practices on such students.

6. From a Harvard course evaluation questionnaire.

7. DeFranco, T. C., & Curcio, F. R. (1997). "A division problem with a remainder embedded across two contexts: Children's solutions in restrictive versus real-world settings". *Focus on Learning Problems in Mathematics, 19*(2), 58–72. Reported by Erik De Corte in a presentation entitled "Connecting Mathematics Problem Solving to the Real World" at a conference on *Mathematics for Living*, Amman, Jordan, November 18–23, 2000.

8. From David Matthews, University of Central Michigan; reported at a conference at the University of Arizona, fall 1993.

9. A student made this request in linear algebra when she wanted a picture showing why a result was true, but was not yet ready to hear the proof.

10. Published in Chick, Stacey, Vincent, and Vincent, eds., *Proceedings of the 12th ICMI Study Conference: The Future of Teaching and Learning Algebra* (University of Melbourne, Australia, 2001), vol. 2: 438–46.

11. Challenges, Issues, and Expectations of Pre-Service Teachers at CBMS/Exxon National Summit on Teacher Preparation, Washington, DC, 2000. Available at http://www.maa.org/cbms/NationalSummit/Speakers/McGowan.pdf.

12. This example may seem improbable; unfortunately, it is real.

13. ⟨http://europe.cnn.com/2001/WORLD/europe/UK/08/10/coniston.dna/index.html⟩. The article described the identification of a body in a lake in the United Kingdom as speed record breaker Donald Campbell. (CNN: August 10, 2001.)

14. ⟨http://www.unfoundation.org/campaign/aids/index.asp⟩; accessed October 31, 2001.

15. In South Africa alone, it is estimated that there will be 2.5 million orphans by the year 2010. From *Impending Catastrophe Revisited,* prepared by ABT Associates (South Africa) and distributed as a supplement to South Africa's *Sunday Times,* 24 June 2001.

16. ⟨http://www.cdc.gov/hiv/pubs/rt/rapidct.htm⟩; accessed July 22, 2001.

17. Reported in *Mass Testing: A Disaster in the Making,* by Christine Johnson at ⟨http://www.healtoronto.com/masstest.html⟩, accessed February 24, 2002.

18. High Risk of False-Positive HIV Tests at ⟨http://www.healtoronto.com/pospre.html⟩, quoting from "To Screen or Not to Screen for HIV in Pregnant Women," by Jeffrey G. Wong, M.D., in *Postgraduate Medicine* 102, 1 (July 1997); accessed February 24, 2002.

19. The word "certain" is not correct here; however, that is not what confuses many students. The central issue is that the large number of false positives is a consequence primarily of the low prevalence of the HIV virus in the U.S. population, not of inaccuracies in the test.

20. Some states apparently give all pregnant women AIDS tests whether or not they consent; others suggest an AIDS test but require consent.

21. Some medical schools explicitly require calculus for admission and many students take calculus as part of their premed program. Statistics is less frequently required for admission.

22. Lewis Carroll, *Through the Looking Glass,* ⟨http://www.literature.org/authors/carroll-lewis/through-the-looking-glass/chapter-05.html⟩; accessed September 9, 2001.

23. Arizona and Massachusetts both have included probability and data interpretation on the state-mandated high school graduation tests; however, the contents of these tests are subject to sudden changes, so there are no guarantees for the future.

24. This was quite reasonable because it was the prevailing view for most of the last century.

The Third R in Literacy

RANDALL M. RICHARDSON AND WILLIAM G. MCCALLUM

The conventional meaning of the word "literate" (able to read and write) leaves the third of the three R's on its own, a separation that is reflected in the traditional curriculum: reading and writing are taught together, and mathematics is taught as a separate subject. The first question to ask in considering quantitative literacy and the curriculum is: Why can't we leave it that way? What is new in the world that prompts us to incorporate mathematics into the definition of literacy, or to believe that mathematics must now be spread across the curriculum rather than contained in dedicated courses? This question is answered persuasively in the opening section of *Mathematics and Democracy: The Case for Quantitative Literacy* (Steen 2001): what is new in the world is the pervasiveness of quantitative information and the necessity of acting on it. Thus the list of things a literate person must be able to read and write has greatly expanded to include the many forms in which quantitative information is represented in everyday life: graphs, charts, tables, maps, diagrams, and algorithms.

Furthermore, acting on quantitative information requires more than the basic level of comprehension that comes from listening to a story or looking at a picture; it requires the ability to extract the relevant pieces from a possibly confusing abundance of data and perform appropriate mathematical operations and reasoning on those pieces. The explosion in both the amount and variety of quantitative information, and the necessity of using such information in daily decisions, make the need for quantitative literacy both new and urgent.

In considering how the school and college curriculum can lead students to achieve quantitative literacy, it is crucial to keep in mind two aspects of quantitative literacy that are captured in a definition of conventional literacy put forth by UNESCO (Fox and Powell 1991): "A literate is a person who, with understanding, can both read and write a short simple statement on his everyday life."

This definition says that simply being able to read and write is not enough for literacy: understanding and engagement with context (everyday life) also are required. The same applies to quantitative literacy, and we might well adopt the modified definition: "A quantitatively literate person is a person who, with understanding, can both read and represent quantitative information arising in his or her everyday life."

Although it might seem unnecessary to mention the criteria of understanding and context explicitly, the fact is that in the traditional curriculum neither goes without saying. Therefore, we start by considering how each might be applied in judging new curricula.

William G. McCallum is Professor of Mathematics at the University of Arizona. A founding member of the Calculus Consortium based at Harvard University, McCallum has done mathematical research at the Institut des Hautes Études Scientifiques in Paris and at the Institute for Advanced Study in Princeton. McCallum's professional interests include both arithmetic algebraic geometry and mathematics education; he has written extensively in both areas.

Randall M. Richardson is Professor of Geosciences and Vice President for Undergraduate Education at the University of Arizona. Richardson is responsible for the university's general education program and recently chaired a university-wide taskforce on mathematics across the curriculum. He is also involved in NSF-sponsored projects for reforming K-12 teacher preparation and for mentoring early-career geosciences faculty.

The Role of Understanding

The ability to perform some of the basic operations of mathematics is necessary for quantitative literacy, but even the ability to perform many of them is not sufficient. Anyone who has taught mathematics, or who has taught a subject requiring the mathematics that students have learned in previous courses, is aware of this fact. Many students are technically capable but unable to make reasonable decisions about which techniques to apply and how to apply them. Mathematicians and their colleagues in other departments share frustration at the fragility of what students learn in their mathematics classes. We hesitate to call literate a person who reads haltingly, picking out words one at a time with no appearance of understanding what is being read; yet too many of the students leaving mathematics courses use mathematics haltingly if at all. Too many appear to be lacking in conceptual understanding.

We make a distinction here between conceptual understanding and formal mathematical understanding. The latter refers to an ability to formulate precise mathematical arguments that are universal in the sense that they work for all numbers or all polygons. Conceptual understanding is understanding of a less formal nature, more like what mathematicians sometimes call intuitive understanding. It refers to an ability to recognize underlying concepts in a variety of different representations and applications. For example, a student who understands the concept of rate knows that the velocity of a moving object, the slope of its position graph, and the coefficient of t in a formula giving its position as a function of time t are all manifestations of the same underlying concept, and knows how to translate between them.

Even though recent efforts to reform mathematics education have paid attention to conceptual understanding, it is often neglected in mathematics classes. Sometimes, in the K–12 environment, this is the result of drifting curricula that, in the absence of firm guidance, gravitate inevitably toward convenient arrangements between teacher and student, and teacher and parent that concentrate mostly on the correct performance of procedures. At other times, it is a consequence of conscious decisions by curriculum designers who believe in division of labor between mathematics classes, which provide technical skills, and classes in mathematically intensive disciplines, which provide context and understanding.

It is worth listening to the voices of teachers in those disciplines. The Mathematical Association of America (MAA) recently conducted a series of workshops with faculty from different disciplines as part of a project to develop recommendations for the mathematics curriculum in the first two years of postsecondary education. Again and again, the authors of these workshop reports—engineers, physicists, biologists, chemists, computer scientists, statisticians, and mathematicians—explicitly mentioned *understanding* as a key goal of the mathematics curriculum, and they made it clear that they thought that it was a proper role of mathematics classes to teach it (*Curriculum Foundations Project* 2001):

Physics: Students need conceptual understanding *first,* and some comfort in using basic skills; then a deeper approach and more sophisticated skills become meaningful.

Life Sciences: Throughout these recommendations, the definition of *mastery* of a mathematical concept recognizes the importance of both conceptual understanding at the level of definition and understanding in terms of use/implementation/computation.

Chemical Engineering: . . . the "solution" to a math problem is often in the *understanding* of the behavior of the process described by the mathematics, rather than the specific closed form (or numerical) result.

Civil Engineering: Introductory math content should focus on developing a sound understanding of key fundamental concepts and their relevance to applied problems.

Business: Mathematics departments can help prepare business students by stressing conceptual understanding of quantitative reasoning and enhancing critical thinking skills.

Statistics: Focus on conceptual understanding of key ideas of calculus and linear algebra, including function, derivative, integral, approximation, and transformation.

What is striking about these reports is that so many science, mathematics, engineering, and technology (SMET) disciplines feel the need to explicitly request conceptual understanding from mathematics courses preparing their students. All the more must we worry about the state of conceptual understanding in students who are not preparing for SMET disciplines but simply need quantitative literacy as a basic life skill. Thus, our first criterion:

> *A curriculum for quantitative literacy must go beyond the basic ability to "read and write" mathematics and develop conceptual understanding.*

The Role of Context

The UNESCO definition specifies that a literate can read and write a "statement . . . on his everyday life." The term "everyday life" is open to interpretation: everyday life in the examples above from the SMET disciplines might include chemical reactions in a laboratory. The vast majority of students, however, are not headed for SMET careers. For most people, everyday life might include telephone rate plans, nutrition information on packages, or the relative risks of a serious car accident versus being struck by lightning, for example. A quantitatively literate person must be able to think mathematically in context. This requires a dual duty, marrying the mathematical meaning of symbols and operations to their contextual meaning, and thinking simultaneously about both. It is considerably more difficult than the ability to perform the underlying mathematical operations, stripped of their contextual meaning. Nor is it sufficient simply to clothe the mathematics in a superficial layer of contextual meaning. The mathematics must be engaged with the context and be providing power, not an engine idling in neutral. Too many attempts at teaching mathematics in context amount to little more than teaching students to sit in a car with the engine on, but not in gear. The "everyday life" test provides a measure of engagement; everyday life that moves forward must have an engine that is in gear.

We share two local examples outside of the training for traditional SMET careers. The first is a "math for all citizens" example. One of us (RMR) teaches a freshman-level general education science course for nonscience majors. Reading graphs as pictures or graphs as active conveyors of quantitative information is a desired learning outcome for the course. For the past five years we have used, in classes with as many as 325 students, the so-called Keeling CO_2 data set. This data set consists of a nearly continuous 50-year record of monthly atmospheric CO_2 concentration levels at Mauna Loa, Hawaii (Keller 2000; Keeling and Whorf 2001). Working in groups during a single lecture period, students randomly select 15 data points from about a six-year (100-point) portion of the data set. They plot this subset on an overhead transparency and estimate the slope of the data. Using their slopes, they estimate the number of years it will take for CO_2 concentration to double, an important component of all climate models of global warming. Because the small sample size of the data is insufficient to accurately reflect both an annual cycle and a long-term increase, student estimates of slope and doubling times vary by at least a factor of two. When all transparencies are superimposed using an overhead projector, the annual cycle is clearly visible. This exercise, although simple and completed in a single class period, includes basic mathematical operations (slopes, rates, doubling times) and issues of data quality and completeness, as well as a contextual setting that is arguably one of the most important for everyday life in the twenty-first century. (The Mauna Loa CO_2 data set is very rich for quantitative literacy instruction. For example, geologist Len Vacher at the University of South Florida uses the same data set to show that errors in estimating slopes from graphs are very common unless the axes of such graphs are understood.)

Another example is a business mathematics course recently developed at the University of Arizona by a collaboration between the Department of Mathematics and the College of Business and Public Administration. In this course, students use mathematical and technological tools to make business decisions based on realistic (in some cases, real) data sets. In one project, for example, students decide whether to foreclose on a business loan or work out a new payment schedule. They have available some information about the value of the business, the amount of the loan, and the likely future value if the business is allowed to continue but still fails. They also have some demographic information about the person running the business. Using historical records about the success and failure of previous arrangements to work out a payment schedule, they make successively more sophisticated calculations of expected value to arrive at their decision. Students are expected to understand both the mathematics and the business context, and to make professional oral presentations of their conclusions in which they are expected to express themselves mathematically, with clarity, completeness, and accuracy.

A noteworthy feature of this course is the level of involvement of the business college. The impetus to create the course came from the college, as do the basic ideas for projects. The visible involvement of the college makes their students take seriously the requirement to understand the mathematics. Thus, our second criterion:

A curriculum for quantitative literacy must be engaged with a context, be it everyday life, humanities, business, science, engineering, or technology.

Mathematics and Democracy (Steen 2001) lists elements that might compose quantitative literacy: confidence with mathematics, cultural appreciation, interpreting data, logical thinking, making decisions, mathematics in context, number sense, practical skills, prerequisite knowledge, symbol sense. Many of these elements arise naturally in applying the criteria we have given here, and are, in varying proportions, necessary ingredients of a curriculum for quantitative literacy. The precise proportions depend on the educational level and background of the students. Symbol sense, for example, is a rich vein in the everyday life of students in the physical and social sciences and engineering, but perhaps not as important to students in art or literature. On the other hand, because all citizens are bombarded daily with statistical data and inferences from it, reasoning logically and confidently with data is a crucial component of any curriculum for quantitative literacy.

The odd man out in this list is "cultural appreciation." In recent years there has been a proliferation of general education courses, taught by mathematics departments, that study such topics as voting schemes, symmetry, and periodic tilings of the plane. Although these "mathematics appreciation" courses often provide the serious engagement with quantitative information necessary for quantitative literacy, they focus primarily on fostering a general understanding of the uses of mathematics. Although there is certainly a place in the curriculum for mathematics appreciation courses, we believe an important difference exists between such courses and quantitative literacy—just as there is a difference between the ability to appreciate a great work of art and the ability to make some sketches of one's own, however rudimentary. For quantitative literacy, the element of engagement is crucial.

Who Is Responsible for Teaching Quantitative Literacy?

This question has both a vertical dimension (in which grades should quantitative literacy be taught?) and a horizontal dimension (in which departments?). Along the vertical dimension, we are faced with the question of whether quantitative literacy is properly a college subject at all. It can be argued that a good K–12 education should be sufficient to lay the foundations of quantitative literacy, and that the proper role of colleges and universities, typically in general education courses, is not to teach it but to use it.

Whatever the ideal, the reality is that there are well-documented problems with the mathematical performance of students in grades K–12; see, for example, the Third International Mathematics and Science Study (TIMSS). As a local confirmation of a national issue, each year over 35 percent of freshman students entering the University of Arizona, which has a four-year high school mathematics entrance requirement, place *below* college algebra.

Many people, including mathematics faculty, are working to improve the situation. Mathematics faculty have focused on improving the teaching of mathematics in high schools and reforming courses in mathematics departments in the first two years of college. The National Council of Teachers of Mathematics (NCTM) issued standards for K–12 mathematics in 1989 (NCTM 1989) and revised them in 2000 (NCTM 2000). Many states and localities have endeavored to improve mathematics education by implementing standards, frameworks, or high-stakes tests. At the college level, the National Science Foundation (NSF) has funded projects to reconsider curricula in pre-calculus, calculus, differential equations, and linear algebra. More recently, the Curriculum Foundations Project of the Mathematical Association of America, cited above, has initiated an ambitious undertaking aimed at formulating recommendations for the first two years of undergraduate mathematics.

Would improvements in mathematics education be sufficient to remedy current deficiencies in quantitative literacy? Attempts to change the mathematics curriculum—to make room earlier for statistics and probability (as recommended by NCTM), to teach mathematics in context, to pay attention to conceptual understanding, and to improve the mathematics education of K–12 teachers—would certainly move partway toward the changes needed to improve quantitative literacy. Such improvements are necessary. However, although the way mathematics is taught has a lot to do with quantitative literacy, so do other things.

Quantitative literacy cannot be taught by mathematics teachers alone, not because of deficiencies in teaching but because quantitative material must be pervasive in all areas of a student's education. Quantitative literacy is not simply a matter of knowing how to do the mathematics but also requires the ability to wed mathematics to context. This ability is learned from seeing and using mathematics regularly in contexts outside the mathematics classroom: in daily life, in chemistry class, in the business world. Thus, quantitative literacy cannot be regarded as the sole responsibility of high school mathematics teachers or of college teachers in mathematics departments. It has long been recognized, for example, that instruction in writing literacy, isolated in English composition courses, cannot succeed. Students quickly recognize that a requirement satisfied by a course or two in a single department is a local "hoop" to be jumped through, not a global requirement central to their education. Students often behave as if mathematical ideas are applicable only in mathematics courses, so that once they enter the world of their chosen major they can safely forget whatever they learned in those courses.

It must therefore be the common responsibility of both mathematicians and those in other disciplines to provide students with basic skills, to develop conceptual understanding, and to model the systematic use of mathematics as a way of looking at the world. The pervasiveness of quantitative information in the world outside the classroom also must be reflected throughout academe. A beautiful example of this pervasiveness is the recent foray into art history by optical scientist Charles Falco and contemporary artist David Hockney. These two have recently challenged traditional art historian interpretations of fifteenth-century art. Using simple optics, they have argued persuasively that a number of important painters of the fifteenth century, from van Eyck to Bellini, used lenses or mirrors to produce some of their paintings nearly 200 years earlier than had been believed possible. They argue that the use of such optical instruments accounts for the sudden surge in the reality of portraits in the fifteenth century (Hockney and Falco 2000). We can easily envision a wonderful application of quantitative literacy in fine arts education if their arguments stand the test of further scrutiny.

A persuasive argument can be made that the skills component of quantitative literacy is essentially precollege in nature. What, this argument goes, beyond the topics of precollege education (graphs, algebra, geometry, logic, probability, and statistics) is foundational to quantitative literacy for everyday life? Looking at the curriculum as a list of topics, however, misses an important point: quantitative literacy is not something that a person either knows or does not know. It is hard to argue that precollege education in writing fails to cover the basics of grammar, composition, and voice, for example. Yet it is widely accepted that writing is a skill that improves with practice in a wide variety of settings at the college level. We argue here that quantitative literacy at the college level also requires an across-the-curriculum approach, providing a wide variety of opportunities for practice.

The challenges to incorporating quantitative literacy across the curriculum are many, including math anxiety on the part of both faculty and students, lack of administrative understanding and support, and competing pressures for various other literacy requirements. We discuss below a variety of approaches that have demonstrated success at the college level in moving quantitative literacy across the curriculum. A more comprehensive discussion would address how these approaches should be coordinated with efforts to improve K–12 education, an issue we do not feel qualified to address. It is worth pointing out, however, that improving quantitative literacy at the college level would have an important effect on K–12 education for the simple reason that it would influence the mathematics education of K–12 teachers.

Mathematics Across the Curriculum

The term "mathematics across the curriculum" refers to attempts to incorporate mathematical thinking in courses throughout the university. The following excerpt from the vision statement of the Mathematics Across the Curriculum committee at the University of Arizona expresses the goals (2000):

> The purpose of Mathematics Across the Curriculum at the University of Arizona is to help students recognize the utility of mathematics across disciplines and majors and to improve their skills in mathematics. Just as all students should be able to write an essay in any class they take, all students should be able to look at a problem or situation in any class and be able to formulate appropriate mathematical approaches to finding solutions. They should also have the mathematical skills to know how to seek solutions. Particular attention must be paid to such fundamental processes as graphic representation of quantitative data; estimation; basic numeracy (i.e., ability to perform "basic" mathematical operations); and logic, among other mathematical concepts and topics.

Various approaches to implementing mathematics across the curriculum have been tried. We consider six approaches here: collaboration between mathematics and other faculty, gateway testing, intensive instructional support, workshops for nonmathematics faculty, quantitative reasoning requirements, and individual initiative by nonmathematics faculty. This is not intended to be an exhaustive list of all possible approaches or all approaches that have been tried, but rather an illustration of the range of possibilities.

"FRIENDLY CONSPIRACIES" BETWEEN MATHEMATICIANS AND OTHERS

Collaboration between mathematics faculty and faculty from other departments is one powerful approach. This could involve a sort of pact between mathematicians and others: mathematicians will add more context to their courses, others will add more mathematical concepts to theirs. Deborah Hughes Hallett writes of the need for friendly conspiracies between mathematicians and other departments to make sure this happens (Hughes Hallett 2001). The two-course business mathematics sequence developed at the University of Arizona is an example of such a conspiracy: students know that the problems they are studying in their mathematics course will come up again in their business courses, because they know that the course was developed with significant input from the business college. Team-teaching arrangements between mathematics and other departments are another example of this collaborative approach.

One cautionary note on such collaborations is illustrated by a survey conducted by the Mathematics Across the Curriculum group at the University of Arizona. This survey was sent to faculty in the College of Social and Behavioral Sciences who teach some of the largest general education courses on campus. The responses, completed by almost 33 percent of the group, included some telling results. More than half responded positively to the question, "Does any course you teach include any mathematical or quantitative elements?" The most common elements included statistics, slopes and rates, analysis of experimental outcomes, graphs, formal reasoning, and decision theory. Faculty were also asked, "Would you be willing to integrate some mathematical elements into your courses?" Again, more than half responded positively, although the response was cautious. For example, even among the positive responses, faculty said, "I don't see this as central to the usefulness of the course. Emphasis on the mathematics might actually distract students from the more important (in this course!) learning," and, "I would be reluctant to assign stats-heavy reading, as most students do not seem to pay close attention to such materials." The faculty responding negatively were split about evenly between "The course doesn't seem compatible with the addition of mathematical content" and "My background in mathematics is insufficient." These responses, typical of faculty everywhere, highlight some of the challenges inherent in establishing these friendly conspiracies.

GATEWAY TESTING IN COURSES OUTSIDE MATHEMATICS

The University of Nevada, Reno, approaches quantitative literacy by offering a set of mathematics competency tests in courses across the university, based on a model described in an article by Steven F. Bauman and William O. Martin (1995). The mathematics covered by the tests is required for success in the courses, and is no more than the students reasonably can be expected to have learned already. The main purpose of the tests is to inform instructors and students. Students may retake a test until they pass (a passing grade is 80 percent). The initial test is held in class during the first week of classes, to make clear that the test is an integral part of the course; after that, a separate office, the Math Center, handles grading and retesting, to make it feasible for instructors to use the system. The Math Center also provides tutors who go over a failed examination with each student and help him or her correct mistakes. Courses that have been involved with this program include agricultural economics, anthropology, art, biology, chemistry, economics, English, environmental studies, geography, geology, mathematics core courses, nutrition, philosophy, physics, political science, psychology, recreation, physical education, dance, sociology, and Western traditions.

MATHEMATICS INSTRUCTIONAL SUPPORT

The Center for Mathematics and Quantitative Education at Dartmouth College (2001) functions as a laboratory support office for the mathematics department, analogous to similar services available in other science departments. It houses equipment for use in mathematics classrooms, books, videos, and prepared laboratory activities. Some of these materials come from Mathematics Across The Curriculum (MATC) courses at Dartmouth. The center also provides consulting, classroom visitation, and videotaping services, and runs a departmental Teaching Seminar during the summer. The center works in collaboration with similar offices in other departments and supports courses in other departments that feature mathematics as a key component. It reviews materials that come out of the university's MATC courses and makes those that are suitable for K–12 available to teachers. It also facilitates links between K–12 teachers and college professors for conversation and collaboration across levels and disciplines.

WORKSHOPS FOR FACULTY OUTSIDE MATHEMATICS

Many disciplines, most commonly the SMET disciplines, have come to recognize the importance of quantitative literacy and some have organized regional or national workshops on the topic. One group that has facilitated such workshops is Project Kaleidoscope (PKAL 2002), an informal national alliance working to build strong learning environments for undergraduate students in mathematics, engineering, and the various fields of science. One PKAL workshop, entitled "Building the Quantitative Skills of Non-Majors and Majors in Earth and Planetary Science Courses," was held in January 1999 at the College of William and Mary. The

workshop brought together over 30 earth and planetary science faculty from research-intensive, and four-year and two-year institutions to work together on such questions as:

- Which quantitative skills are important in our curriculum, and at what levels?

- How do we include appropriate quantitative expectations in our courses for nonmajors without sending some students running for less quantitative offerings elsewhere on campus?

- How can a department work to build the quantitative skills of its majors?

- Many students, nonmajors and majors, bring tremendous fear, or "math anxiety," to our courses. What support is necessary to help students understand, use, and enjoy mathematics in our courses?

Such workshops have had a significant impact on how faculty outside of mathematics view quantitative literacy, and have provided concrete strategies and "best practices" to help them transform their courses. One example is the development of "Q-Courses" (e.g., Marine Environmental Geology and Introduction to Environmental Geology and Hydrology) at Bowdoin College by a geology team that grew out of the 1999 PKAL workshop.

QUANTITATIVE REASONING REQUIREMENTS

Recognizing that quantitative literacy often is not ensured by their entrance requirements, many colleges have instituted quantitative reasoning requirements that must be satisfied by all graduates. At some institutions, such as Harvard University and the University of Michigan, there is an approved list of courses that satisfy the requirement. An example of a more formal quantitative reasoning requirement is the one at Wellesley College (2002). This consists of a basic skills component, which is satisfied either by passing a quantitative reasoning test or by taking a specific course, and an overlay course component. The topics covered by the test are arithmetic, algebra, graphing, geometry, data analysis, and linearity. Overlay courses are taught within departments and engage students in using these skills in reasoning about and interpreting data in specific contexts. Guidelines specify the minimum necessary exposure to data analysis for a course to qualify as an overlay course. For example, such a course must address issues of collecting, representing, and summarizing data and must require a working knowledge of probability, distributions, and sampling. The goals of the overlay requirement are worth quoting for their resonance with the issues of quantitative literacy:

Literacy. The number of topics, and depth of coverage, should be sufficient to ensure that students have the basic knowledge they need in order to function in real-life situations involving quantitative data.

Authenticity. Students should have experience in using authentic numerical data. The experience should arise naturally in the context of the course and actually advance the work of the course. Only with such experience is the literacy goal likely to be realized.

Applicability. The examples used in an overlay class should be adequate to convince the average student that the methods used in the analysis of data are of general applicability and usefulness.

Understanding. A student's experience with data analysis should not be limited to rote application of some involved statistical procedure. Rather, students should understand enough of what they are doing so that their experience of data analysis is likely to stay with them, at least as a residue of judgment and willingness to enter into similar data analyses in the future.

Practicality. The breadth of topics covered, and the depth of coverage, should be consistent with what an average Wellesley student can realistically absorb in a course that devotes only a part of its time to data analysis.

GOOD-CITIZEN MODEL OF CONCERNED NONMATHEMATICS FACULTY

All the previous approaches involve either mathematics faculty or specialized administrative units, but we should never underestimate the power of nonmathematics faculty or departments acting on their own initiative to advance quantitative literacy. There are many such examples of individual faculty revising courses and curricula simply because it is the right thing to do. Examples include Len Vacher at the University of South Florida, Bill Prothero at the University of California at Santa Barbara, Kim Kastens at Columbia University, Larry Braille and Jon Harbour at Purdue University, and Alexandra Moore at Cornell University. These faculty may take advantage of some of the approaches listed above, but they often are essentially lone crusaders for quantitative literacy working in the trenches. Although they may attend workshops or seek NSF funding, for example, just as often they proceed with little administrative support or interaction with mathematics faculty. In fact, some are hampered by administrations that depend on student credit hours as the coin of the realm, or student evaluations that can tend to favor less quantitatively challenging courses.

Given strong evidence of the success of these independent initiatives, we cannot but wonder at how much more effective such efforts could be with the full involvement and cooperation of

mathematics faculty and college or university administrations. We argue that one critical component of quantitative literacy across the curriculum must be the support and nurturing of such initiatives. As one example of administrative support, we cite the reform of the promotion and tenure system in the College of Science at the University of Arizona for faculty whose primary scholarly contribution is in the area of mathematics and science education. This reform was recognized by NSF with one of just 10 Recognition Awards for the Integration of Research and Education (University of Arizona 1998).

Conclusions and Challenges

We have argued that conceptual understanding and everyday life are two aspects of quantitative literacy deserving special attention. The ability to adapt mathematical ideas to new contexts that is part of conceptual understanding is a key component of quantitative literacy. The everyday-life component of quantitative literacy argues forcefully for engagement of faculty across the curriculum. Quantitative literacy thus must be the responsibility of teachers in all disciplines and cannot be isolated in mathematics departments.

We have illustrated curricular approaches to quantitative literacy at the college or university level that range from friendly conspiracies between mathematics and other faculty to administrative structures and requirements to initiatives by individual nonmathematics faculty. All offer success stories as well as war stories, both of which serve as models for how we can work to improve quantitative literacy.

We end with two challenges. The approaches we have illustrated must be only the start of continued and sustained efforts on the parts of faculty and institutions. Significant institutional change must occur to achieve the sort of pervasive use of mathematical ideas that we think essential in teaching quantitative literacy. Neither administratively imposed solutions nor grassroots movements will succeed alone; initiatives solely from within mathematics departments or solely from without are bound to fail. The first challenge, therefore, is to cross the boundaries that separate disciplines and levels of administration. Administrators of university-wide requirements must talk with the faculty who do the teaching on the ground; pioneers in the classroom must talk to each other and to administrators; departments of mathematics must collaborate with other departments.

Second, we must not lose sight of the fact that our goal is student learning. It is far too easy, in the heat of battle over establishing quantitative literacy requirements, setting up support centers, or revising our individual courses, to forget that the student must be the focus of our efforts. The question of "what works best" must be answered in terms of student learning. To do this, we must establish clearly defined student learning outcomes in quantitative literacy. We must be able to develop measures for these outcomes as part of an ongoing assessment program. Key to the success of such an assessment program is feedback on the way we are teaching quantitative literacy. Without such formative assessment, debates on how to improve quantitative literacy will be driven by anecdotal experience and the force of individual personality. Students deserve better.

We welcome the national focus on quantitative literacy and are hopeful that the kinds of approaches described here may serve as models for others.

Acknowledgments

The authors wish to thank H. Len Vacher and Stephen Maurer for very constructive reviews of a preliminary version of this manuscript.

References

Bauman, Steven F., and William O. Martin. 1995. "Assessing the Quantitative Skills of College Juniors." *College Mathematics Journal* 26: 214.

Mathematical Association of America. 2001. *Curriculum Foundations Project.* Washington, DC.: Mathematical Association of America. Retrieved at: http://academic.bowdoin.edu/faculty/B/barker/dissemination/Curriculum_Foundations/.

Center for Mathematics and Quantitative Education at Dartmouth College. 2002. Hanover, NH: Dartmouth College. Retrieved at: http://hilbert.dartmouth.edu/~mged.

Fox, J., and J. Powell. 1991. *A Literate World.* Paris, France: UNESCO-International Bureau of Education.

Hockney, David, and Charles M. Falco. 2000. "Optical Insights into Renaissance Art." *Optics and Photonics News* 11(7): 52–59.

Hughes-Hallett, Deborah. 2001. "Achieving Numeracy: The Challenge of Implementation." In *Mathematics and Democracy: The Case for Quantitative Literacy,* edited by Lynn Arthur Steen, 93–98. Princeton, NJ: National Council on Education and the Disciplines.

Keeling, C. D., and T. P. Whorf. 2001. "Atmospheric CO^2 Records from Sites in the SIO Air Sampling Network." In *Trends: A Compendium of Data on Global Change.* Oak Ridge, TN: Carbon Dioxide Information Analysis Center, Oak Ridge National Laboratory, U.S. Department of Energy. See also http://cdiac.esd.ornl.gov/trends/co2/sio-mlo.htm and http://cdiac.esd.ornl.gov/ftp/maunaloa-co2/maunaloa.co2.

Keller, Edward A. 2000. *Environmental Geology,* 2nd ed. Englewood Cliffs, NJ: Prentice Hall.

Math Across the Curriculum. 2000. "A Vision Statement for Math Across the Curriculum at UA." Retrieved at: http:math-across.Arizona.edu/MACvision.htm.

National Council of Teachers of Mathematics. 1989. *Curriculum and Evaluation Standards for School Mathematics.* Reston, VA: National Council of Teachers of Mathematics.

National Council of Teachers of Mathematics. 2000. *Principles and Standards for School Mathematics.* Reston, VA: National Council of Teachers of Mathematics.

Project Kaleidoscope. 2002. Washington, DC. Retrieved at: http://www.pkal.org/.

Steen, Lynn Arthur, ed. 2001. *Mathematics and Democracy: The Case for Quantitative Literacy.* Princeton, NJ: National Council on Education and the Disciplines.

Third International Mathematics and Science Study. National Center for Education Statistics. Retrieved at: http://nces.ed.gov/timss/.

University of Arizona. 1998. "Integrating Research and Education." *Report on Research*, Vol. 14, No. 2.

Wellesley College. *Quantitative Reasoning.* 2002. Wellesley, MA: Wellesley College. Retrieved at: http://www.wellesley.edu/QR/home.

Articulation and Mathematical Literacy: Political and Policy Issues

MICHAEL W. KIRST

Articulation of the mathematics curriculum is very difficult to attain at any grade level, but particularly for grades 11 through 14. Fragmented decision making concerning K–12 mathematics curricula and lack of linkage between higher and lower education pose major problems for articulation.

Higher education influences what is taught in secondary schools. Every secondary school reacts to changes in college admissions requirements that involve different courses or major changes in content emphasis within a subject. For example, changes in admissions weighting such as more emphasis on Advanced Placement, or honors courses elicit a response from secondary schools. Higher education's impact is often blunted, however, by incomplete or confusing signals sent to secondary schools and to high school students concerning what knowledge is most worth knowing. In part, these unclear signals reflect uncertainty about priorities within the entire scope of the mathematics curriculum, including quantitative literacy: "Almost everyone believes quantitative literacy to be important, but there is little agreement on just what it is" (Steen 2001).

The potential leverage of higher education on the K–16 system, therefore, may or may not be effective. A clear signal within an articulated K–16 system is required so that students know what they should be learning.

In this essay, I take the mathematics curriculum to encompass three related literacies:

- Mathematical Literacy (ML): The basic skills of arithmetic, algebra, and geometry that historically have formed the core of school mathematics;

- Quantitative Literacy (QL): Reasoning with data in their natural contexts, especially in situations that citizens encounter in judging public issues (e.g., pollution, taxes) or private decisions (e.g., cell phone plans); and

- Symbol Literacy (SL): Fluent use of algebraic notation as a second language, typical of students in science and engineering, but at a level beyond what states or districts would consider as a requirement for all students.

Although these same terms often are used by others with different interpretations, these are the definitions that apply throughout this essay.

K–16 Content and Articulation of Assessment

There is no agreement, nor even a forum in which to deliberate about a possible consensus, concerning mathematical or quantitative literacy in the U.S. K–16 education system. Educational policy in the United States is decentralized. Moreover, within each state—and at the federal level as

Michael W. Kirst is Professor of Education at Stanford University. A member of the National Academy of Education, Kirst is co-director of Policy Analysis for California Education (PACE), a policy research consortium including Stanford and UC Berkeley. Previously, he served as staff director of the U.S. Senate Subcommittee on Manpower, Employment, and Poverty and as President of the California State Board of Education. His current research centers on the relationship between state education reform efforts and educational outcomes.

well—an additional, less overt, division exists, one that is based on the historical and pervasive assumption that K–12 schools and colleges and universities should be guided by policies exclusive to each sector. As a result of this premise, public policy tools that influence one sector—funding, accountability, and governance systems, for instance—have little in common with the policy tools that influence the other. Given this division, it is not surprising that the most serious questions about quality in American education have been directed primarily toward one side of the educational divide: the K–12 public schools.

THE DISJUNCTURE BETWEEN K–12 AND HIGHER EDUCATION

The origin of the disjuncture between lower and higher education in the United States stems, in part, from the laudable way the nation created mass education systems for both K–12 and higher education. In Europe, in contrast, the higher grades of secondary education were designed for an elite group who would be going on to universities. European universities have long played a major role in determining both the content of the secondary school curriculum and the content and format of secondary school examinations. For example, professors at British universities such as Oxford and Durham grade the A levels taken by students during their last year of secondary education, and these essay examinations figure crucially in a student's chances for university admission.

Over time, the chasm between lower and higher education in the United States has grown wider than that in many other industrialized nations (Clark 1985). Nonetheless, at one time U.S. colleges and universities did play an important role in the high schools. In 1900, for example, the College Board set uniform standards for each academic subject and issued a syllabus to help students prepare for college entrance subject-matter examinations. (These College Board examinations were used by some colleges and universities until after World War II.) Some state universities developed their own systems for reviewing high school curricula. Until the 1930s, for example, the University of California accredited high schools to make sure that their curricula were adequate for university preparation; however, as more high schools sent students on to postsecondary education, the process became unmanageable.

In the postwar years, the notion of K–16 mathematics academic standards vanished. "Aptitude" tests such as the SAT replaced subject-matter standards for college admissions, and secondary schools added elective courses in nonacademic areas, including vocational education and life skills. Today, K–12 faculty and college mathematics faculty are organized into separate professional organizations and rarely meet in professional contexts. K–12 mathematics policymakers and higher education policymakers

cross paths even less often. The only large-scale, nationally aligned K–16 standards effort that involves K–16 faculty is the Advanced Placement Program (AP)—a stalactite extending from universities to high schools that influences the course syllabus and examination. An examination grade of 3, 4, or 5 on an AP examination is one indicator of college preparation. But roughly one-third of all AP students do not take the AP Examination, which means that many AP students may not be benefiting much from AP's close link to postsecondary standards (Lichten 2000).

With the exception of the AP Program, there are no major efforts to provide curricular coherence and sequencing for grades 10 to 14. Nor has anyone proposed a conception of liberal education that relates the academic content of mathematics in secondary schools to the first two years of college. Instead, students face an "eclectic academic muddle in grades 10 to 14" (Orrill 2000) until they select a college major. In Ernest Boyer's metaphor, postsecondary general education is the "spare room" of the university, "the domain of no one in particular" whose many functions make it useless for any one purpose (Boyer and Levine 1981). The functional "rooms," those inhabited by faculty, are the departmental majors.

There are no recent assessments of the status of general education. C. Adelman (1992) analyzed college students' transcripts from the National Longitudinal Study, containing data from the early to mid-1970s, which proved to be a low point in general education requirements. He reported that students took very few courses in the fields comprised by general education. Less than one-third of college credits were from courses that focused on cultural knowledge, including Western and non-Western culture, ethnic, or gender studies. Among bachelor's degree recipients, 26 percent did not earn a single college credit in history, 40 percent did not study any English or American literature, and 58 percent had no course work in foreign languages.

When attention is paid to general education, two contending theories predominate. One holds that courses used for general education should be the same courses as those used to prepare prospective majors for upper-division specialization. Another view contends that the purpose of general education is as an antidote to specialization, vocationalism, and majors. Clark (1993) hoped that somehow the specialized interests of the faculty could be arranged in interdisciplinary forms that would provide a framework for mathematical literacy, but there is little evidence that this is happening.

In sum, the high school curriculum is unmoored from any continuous vision of quantitative literacy. Policymakers for secondary and postsecondary schools work in separate orbits that rarely interact, and the policy focus for community colleges has been more concerned with access to postsecondary education than with academic preparation. Access, rather than preparation, is also the theme of many of the professionals who mediate between high schools and universities: high school counselors, college recruiters, and college admissions and financial aid officers.

The number and influence of mediating groups is, for C. Stocking (1985, 263), an indicator of the "amount of disorder and confusion that has grown through the years in the relationship between the school and the university in America." In addition to the mediating professionals employed by the high schools and the colleges, "A major role is assumed by the major private testing organizations, whose mathematics tests have become powerful tools for allocating students to different types of universities and colleges." Appendix I demonstrates that these testing organizations must be involved in any revision of the balance between quantitative and mathematical literacy.

THE STANDARDS MOVEMENT AND THE K–16 DISJUNCTURE

In recent years, the standards movement has swept across the United States. Forty-six states have developed K–12 content standards in most academic subjects, and all but Iowa and Nebraska have statewide K–12 student achievement tests. These state-directed efforts have two interrelated goals: clarifying what students must know and be able to do in the K–12 grades and aligning standards, assessments, textbook selection, and accountability measures in those grades. These reforms, however, have ignored the lack of coherence in content and assessment standards between K–12 and higher education. Until educators address this issue, secondary schools and their students will have no clear sense of what knowledge and skills constitute mathematical literacy.

Colleges and universities rely on the SAT and ACT to provide some uniform national assessment, but neither of these tests was designed to measure quantitative literacy as defined by the National Council on Education and the Disciplines (Steen 2001, 1). The relationship between K–12 mathematics standards and college placement tests is even more chaotic. In 1995, for example, universities in the southeastern United States devised 125 combinations of 75 different placement tests, with scant regard to secondary school standards.

Tests at each level—K–12 achievement tests, standardized college entrance examinations, and college placement assessments—use different mathematics formats, emphasize different content, and are given under different conditions, for example:

- California's newly augmented K–12 assessment, the Standardized Testing And Reporting (STAR) program, includes mathematics that is considerably more advanced and difficult than the SAT or ACT, but Texas' high school assessment, Texas Assessment of Academic Skills (TAAS) includes less algebra and geometry than the SAT.

- Some state K–12 assessments permit students to use calculators, but many college placement examinations do not.

- Texas has a statewide postsecondary placement test, the Texas Academic Skills Program (TASP), but many Texas universities also use their own mathematics placement examinations. High school students in Texas are either confused by or ignorant of college placement standards (Venezia 2000).

Universities provide some good arguments to explain why they pay little attention to K–12 standards or assessments. First, universities emphasize that they are not involved in the development or refinement of the K–12 standards. Second, universities observe that both politics and technical problems affect frequent changes in state K–12 standards. Third, they note that K–12 assessments have not been evaluated to see how well they predict freshman grades (although such evaluations are not difficult to conduct).

Many universities are wary of being subjected to a postsecondary version of K–12 state accountability systems and the political quagmire surrounding high-stakes testing. Mathematics curriculum policy disjunctures between K–12 and higher education will be hard to mend in the absence of a national institutional center and institutions in each state whose mission is K–16 alignment and reform. Without new deliberative bodies, more influence is left to textbook publishers and private testing firms. Currently, there are few opportunities for K–12 educators to discuss, much less resolve, questions about mathematics articulation with college and university faculty or policymakers. Very few states have any policy mechanism for specific decisions concerning K–16 standards and assessment, and higher education coordinating bodies do not include K–16 standards alignment within their purview. The disciplinary and professional associations have the potential to serve as a locus for such discussion, but these are organized into separate K–12 and postsecondary units.

The governor's office might seem the logical place for states to align their fractured K–16 standards, but higher education leaders (especially those at private universities) want to guard their political independence from gubernatorial and legislative interference in admissions criteria. Nor is it clear what can be done at the federal level, given that each state has its own K–12 standards and assessment system. When President Clinton spoke in support of voluntary national testing, he was silenced by protestors championing states' rights, local control of schools, and students' freedom and opportunity to learn.

HIGH SCHOOL STUDENTS FACE A BABEL OF ASSESSMENTS

High school students receive confusing messages about the mathematical knowledge and skills that they need to acquire in high school to succeed in college. In deciding how many years of math-

Table 1.

Distribution of Topics on Standardized Mathematics Tests

Percentage of questions devoted to:

	Algebra I	Geometry	Data, Probability, Statistics	Number Theory, Arithmetic, Logic, Combinatorics	Algebra II	Trigonometry, Pre-Calculus
Privately developed high school assessment tests						
TerraNova	14	29	23	21	0	0
Stanford 9 m/c	29	25	25	21	0	0
State high school assessment tests						
Kentucky (CATS)	9	33	17	18	20	0
Massachusetts (MCAS 10)	23	28	13	18	13	5
New York	29	26	9	26	9	3
Texas (TAAS)	12	23	3	53	0	0
College admissions examinations						
SAT-I	47	23	3	23	3	0
ACT	25	27	5	18	12	8
Privately developed college placement tests						
Compass	14	23	0	19	25	15
Accuplacer (algebra)	25	0	0	0	75	0
Accuplacer (calculus)	16	0	0	0	63	21

Source: Education Trust, 2000. "Thinking K–16," 3(2): 27.

Note: Numbers may not add to 100% because some items could not be classified or overlapped categories.

ematics to take, students look at their high school graduation and college admissions requirements; the former reflect the content of any statewide grades 10 to 12 mathematics assessments, and the latter entail mastering the content that appears in the mathematics sections of the SAT-I or the ACT. As a recent analysis shows (see Table 1), the content of statewide high school mathematics assessment tests and the content of the mathematics portions of the SAT-I and ACT are fairly similar: they tend to emphasize basic algebra, geometry, probability and statistics, and numbers (number theory, arithmetic, combinatorics, and logic) and to ignore intermediate algebra, trigonometry, and pre-calculus.

But the differences between the above tests and college placement tests are enormous. College placement examinations, such as Compass and Accuplacer, produced by national testing companies, which are used by community colleges, put considerable emphasis on intermediate algebra and trigonometry. Many colleges, even some major universities, use local placement tests written by the mathematics departments without any special oversight or blessing by the university as a whole. These tests are more accurately described as departmental placement examinations, and their quality is very uneven. Students thus prepare for and are

admitted to college based on one set of skills but then are given placement tests that cover different topics.

Higher education must be an integral part of any attempt to improve mathematics articulation. Higher education policymakers need to be involved in the design and implementation of K–12 standards and assessments to ensure K–16 mathematics articulation. Some states, such as Illinois, California, and New York, are moving ahead on this. Illinois is giving ACT mathematics to all eleventh graders, but augmenting it with test items based on the Illinois mathematics K–12 standards. The 19 campuses in the California State University (CSU) system are eliminating the placement test designed by CSU faculty and using the K–12 California standards test for placement. The City University of New York (CUNY) system allows students with high scores on the K–12 Regents examination in mathematics to be exempt from taking CUNY mathematics placement tests.

Some K–12 state assessments are rigorous, with content that more closely resembles college placement tests than the SAT-I. The Massachusetts and Kentucky K–12 assessments include intermediate algebra and trigonometry. Then again, many state K–12 tests, including the California Stanford 9 and the Texas TAAS, stress data, probability, and statistics—topics that college admissions and placement tests largely ignore. The content and topical differences in the major national assessments and in those in California are shown in Appendix I.

Is it any wonder that high school juniors and seniors are confused? They are focused on high school graduation (state assessment tests) and college admission (SAT-I), not on college placement examinations, undergraduate general studies, or distribution requirements. Many do not realize the importance of taking mathematics in their senior year as part of their preparation for college.

REACHING CONSENSUS ON MATHEMATICAL LITERACY

Suppose that a representative K–16 commission was created to formulate an articulated K–16 mathematical literacy curriculum. Such a group would immediately confront a number of difficult issues:

1. Who must be involved in the process to certify that it is inclusive? Students? Business? If you exclude groups, this will lead to charges of bias. If you include every group that is suggested, this will lead to a cumbersome and slow process.

2. If you choose standards that achieve a broad consensus in a field, "leading-edge thinkers" will object. You will be accused of certifying "what is" rather than "what ought."

3. If you choose standards that achieve consensus in a field, you will *not* be able to satisfy demands for "less is more." Consensus expands topics rather than cutting them.

4. If you choose standards that reflect a consensus on current content, this will lead to criticism that you have not sufficiently stressed interdisciplinary content. There is limited support for interdisciplinary content in any of the subject-matter organizations such as the National Council of Teachers of Mathematics (NCTM).

5. If you approve standards that are too general, or that do not contain pedagogy, critics will say that there is insufficient instructional guidance for teachers and the content gaps will be filled by tests or assessment. If you do approve pedagogy or detailed standards, you will be criticized because the standards are too long, complex, and overly control local practice.

6. If you do not hear appeals from the public for specific content changes (e.g., inclusion of calculators), you will be criticized for not having public participation at the highest level and leaving crucial decisions to a technical panel of nonelected officials. If the commission hears all these protests, it will become bogged down in time-consuming and fractious disputes.

7. If you wish to have standards in place by 2004, you are contradicting findings that it takes closer to five years than two years to formulate national content standards.

Articulation and K–12 Mathematics Curriculum Policymaking

To help understand why K–16 articulation issues are so challenging, it is useful to analyze how K–12 mathematics curriculum policy is made and the political issues that surround articulation. Many institutions and actors influence mathematics curriculum policy in the dispersed and fragmented U.S. education system. The following list illustrates the multiple actors who have some potential to help define and promulgate mathematical literacy and who need to be involved in building a coalition for articulation:

- Insiders
  - Higher education policymakers
  - Professors in mathematics, mathematics education, and related disciplines
  - State curriculum framework policymakers
  - Textbook publishers/testing agencies (private industry)
  - National Science Foundation (NSF) collaboratives, partnerships, and curriculum development projects
  - Legislative leaders in educational policy

- Near Circle
  - Teacher preparation institutions
  - Teacher certification organizations (e.g., National Council on Accreditation of Teacher Education (NCATE), National Board for Professional Teaching Standards (NBPTS), American Association of Colleges for Teacher Education (AACTE))
  - Ideological interest groups
  - Federal agencies (Office of Educational Research and Improvement (OERI), National Science Foundation (NSF), U.S. Department of Education (DOE))

- Far Circle
  - National Governors' Association
  - Education Commission of the States
  - Council of Chief State School Officers
  - National Academy of Sciences

- Sometimes Players
  - School accrediting agencies (e.g., North Central)
  - Business organizations, minority organizations
  - National Research Council

Different influence configurations will arise in different states and localities, but there are significant national actors as well. The groups listed above have different philosophies and priorities for mathematical literacy; they therefore will need to bargain and deliberate concerning their conflicts. In California, for example, the state board of education does not agree with some standards of the NCTM or some views of the NSF and the National Academy of Sciences on mathematical literacy. A K–16 coalition in favor of articulation must be created and sustained. It must include both public and private higher education as well as K–12 teacher, administrator, and mathematics curriculum specialists. Crucial policy instruments including assessments, content standards, and textbooks need to be aligned through a dominant K–16 political coalition that has bargained and compromised its conceptual, content, and pedagogical disputes. I now provide an overview of the multiple political and policy influences on potential mathematics articulation.

MATHEMATICS ARTICULATION AND POLITICAL AND VALUE CONFLICTS

As the national debate about curriculum content standards demonstrates, policymaking concerning mathematics content and standards is a political as well as a technical process (Ravitch 1995). Disputes over such issues as the inclusion of AIDS education or creation science in a curriculum highlight the existence of value conflicts embedded in the development and maintenance of curriculum standards (Wirt and Kirst 1992). The "math wars" in the California standards debate of 1997 included intense debate concerning the relative emphasis on mathematical literacy versus quantitative literacy. Because of these conflicts, curriculum policymaking often requires complex trade-offs between groups of competing interests. Articulation of the mathematics curriculum in grades 11 to 14 not only involves these conflicts but also others surrounding the relative priority of symbol literacy in the total mathematics curriculum linking lower and higher education in such fields as science and engineering.

The most common way to determine curriculum standards is to endow an individual or group (e.g., a state school board or a national subject-matter association) with the authority to make decisions about curricular content using professional and, presumably expert, judgment (Massell and Kirst 1994). But what procedures do the developers of curriculum standards follow? Past efforts best can be described by what Lindblom and Braybrooke (1963) call disjointed incrementalism, a strategy in which decision makers use pragmatic methods that result in minimal changes at the margin. Conflict is avoided by adopting vague language concerning standards and covering so many topics that no major interest group feels left out. Content priority is sacrificed to the political necessity of coverage. Disjointed incremental strategies, however, will not solve the grades 11 to 14 mathematical literacy

problem; this essay therefore makes several suggestions for more fundamental change.

The development of state mathematics standards in the 1990s was an attempt to replace disjointed incrementalism with a nonincremental reconceptualization that involved a thorough overhaul of subject-matter standards and examinations. For example, in mathematics this included more emphasis on data analysis and statistics in K–12 education.

The politics of developing state standards are complex, as one observer of NCTM's efforts noted (Ball 1992, 2–3):

> Twin needs propelled the development of NCTM's standards for school mathematics: the need to gain consensus and the need to promote change. On the one hand, if these standards were to stand as the banners of the community, then they had to reflect shared values and commitment. On the other hand, if change was desired, then these standards had to do more than reflect current practice. New ideas were needed, ideas that departed from extant assumptions and practices.

In short, the development of grades 11 to 14 mathematics standards requires complex trade-offs. There is no way to avoid conflict and the sense of winners and losers. In California, for example, the NCTM standards were challenged by a statewide group called Mathematically Correct. Difficult choices were made concerning the standards and the procedures by which mathematics content priorities were established.

Merely following the "right" procedural steps is not sufficient because there are many constraints on the total mathematics content that can be included (e.g., length of the school year). The history of standards development has been one of jockeying for priority in an overcrowded school schedule and incorporating some interest groups' priorities into the curriculum because of political considerations while others' priorities are neglected. For example, organized proponents of driver education and vocational education have been more effective politically than those of music education (Wirt and Kirst 1975).

Efforts to formulate mathematics curriculum standards have provoked conflict over the proper foundations for deciding what to teach. For example, should schools teach those things that are likely to be useful immediately in life outside of school or those most fundamental to an understanding of organized knowledge? Should they emphasize the development of individuality or conformity to the needs of higher education? As long as people disagree on how to evaluate curricula, they are bound to quarrel over its composition. The basis for this disagreement is evidenced by the University of California dispute concerning the use of SAT-I or SAT-II mathematics for admissions.

TRENDS IN THE POLITICS OF MATHEMATICS REFORM

Until the 1950s, mathematics curricula were selected by individual school systems in response to the perceived desires of local communities. The successful launch of Sputnik I in 1957 created demands for stronger federal and state roles in the education system using two broad strategies: more mathematics content at all levels and different content and instructional foci (Yee and Kirst 1994). Nevertheless, there were strong demands for preserving local control over some traditional curriculum matters, and the political conflict surrounding curricula escalated in the 1970s (Dow 1991).

An attempt by a federal agency to influence the development of all subjects in the local curriculum was rebuffed in the 1970s when Congress cut back the role of the federal government in social studies curriculum development (Dow 1991). An example of resistance to the federal government's efforts was the charge by Congressman John Conlan (R.-Ariz.) that this curriculum was a federal attempt to "use classrooms for conditioning, to mold a new generation of Americans toward a repudiation of traditional values, behavior, and patriotic beliefs" (cited in Wirt and Kirst 1992, 102). Yet 20 years earlier, the federal government had entered the curriculum and text development field because of concern that mathematics and science curricula were outdated, inaccurate, dull, and lacking in diversity (Dow 1991). Scholars and experts in education who advise federal and state governments have been criticized for trying to impose their own cosmopolitan and secular values on diverse local communities. Curricular reform itself has become professionalized through government and foundation grants. No longer are perceived crises such as the economic recession of 1980 to 1983 required to generate curricular change because curricular change now has a self-starting capacity.

Curricular conflict has many roots. Military threats or changes in public sentiment about issues such as the women's movement generate value conflicts about curriculum. Other forces, such as court decisions favoring bilingual education or the pronouncements of influential individuals, can result in changes to the curriculum without the direct development of new materials. To incorporate all these influences, the process of new mathematics textbook creation is "managed," whereby a writing team prepares a series of texts. The actual author is frequently the publisher's internal editor, not the authors listed on the title page. States that adopt textbooks (mostly in the Southeast) have disproportionate influence on what is offered in the national market. Thus any attempt to change mathematics curriculum must involve rethinking textbook creation and adoption policies.

The limited impact of the "new math" curricular reform of 25 years ago, widely regarded as a failure, suggests the obstacles for articulation in grades 11 to 14 unless there are powerful constituencies and organized forces backing change. Parents may be confused and many will want to revert back to the traditional pattern of mathematics education that they experienced during their K–12 schooling. Consequently, if change is to occur, higher education must be a united and firm supporter of mathematical literacy articulation in grades 11 to 14.

This will not be easy or swift. In California, the 1996 to 1999 reading wars were easier and quicker to resolve than the mathematics conflicts. In the case of mathematics, higher education was represented by mathematics professors with specific views, but not by their institutions, or by those who make policy concerning admissions or placement. No state body except the New York Regents has a K–16 institutional center that could provide a forum to settle these disputes. Professional mathematics associations such as NCTM include some higher education mathematicians but not many postsecondary policymakers. Moreover, because NCTM has been a major protagonist in the mathematics standards debate, it may not be able to play a major role in building a coalition for articulation.

THE COMPLEXITIES OF SYSTEMIC CHANGE

Curricular developments in the 1990s underline the need to change the entire education system, but this strategy confronts considerable political obstacles. The systemic reform strategy currently in use departs from the traditional practice of leaving content determination solely to individual teachers and local schools (Fuhrman 1993). Frequent elections and turnover of key leaders at the state and school board level make it very difficult for mathematics curriculum changes to persist long enough for systemwide implementation. The difficulty of reelecting state leaders combined with fractured mathematics interest groups tends to preserve local control. Several states limit legislative terms to six years.

Historically, the education system in the United States, supported by federal and state policies, has tended to reinforce the use of textbooks and low-level, basic skills curricula that in turn have become the de facto national curricula (Elmore and Fuhrman 1994). Textbook publishers can broaden their market potential by gearing standards to the lowest common denominator (Kirst 1984). For example, it has been typical for schools and teachers to make their decisions as to what will be taught by deferring to textbook publishers' tables of contents and letting standardized tests required by states and districts define the skills children should learn (Elmore and Fuhrman 1994). State-mandated multiple-choice tests and basic skills examinations typically emphasize single, correct answers and often do not adequately emphasize analysis, statistical inference, multistep mathematical problem solving, synthesis, and complex reading (Kirst 1994).

Many states are trying to change this with new mathematics standards assessments, but there is little motivation for students because teachers typically do not use students' scores on state assessments to determine grades. State tests rarely are used for college entrance or placement, and employers rarely ask to see a high school transcript (Kirst 1994). With the lack of any explicit consensus, low-level skills that are familiar and relatively easy to teach become the curriculum (Fuhrman 1993; Smith and O'Day 1991). If a school system has no clear mathematics goals or directions, it cannot develop any authentic means by which to judge its progress; schools are left with no independent means of assessing students' achievement apart from the grades assigned by teachers.

Because of support for local control, state policymakers have historically avoided determining the articulation of mathematics content. For the most part, educators have not tried to change the status quo and, in fact, many have argued against state "policy interference" (Fuhrman 1993). Educators have tended to be highly skeptical of state policymakers' ability to develop ambitious and challenging student achievement standards that can actually be carried out in the classroom. Their skepticism is based on the fact that until recently, politicians found it was easiest to set standards at levels that school systems could readily achieve; however, from 1995 to 2000, several states established mathematics graduation standards that failed about 50 percent of the students. When standards are set too high, educators complain because they feel unfairly held to impossibly high standards (Ravitch 1995).

Because many educators do not believe that state government is able to make enlightened educational policy using top-down state tests linked to sanctions and incentives, they have placed their hope for mathematics improvement on individual school efforts or bottom-up reform (Cohen 1983; Cuban 1984; Elmore 1990; Fuhrman 1993; Purkey and Smith 1983). But as long as there is a school-based "us versus them" attitude at the policy level, articulation in grades 11 to 14 may never be successful. An alternative is the integration of top-down and bottom-up reform strategies, with both state and local policymakers working together to help change the system.

Mathematics Articulation and Coalition Building

Today, mathematics and science curriculum developers are bridging the gap between legislation and the classroom by specifying content, assessment, and performance standards, while at the same time trying to give teachers and local school districts a meaningful "zone of local discretion" over how to achieve the goals of the legislation (Elmore and Fuhrman 1994; O'Day and Smith 1993). There are, however, five main areas of political tension that make it difficult to develop a supportive coalition for mathematics articulation inside and outside the schools: the tension between leadership and political consensus, between flexible and specific standards, between up-to-date, dynamic standards and reasonable expectations for change in the system, and between professional leadership and public understanding (Massell 1994a). The most recent tension is between expectations and requirements—how to specify high mathematics expectations that provide worthy goals and, at the same time, calibrate high school graduation requirements to accommodate those who will not have met these high expectations.

THE TENSION BETWEEN LEADERSHIP AND POLITICAL CONSENSUS

Previous education reform efforts, especially large-scale curriculum reforms, often have been criticized for ignoring the social, political, and technical realities of implementation in schools and classrooms (Dow 1991; McLaughlin 1991; Yee and Kirst 1994). The new math projects that were sponsored by the National Science Foundation from the 1950s to the 1970s are good examples of programs that were criticized because parents, teachers, community leaders, administrators, and others "had only limited, if any, involvement in the development of the new curriculum, were uninformed about the changes they were expected to make, and were ill-prepared to defend the reforms when challenges arose at the local levels" (Massell 1994a, 186-87). Because of the failure of these past reform efforts, today's educators are well aware of the types of problems that will arise if notions of change are not widely shared at the community level (Carlson 1995). Most of today's K–12 standards projects thus try to gather diverse input by engaging in a broad review and feedback process with professional educators, business, community members, and others who have an interest in the standards. Gathering diverse input alone, however, will not achieve the development and implementation of leading-edge content standards because the broad range of ideas frequently blocks consensus. Might a variety of passionate individuals pursuing very different goals in very different ways produce much greater student learning and commitment than the same individuals constrained by a forced consensus?

NCTM achieved a degree of initial consensus around the content standards that they designed in 1989 (Massell 1994a). The impact of those standards was enhanced by a long period of preparation prior to convening the writing committees. This preparation laid some of the intellectual groundwork for mathematics reform and ensured broad involvement in the developmental process. In contrast to past large-scale curriculum reform efforts, NCTM engaged more educators as well as subject-matter specialists on its drafting committees. Its efforts also were enhanced by far-reaching review and feedback processes. The organization embarked on an extensive consensus-building process among thousands of practitioners, academics, and other professionals as well as among members of the general public. NCTM received the endorsement of major professional associations prior to the release of its standards document. Even after the standards were drafted, NCTM continued its consensus- and capacity-building efforts (Massell 1994a, 1994b). Yet even this extensive process of involvement did not prevent major challenges to the NCTM standards.

D. Massell (1994a, 188) described the unique characteristics of mathematics that helped NCTM in the formation of its standards:

> Mathematics, unlike science, is not fragmented into a large number of competitive sub-disciplines; furthermore, the sub-areas that do exist (i.e., geometry, algebra, calculus) share a common conceptual base and language that facilitates discussions across them and makes goals like "depth over breadth" more easily achieved. In contrast to science, mathematics does not tend to galvanize debate on pressing social issues or political concerns. The mathematics community has relatively few national organizations, and many have overlapping membership. These elements strengthen communication and provide a more solid foundation for consensus.

Compared with the National Research Council's (1996) development of the *National Science Education Standards* in the mid-1990s, the development of the NCTM standards was facilitated by the less-turbulent political atmosphere surrounding the issue in the late 1980s. In fact, NCTM had to use its own resources to produce the mathematics standards because "federal and foundation actors did not think a national curriculum document was a good idea" (Massell 1994a, 188). Because NCTM had no external support, it had to recruit support for the standards project from within the ranks of its own membership. NCTM also was able to take its time (seven to nine years, depending on how you count it) in developing the standards, a luxury today's standards developers do not have.

Professional disputes arose during the NCTM formation process that still linger today even after NCTM's recent revisions to its standards. For example, NCTM members have continuing paradigmatic arguments about whether basic skills should be taught first and applications second, along with disagreements over the timing of the introduction of problem solving. NCTM members who prefer a behavioral approach to learning argue for a teacher-centered direct instructional method. They also argue that:

> You have to crawl/walk before you can run. If formulas aren't memorized, there will be no basis for the mathematical reasoning. If there is no mechanistic answer finding, there will

be no conjecturing, inventing, and problem solving. If you don't know a body of so-called isolated concepts and procedures, there won't be any connecting mathematics and its applications. Judicious use of old-fashioned rote memory and drill are as necessary today as they were in generations past (Carlson 1995, 9).

Other mathematics educators believe that classrooms should be student centered with emphasis on mathematical reasoning learned through constructing and solving problems. Their "timing" argument, and the one that NCTM used in the 1980s, was that skills and concepts can and do emerge during the process of problem solving and should proceed in tandem (Massell 1994b). *Curriculum and Evaluation Standards for School Mathematics* (NCTM 1989, 9) stated:

> Two general principles have guided our descriptions [of student activities related to mathematics]: First, activities should grow out of problem situations; and second, learning occurs through active as well as passive involvement with mathematics. Traditional teaching emphases on practice in manipulating expressions and practicing algorithms as a precursor to solving problems ignore the fact that knowledge often emerges from the problems. This suggests that instead of the expectation that skill in computation should precede word problems, experience with problems helps develop the ability to compute.

The development and impact of the NCTM standards reflect continuing debates about the relative emphasis on quantitative literacy versus mathematical literacy. This experience shows that any attempt to improve mathematics articulation in grades 11 to 14 will encounter difficulties in reaching and sustaining a consensus. NCTM used a number of promising strategies but still was engulfed in conflict in states such as California because groups such as Mathematically Correct opposed the NCTM content.

THE TENSION BETWEEN FLEXIBLE AND SPECIFIC STANDARDS

Recently, local control of curricula has decreased in favor of increased roles for the states and the federal government. For articulated standards in mathematics to be accepted, the people of this nation must want to have them, and the standards must be flexible enough to allow for local elaboration and variation. Keeping this in mind, Smith and O'Day (1991, 254) propose to simultaneously:

> . . . increase coherence in the system through centralized co-ordination and increase professional discretion at the school site. Thus while schools have the ultimate responsibility to educate thoughtful, competent, and responsible citizens, the state—representing the public—has the responsibility to define what "thoughtful, competent, and responsible citizens" will mean in the coming century.

Today, the term "standard" is typically used as a flag that reflects the valued goals around which educators can rally and decide for themselves how these goals will be accomplished in their schools and classrooms (Ravitch 1995). Developers of standards for mathematics thus may find it undesirable to enforce a particular set of practices or materials. Rather, mathematics articulation could be designed to direct and guide local choice instead of determining and prescribing practice and teaching. No rigid or specific implications for practice would be inferred from the standards (Ball 1992; Myers 1994; Sykes and Plastrik 1992). In allowing this flexibility, however, policymakers trying to link high school mathematics courses to the first two years of university may confront the problem of not knowing when their standards lack the specificity required to provide strong leadership (Massell 1994a). This same concern emerged among experts who were trying to design teacher knowledge assessments for the National Board for Professional Teaching Standards:

> By not creating standards at what we would call a fine-grained level . . . standard writers leave the critical work of operationalizing standards for exercises and judging to the assessment developers. We, not the standards committee . . . imagined the vignettes or examples of accomplished teaching, we attempted to ground the standards in research, and we think the standards committee should have been involved in the assessment effort to operationalize standards (Pence and Petrosky 1992, 12).

Therefore, "a certain level of detail in the content standard is necessary to guide the construction of Grades 11 to 14 course sequence standards, which will then guide test specifications, and finally the development of the tests themselves" (Massell 1994a, 192). If the mathematics content standards do not provide sufficient detail, they will not pave the way for other policy components such as assessment and instructional materials; this is the problem mathematics frameworks are struggling with today. Thus, the national debate on mathematics and science standards:

> ". . . must go beyond generally worded standards to include the development of curricula specific enough to guide teaching and assessment. These must be the first steps; a syllabus-based examination system will have to wait until standards are established, because we cannot ensure that students have a fair chance to learn what is tested until we have a curricula in place" (Koretz, Madaus, Haertel, and Beaton, 1992, 12).

But with more specificity comes less flexibility for individuals at various levels in the system and the potential for greater politically based opposition to policymakers telling teachers what to teach. A possible solution to the flexibility/specificity dilemma is to develop numerous, relatively detailed strands of content for grades 11 to 14 keyed to a common set of standards. These standards could include relative emphasis and sequencing for quantitative, mathematical, and symbol literacy.

THE TENSION BETWEEN UP-TO-DATE, DYNAMIC STANDARDS AND REASONABLE EXPECTATIONS FOR CHANGE IN THE SYSTEM

We already know how difficult it is to develop standards, and given all the interlocking systemic components such as teacher repertoires, instructional materials, and assessments that take time and significant resources to develop, frequent revisions are not practical. California currently revises its curricular frameworks on a staggered eight-year schedule. That is, each particular content-area framework is reviewed every eight years, with a new subject being addressed each year by state policymakers. Eight years may seem like a long time, but if we break the process up into the time it takes to complete each step we can see that eight years can become a very short time. For example, it takes approximately two years to revise the curricular framework, and then publishers must be given enough time to align their textbooks accordingly. Furthermore, staff development programs, assessments, and other facets of the system must be constructed and implemented in the schools.

California frequently has been criticized for having its frameworks and assessments ready before the staff development programs and curriculum materials were in place (Massell 1994a). Although the staggered schedule does not present a great burden for middle school and high school teachers, it does for elementary school teachers because they are responsible for the whole range of subjects and, therefore, have to reassess a key component of their curriculum every year (Massell 1994a). The district curriculum supervisors have the same problem (Marsh and Odden 1991). Thus, mathematics standards developers must set a time line that is practical and feasible; revised standards do nothing to help educate our students if our educational resources and systems cannot keep up with them.

Many educational frameworks, standards, and materials for mathematics disciplines are also criticized because they tend to "cover the waterfront" instead of focusing only on a few key points or topics in great detail; that is, they cover a wide range of material superficially instead of emphasizing in-depth learning of key concepts. Typically, such broad frameworks do not push publishers to develop high-quality materials, have little impact in the classroom, and are "seen as little more than 'good doorstops'" (Massell 1994b, 119) because of the intentionally vague language. Instead of working together and compromising to provide in-depth coverage of a few key topics, developers try to include everything. By using vague terms, developers avoid offending advocates of the various sub-areas, a likely result if topics from one sub-area are emphasized more strongly than those from another.

THE TENSION BETWEEN PROFESSIONAL LEADERSHIP AND PUBLIC UNDERSTANDING

Parents, religious groups, and other factions in society will continue to have an effect on the wording and content of articulation documents that better link high school mathematics curriculum to college and university courses, as well as on what teachers choose to teach in their classrooms. Challenges to public school programs and materials are nothing new in America. As M. McCarthy (1995, 55) noted:

> For decades civil rights groups have been challenging materials as racist or sexist or as curtailing free speech; consumer groups have been contesting materials that promote bad health habits; environmentalists have been critical of texts that do not encourage global responsibility; and parents and religious groups have objected to the language and orientation of particular books, courses, and activities.

Recent disputes, however, are different from these challenges in several ways. In the 1960s and 1970s, "the most vociferous critics of public education usually came from the politically left" (Whitty 1984, 52). Since the 1980s, however, more and more critics of public education have come from conservative citizen groups who have been labeled the "new right." Also, the number of challenges has increased dramatically, and their central focus has broadened from single books to entire programs and strategies to redesign schooling (McCarthy 1995). In addition, the disputes have galvanized considerable media coverage: "Battle lines are clearly drawn, misinformation abounds, vicious accusations are being hurled, logic is often replaced by emotion, and there seems to be little desire to compromise" (McCarthy 1995, 55). The conflicts today seem to reflect the different values and world views of educators, parents, business leaders, and policymakers with regard to the purpose of schooling and the relationship between quantitative and mathematical literacy (McCarthy 1995; Marzana 1993–94).

SUMMARY OF POLICY AND POLITICAL ISSUES

Articulation of mathematics content standards and examinations for grades 11 to 14 could be another chapter in the long-running saga of U.S. curriculum politics. Decisions on what knowledge is most worth knowing are at the center of school politics, even though school finance usually attracts more media attention. Curriculum standards are the crucial components of the overall vision of systemic reform (Smith and O'Day 1991). Content standards are a beginning for subsequent state and local policy alignment of textbooks, assessment, staff development, categorical programs, and accreditation. All these policy areas must be linked to teaching articulated standards in U.S. classrooms for systemic reform to succeed. Consequently, "standards for mathematics" is high-stakes politics.

Some potentially useful political strategies for mathematics and science curriculum developers include better public engagement and parent involvement; coalition building with business, higher education, vocational education, and teacher organizations; and a recognition that some value conflicts are so deep that no reasonable compromise is possible. In *Transforming Education: Overcoming Barriers* (David and Goren 1993), the National Governors' Association offered six guidelines: (1) send clear and consistent signals; (2) give priority to professional development; (3) balance top-down and bottom-up strategies; (4) create feedback mechanisms; (5) make mid-course corrections; and (6) focus attention on education as a public good. These guidelines offer insight for educators and policymakers at all levels who want to pursue articulation.

PROMISING POLICIES

Despite these complex issues, some progress has been made. For example, NCTM content revisions in 2000 appear to have reduced objections by opponents. CUNY has agreed to use the New York Regents mathematics tests for initial freshman placement, and Oregon has developed a system for K–16 educators to rate high school student work samples in their college preparatory courses as one criterion for university admissions. Representatives of the University of California, California State University, California community colleges, and K–12 are devising a college admissions test that will be an integral part of the California state secondary school assessment. Georgia has regional P–16 Councils that help improve student preparation for postsecondary education. These diverse K–16 efforts have the potential to send clearer signals to students, but articulation requires that these signals be received: they must culminate in specific and clear student understanding of mathematical literacy.

Signaling theory suggests that streamlined messages have a positive impact on students' learning and achievement but that mixed signals—the current state of affairs—have the opposite effect. Crucial aspects of signals and incentives are clarity and consistency. Consistency occurs when signals and institutional policies are aligned—for example, when state and local K–12 assessments are coordinated with the ACT and SAT. In the emerging climate, a simple rule of thumb will likely apply: the more that incoherent and vague signals are sent by universities to students, the less adequate student preparation for higher education will become. Better mathematics articulation will require basic changes in curriculum policymaking and K–16 integration. It can be done but will require persistent leadership and institutional structures that provide effective deliberative forums. The United States has made some initial promising steps but there is still a long way to go. The incentives for the higher education community to work with K–12 to develop quantitative literacy are weak, so this must become a higher priority for college and university presidents, provosts, deans, and faculty.

Appendix I
Structural, Content, and Cognitive Features of the Mathematics Tests

Test	Format				Context	Graphs			Diagrams			Formulas		Content								Cognitive Requirements		
	MC	QC	GR	OE	C	S	RO	P	S	RO	P	M	G	PA	EA	IA	CG	PG	TR	SP	MISC	CU	PK	PS
ACT	100	0	0	0	22	5	2	0	13	0	0	15	0	17	22	5	15	25	8	3	5	40	53	7
Algebra Readiness	100	0	0	0	26	12	0	0	12	0	0	8	2	42	20	0	2	12	0	8	0	16	84	0
CSU	100	0	0	0	24	0	0	0	16	0	0	18	0	6	32	8	16	14	2	22	0	28	70	2
GSE (Algebra)	95	0	0	5	15	0	5	0	10	0	0	10	0	0	52	0	19	14	0	10	5	19	76	5
GSE (Geometry)	95	0	0	5	10	0	0	5	75	0	0	25	0	0	0	0	5	86	10	0	0	52	38	10
GSE (HS Math)	92	0	0	8	33	0	5	0	23	0	5	15	0	23	15	0	23	23	0	15	0	62	23	15
Math Analysis	100	0	0	0	7	0	2	0	18	0	0	18	0	2	31	31	7	29	0	0	0	13	82	4
SATI	58	25	17	0	25	7	0	0	18	0	0	1	8	13	37	2	6	19	0	13	11	32	53	15
SATII-Level IC	100	0	0	0	18	8	0	0	26	0	0	12	0	2	30	10	12	28	4	8	6	34	58	8
SATII-Level IIC	100	0	0	0	12	12	2	0	2	0	0	10	0	2	14	22	12	14	18	6	12	26	54	20
Second year Algebra	100	0	0	0	7	7	4	0	22	0	0	16	0	2	60	0	4	33	0	0	0	16	82	2
Stanford 9	100	0	0	0	58	21	4	0	42	0	0	6	6	0	13	2	19	19	4	40	4	63	31	6

Legend:

CSU = California State University Placement Test

GSE = A California state exam based on the New York Regents end-of-course structure.

Format

MC = multiple-choice items

QC = quantitative comparison items

GR = fill-in-the-grid items

OE = open-ended items

Context

C = contextualized items

Graphs/Diagrams

S = graph/diagram within item-stem

RO = graph/diagram within response options

P = graph/diagram needs to be produced

Formulas

M = formula needs to be memorized

G = formula is provided

Content

PA = prealgebra

EA = elementary algebra

IA = intermediate algebra

CG = coordinate geometry

PG = plane geometry

TR = trigonometry

SP = statistics and probability

MISC = miscellaneous topics

Cognitive Requirements

CU = conceptual understanding

PK = procedural knowledge

PS = problem-solving

Source: Vi-Nhuan Le, Alignment Among Secondary and Post-secondary Assessments (Santa Monica: Rand Corporation, 2002).

References and Related Papers

Adelman, C. 1992. *Tourists in Our Own Land: Cultural Literacies and the College Curriculum.* Washington, DC: U.S. Department of Education.

Archibald, D. A., and F. Newman. 1988. *Beyond Standardized Testing: Assessing Authentic Academic Achievement in Secondary School.* Reston, VA: National Association of Secondary School Principals.

Ball, Deborah. L. 1992. *Implementing the NCTM Standards: Hopes and Hurdles.* (Issue Paper 92–2). East Lansing, MI: National Center for Research on Teacher Learning.

Boyer, Ernest L., and Arthur Levine. 1981. *A Quest for Common Learning.* Princeton, NJ: Carnegie Foundation for the Advancement of Teaching.

Carlson, C. G. 1995. "The Metamorphosis of Mathematics Education." Focus, 27 (Princeton, NJ: Educational Testing Service).

Clark, B. 1985. *The School and the University.* Berkeley, CA: University of California Press.

Clark, B. 1993. *The Problem of Complexity in Modern Higher Education.* Cambridge, UK:Cambridge.)

Collins, A. 1995. "National Science Education Standards in the U.S.: A Process and Product." *Studies in Education Science* 26: 7–37.

Cohen, M. 1983. "Instructional Management and Social Conditions in Effective Schools." In *School Finance and School Improvement Linkage for the 1980s,* edited by A. Odden and L. D. Webb, 17–50. Cambridge, MA: Ballinger.

Cuban, L. 1984. "School Reform by Remote Control: SB813 in California." *Phi Delta Kappan* 66: 213–15.

David, J. L. and P. D. Goren. 1993. *Transforming Education: Overcoming Barriers.* Washington, DC: National Governors' Association.

Dow, P. B. 1991. *Schoolhouse Politics: Lessons from the Sputnik Era.* Cambridge, MA: Harvard University Press.

Education Trust, 2000. "Thinking K–16," 3(2): 27. Washington, DC.

Elmore, R. F. 1990. *Restructuring Schools: The Next Generation of Educational Reform.* San Francisco: Jossey-Bass.

Elmore, R. F., and S. Fuhrman. 1994. *The Governance of the Curriculum.* Alexandria, VA: American Society for Curriculum and Development.

Frederickson, N. 1984. "The Real Test Bias: Influences of Testing on Teaching and Learning." *American Psychologist* 39: 193–202.

Fuhrman, S. H. 1993. "Politics of Coherence." In *Designing Coherent Policy: Improving the System,* edited by S. H. Fuhrman, 1–32. San Francisco: Jossey-Bass.

Kirst, M. W. 1984. "Choosing Textbook." *American Educator* (Fall).

Kirst, M. W. 1994. "The Politics of Nationalizing Curricular Content." *American Journal of Education* 102: 383–93.

Koretz, D. M., G. Madaus, E. Haertel, and A. Beaton. 1992. National

Educational Standards and Testing: A Response to the Recommendations of the National Council on Educational Standards and Testing." Santa Monica, CA: RAND.

Lichten, William, 2000. "Wither Advanced Placement?" *Education Policy Archives* 8(29), June 24, 2000 (on-line journal).

Lindblom, C., and D. Braybrooke. 1963. *A Strategy of Decision.* New York, NY: Free Press.

Marsh, D. D., and A. R. Odden. 1991. "Implementation of the California Mathematics and Science Curriculum Frameworks." In *Education Policy Implementation,* edited by A. R. Odden, 219–40. Albany, NY: State University of New York Press.

Marshall, C., D. Mitchell, and F. Wirt. 1989. *Culture and Educational Policy in the American States.* New York, NY: Falmer.

Marzana, R. J. 1993–94. "When Two World Views Collide." *Educational Leadership* 15(4): 18–19.

Massell, D. 1994a. "Three Challenges for National Content Standards. *Education and Urban Society* 26: 185–95.

Massell, D. 1994b. Setting Standards in Mathematics and Social Studies. *Education and Urban Society* 26: 118-40.

Massell, D., and M. Kirst, (eds.). 1994. "Setting National Content Standards" [Special issue]. *Education and Urban Society* 26(2).

McCarthy, M. 1995. "Challenges to the Public School Curriculum: New Targets and Strategies." *Phi Delta Kappan* 75: 55–60.

McLaughlin, M. W. 1991. "The RAND Change Agent Study: Ten Years Later. In *Education Policy Implementation,* edited by A. R. Odden, 143–55. Albany, NY: State University of New York Press.

Myers, M. 1994. "Problems and Issues Facing the National Standards Project in English." *Education and Urban Society* 26: 141–57.

National Council of Teachers of Mathematics. 1989. *Curriculum and Evaluation Standards for School Mathematics.* Reston, VA: National Council of Teachers of Mathematics.

National Council on Educational Standards and Testing. 1992. *Raising Standards for American Education.* Washington, DC: U.S. Government Printing Office.

National Research Council. 1996. *National Science Education Standards.* Washington, DC: National Academy Press.

O'Day, J. A., and M. S. Smith. 1993. "Systemic Reform and Educational Opportunity." In *Designing Coherent Education Policy: Improving the System,* edited by S. Fuhrman, 250–312. San Francisco: Jossey-Bass.

Orrill, Robert, "Grades 11–14: The Heartland or Wasteland of American Education," unpublished paper, 2000.

Pence, P., and A. Petrosky. "Defining Performance Standards and Developing an Assessment for Accomplished English Language Arts Teaching of Young Adolescents. Paper presented at annual meeting of National Council on Measurement in Education, San Francisco, April 1992.

Purkey, S. C., and M. Smith. 1983. "School Reform: The District Policy Implications of the Effective Schools Literature." *Elementary School Journal* 85(4): 358–89.

Ravitch, D. 1995. *National Standards in American Education.* Washington, DC: Brookings Institution.

Smith, M., and J. O'Day. 1991. "Systemic School Reform." In *The Politics of Curriculum and Testing,* edited by S. Fuhrman and B. Malen, 223–67. New York, NY: Taylor & Francis.

Steen, Lynn Arthur, ed. 2001. *Mathematics and Democracy: The Case for Quantitative Literacy.* Princeton, NJ: National Council on Education and the Disciplines.

Stocking, C. 1985. "The United States." In *The School and the University.* Berkeley, CA; University of California Press.

Sykes, G., and P. Plastrik. 1992. Standard-Setting as Educational Reform. Paper prepared for the National Council on Accreditation of Teacher Education, Washington, DC.

Tyson-Bernstein, H. 1988. "The Academy's Contribution to the Impoverishment of American Textbooks." *Phi Delta Kappan* 70: 193–98.

Venezia, A. 2000. *Texas Case Study: Bridge Project Report.* Palo Alto, CA.: Bridge Project, Stanford University School of Education. www.stanford.edu/group/bridgeproject.

Vi-Nhuan, Le, *Alignment Among Secondary and Post-secondary Assessments* (Santa Monica: Rand Corporation, 2002).

Whitty, G. 1984. "The Privatization of Education." *Educational Leadership* 41(7): 51–54.

Wirt, F., and M. Kirst. 1975. *Political and Social Foundations of Education.* Berkeley, CA: McCutchan.

Wirt, F., and M. Kirst. 1992. *Schools in Conflict.* Berkeley, CA: McCutchan.

Yee, G., and M. Kirst. 1994. "Lessons from the New Science Curriculum of the 1950s and 1960s." *Education and Urban Society* 26(2): 158–71.

"Get Real!" Assessing for Quantitative Literacy

GRANT WIGGINS

"OK, people, settle down. It's time to take out some paper and pencil, we're going to have a pop quiz today in Quant. Lit. 101. Stop the groaning please! You have 40 minutes only. As always, you can consult any resource, including other people in the room, but budget your time wisely and note all texts and people consulted for each answer. . . . Here are the questions."

1. What is the meaning of the phrase "statistical tie" in the sentence "The result of the 2000 election in Florida was a statistical tie, even though George Bush was declared the winner"? Extra credit: Sketch out a mathematically sound and politically palatable solution to the problem of close elections.

2. Respond to the following claim, made by a student to his geometry teacher: "Well, you may have proven the theorem today, but we may discover something tomorrow that proves the theorem wrong."

3. Guesstimate quickly, please: If you want the most money for your retirement, should you (a) invest $500 per year in an index-based mutual fund from the time you are 16 years old to the time you are 30, or (b) invest $1,000 per year in a bank savings account from the time you are 25 until you are 65?

4. Is mathematics more like geography (a science of what is really "out there") or more like chess (whose rules and logical implications we just made up)? Did we "discover" the truth that $1 + 1 = 2$, or did we "invent" it? Based on our work this semester, give two plausible reasons for each perspective. Then give your own view, with reasons.

5. Study the data on the last 10 years of AIDS cases in the United States from the newspaper clipping in front of you. What are two trends for charting future policy?

6. "At current rates of revenue and payout the Social Security fund will be bankrupt by the time you retire." Explain how this statement could be both true and false, mathematically speaking, depending on the definitions and assumptions used.

7. Comment on this proof, please:[1]
   Solve $6x - 10 = 21x - 35$ for x.
   Solution: $2(3x - 5) = 7(3x - 5)$
   Therefore $2 = 7$

Grant Wiggins is the President and Director of Programs for Relearning by Design, a not-for-profit educational organization that consults with schools, districts, and state education departments on a variety of issues, notably assessment and curricular change. Wiggins is the author of *Educative Assessment (1998)*, *Assessing Student Performance (1999)*, and (with Jay McTighe) *Understanding by Design* (2000). Wiggins' many articles have appeared in such journals as *Educational Leadership* and *Phi Delta Kappan*.

8. "Hoops" McGinty wants to donate millions of dollars from his salary and sports-drink earnings toward a special exhibit in the new Rose Planetarium area of the American Museum of Natural History in New York. Hoops wants the exhibit to include a three-dimensional scale model of the solar system in which the size of the planets and the distance of each planet from the sun would be exactly to scale. There is a catch, however: the sun is to be represented by a regulation NBA basketball. The nervous folks in the gifts department of the museum call on you because of your expertise in astronomy and matters of scale. What can you advise them—quickly—about the feasibility of McGinty's plan? What approach will work best to ensure a basketball-related design in the display?

9. Discuss the following statement, picking a key axiom as an example to support your observations: "The axioms in any mathematical system may *logically* precede the theorems, but it does not follow (and indeed is not true historically) that they were all formulated *prior in time* to the theorems. Axioms are *not* self-evident truths. They may even sometimes be less obvious than theorems, and formulated late in the game. They are necessary 'givens', shaped by what we wish to be able to prove."

10. Write a memo to the House Education Committee on the accuracy and implications of the following analysis:

    New York Times, August 13, 2001

    Rigid Rules Will Damage School
    By Thomas J. Kane and Douglas O. Staiger

    As school was about to let out this summer, both houses of Congress voted for a dramatic expansion of the federal role in the education of our children. A committee is at work now to bring the two bills together, but whatever the specific result, the center of the Elementary and Secondary Education Act will be identifying schools that are not raising test scores fast enough to satisfy the federal government and then penalizing or reorganizing them. Once a school has failed to clear the new federal hurdle, the local school district will be required to intervene.

    The trouble with this law . . . is that both versions of this bill place far too much emphasis on year-to-year changes in test scores. . . . Because the average elementary school has only 68 children in each grade, a few bright kids one year or a group of rowdy friends the next can cause fluctuations in test performance even if a school is on the right track.

    Chance fluctuations are a typical problem in tracking trends, as the federal government itself recognizes in gath-

    ering other kinds of statistics. The best way to keep them from causing misinterpretations of the overall picture is to use a large sample. The Department of Labor, for example, tracks the performance of the labor market with a phone survey of 60,000 households each month. Yet now Congress is proposing to track the performance of the typical American elementary school with a sample of students in each grade that is only a thousandth of that size.

    With our colleague Jeffrey Geppert of Stanford, we studied the test scores in two states that have done well, investigating how their schools would have fared under the proposed legislation. Between 1994 and 1999, North Carolina and Texas were the envy of the educational world, achieving increases of 2 to 5 percentage points every year in the proportion of their students who were proficient in reading and math. However, the steady progress at the state level masked an uneven, zigzag pattern of improvement at the typical school. Indeed, we estimate that more than 98 percent of the schools in North Carolina and Texas would have failed to live up to the proposed federal expectation in at least one year between 1994 and 1999. At the typical school, two steps forward were often followed by one step back.

    More than three-quarters of the schools in North Carolina and Texas would have been required to offer public school options to their students if either version of the new education bill had been in effect. Under the Senate bill a quarter of the schools in both states would have been required to restructure themselves sometime in those five years—by laying off most of their staffs, becoming public charter schools or turning themselves over to private operators. Under the more stringent House bill, roughly three-quarters of the schools would have been required to restructure themselves.

    Both bills would be particularly harsh on racially diverse schools. Each school would be expected to achieve not only an increase in test scores for the school as a whole, but increases for each and every racial or ethnic group as well. Because each group's scores fluctuate depending upon the particular students being tested each year, it is rare to see every group's performance moving upward in the same year. Black and Latino students are more likely than white students to be enrolled in highly diverse schools, so their schools would be more likely than others to be arbitrarily disrupted by a poorly designed formula. . . .

    In their current bills, the House and Senate have set a very high bar—so high that it is likely that virtually all school systems would be found to be inadequate, with many schools failing. And if that happens, the worst schools would be lost in the crowd. The resources and energy required to reform them would probably be dissipated. For these schools, a poorly designed federal rule can be worse than no rule at all.[2]

11. "It is fair to say that no more cataclysmic event has ever taken place in the history of thought." Even though we have not read the text from which this quote comes, mathematician Morris Kline was referring to a mid-nineteenth-century development in mathematics. To what was he *most likely* making such dramatic reference? Why was it so important in the history of thought?

* * *

In an essay designed to stimulate thought and discussion on assessing quantitative literacy (QL), why not start with a little concrete provocation: an attempt to suggest the content of questions such an assessment should contain? (Later I will suggest why the typical form of mathematics assessment—a "secure" quiz/test/examination—can produce invalid inferences about students' QL ability, an argument that undercuts the overall value of my quiz, too.)

Note that the questions on my quiz relate to the various proposed definitions of QL offered in *Mathematics and Democracy: The Case for Quantitative Literacy* (hereafter "case statement").[3] As part of a working definition, the case statement identified 10 overlapping elements of quantitative literacy:

A. Confidence with Mathematics

B. Cultural Appreciation

C. Interpreting Data

D. Logical Thinking

E. Making Decisions

F. Mathematics in Context

G. Number Sense

H. Practical Skills

I. Prerequisite Knowledge

J. Symbol Sense

to which I would peg my quiz questions categorically as follows:

1.	Statistical Tie	C, E, F, H
2.	Fragile Proof	A, D, I
3.	Investment Estimate	E, F, G, H
4.	Discover or Invent	A, B, D, I
5.	AIDS Data	C, F, G, I
6.	Social Security	A, B, D, E, G, H
7.	Silly Proof	D, I
8.	Solar System	C, E, F, G, H
9.	Axioms and Truth	D, I, J
10.	Testing Memo	C, D, E, F, H
11.	Cataclysmic	B

If we wish for the sake of mental ease to reduce the 10 overlapping elements of quantitative literacy to a few phrases, I would propose two: *realistic mathematics in context* and *mathematics in perspective*. Both of these can be summed up by a familiar phrase: quantitative literacy is about mathematical understanding, not merely technical proficiency. Certainly, the call for a more realistic approach to mathematics via the study of numbers in context is at the heart of the case for QL. The importance of context is underscored repeatedly in *Mathematics and Democracy*,[4] and not only in the case statement:

> In contrast to mathematics, statistics, and most other school subjects, quantitative literacy is inseparable from its context. In this respect it is more like writing than like algebra, more like speaking than like history. Numeracy has no special content of its own, but inherits its content from its context.[5]

> . . . mathematics focuses on climbing the ladder of abstraction, while quantitative literacy clings to context. Mathematics asks students to rise above context, while quantitative literacy asks students to stay in context. Mathematics is about general principles that can be applied in a range of contexts; quantitative literacy is about seeing every context through a quantitative lens.[6]

But what exactly is implied here for assessment, despite the surface appeal of the contrast? To assess QL, we need to make the idea of "context" (and "realistic") concrete and functional. What exactly *is* a context? In what sense does mathematics "rise above context" while QL asks students to "stay in context"? Does context refer to the content area in which we do QL (as suggested by one of the essays in *Mathematics and Democracy*[7]) or does context refer to the conditions under which we are expected to use mathematical abilities in any content area? If QL is "more like writing," should we conclude that current writing assessments serve as good models for contextualized assessment? Or might not the *opposite* be the case: the contextual nature of writing is regularly undercut by the canned, bland, and secure one-shot writing prompts used in all large-scale tests of writing? If context is by definition unique, can we *ever* have standardized tests "in context"? In other words, is "assessing performance in context" a contradiction in terms?

What about assessing for mathematics in perspective, our other capsule summary of QL? As quiz questions 2, 4, 9, and 11 suggest, such an assessment represents a decidedly unorthodox approach to teaching and assessment for grades 10 to 14. Some readers of this essay no doubt reacted to those questions by thinking, "Gee, aren't those only appropriate for graduate students?" But such a reaction may only reveal how far we are from understanding how to teach and assess for understanding. We certainly do not flinch from asking high school students to read and derive important meaning from Shakespeare's *Macbeth,* even though our adult hunch might be that students lack the psychological and literary wisdom to "truly" understand what they read. Reflection and meaning making are central to the learning process, even if it takes years to produce significant results. Why should mathematics assessment be any different?

In fact, I have often explored questions 4 and 9 on the nature of "givens" and proof with high school mathematics classes, with great results, through such questions as: Which came first: a game or its rules? Can you change the rules and still have it be the same game? Which geometry best describes the space you experience in school and the space on the surface of the earth? Then why is Euclid's the one we study? In one tenth-grade class, a student with the worst grades (as I later found out from the surprised teacher) eagerly volunteered to do research on the history of rule changes in his favorite sports, to serve as fodder for the next class discussion on "core" versus changeable rules. (That discussion, coincidentally, led to inquiry into the phrase "spirit versus letter of the law"—a vital idea in United States history—based on the use of that phrase in a ruling made by the president of baseball's American League in the famous George Brett pine-tar bat incident 20 years ago.)

I confess that making mathematics more deliberately meaningful, and then assessing students' meaning making (as we do in any humanities class), is important to me. Although some readers sympathetic to the case statement may disagree, they only need sit in mathematics classrooms for a while (as I have done over the past 20 years) to see that too many teachers of mathematics fail to offer students a clear view of what mathematics *is* and why it matters

intellectually. Is it any accident that student performance on tests is so poor and that so few people take upper-level mathematics courses?

Without anchoring mathematics on a foundation of fascinating issues and "big ideas," there is no intellectual rationale or clear goal for the student. This problem is embodied in the role of the textbook. Instead of being a resource in the service of broader and defensible priorities, in mathematics classes the textbook *is* the course. I encourage readers to try this simple assessment of the diagnosis: ask any mathematics student midyear, "So, what are the few really big ideas in this course? What are the key questions? Given the mathematics you are currently learning, what does it enable you to do or do better that you could not do without it?" The answers will not yield mathematics teachers much joy. By teaching that mathematics is mere unending symbol manipulation, all we do is induce innumeracy.

Quiz question 11 interests me the most in this regard because, whether or not I agree with Kline, I would be willing to bet that not more than one in 100 highly educated people know anything about the development in question—even if I were to give the hint of "Bolyai and Lobachevski." More important, most would be completely taken aback by Kline's language: how can any development in mathematics be intellectually cataclysmic? (I can say without exaggeration that I was utterly roused to a life of serious intellectual work by becoming immersed in the controversies and discoveries Kline refers to. I had no idea that mathematics could be so controversial, so thought provoking, so important.)

Regardless of my idiosyncratic St. John's College experience, should not all students consider the meaning of the skills they learn? That is what a liberal education is all about: So what? What of it? Why does it matter? What is its value? What is assumed? What are the limits of this "truth"? These are questions that a student must regularly ask. In this respect, quantitative literacy is no different from reading literacy: assessment must seek more than just decoding ability. We need evidence of fluent, thoughtful meaning making, as Peter T. Ewell noted in his interview in *Mathematics and Democracy.*[8]

Talking about quantitative literacy as part of liberal education may make the problem seem quaint or "academic" in the pejorative sense. The QL case statement is in fact *radical,* in the colloquial and mathematical sense of that term. As these opening musings suggest, we need to question the time-honored testing (and teaching) practices currently used in *all* mathematics classes. We are forced to return to our very roots—about teaching, about testing, about what mathematics is and why we teach it to nonspecialists—if the manifesto on quantitative literacy is to be realized, not merely praised.

The result of students' endless exposure to typical tests is a profound lack of understanding about what mathematics is: "Perhaps the greatest difficulty in the whole area of mathematics concerns students' misapprehension of what is actually at stake when they are posed a problem. . . . [S]tudents are nearly always searching for [how] to follow the algorithm. . . . Seeing mathematics as a way of understanding the world . . . is a rare occurrence."[9] Surely this has more to do with enculturation via the demands of school, than with some innate limitation.[10]

Putting it this way at the outset properly alerts readers to a grim truth: this reform is *not* going to be easy. QL is a Trojan horse, promising great gifts to educators but in fact threatening all mainstream testing and grading practices in all the disciplines, but especially mathematics. The implications of contextualized and meaningful assessment in QL challenge the very conception of "test" as we understand and employ that term. Test "items" posed under standardized conditions are decontextualized by design.

These issues create a big caveat for those cheery reformers who may be thinking that the solution to quantitative illiteracy is simply to add more performance-based assessments to our repertoire of test items. The need is not for performance tests (also out of context)—most teacher, state, and commercial tests have added some—but for an altogether different approach to assessment. Specifically, assessment must be designed to cause questioning (not just "plug and chug" responses to arid prompts); to teach (and not just test) which ideas and performances really matter; and to demonstrate what it means to *do* mathematics. The case statement challenges us to finally solve the problem highlighted by John Dewey and the progressives (as Cuban notes[11]), namely, to make school no longer isolated from the world. Rather, as the case statement makes clear, we want to regularly assess student work with numbers and numerical ideas in the field (or in virtual realities with great verisimilitude).

What does such a goal imply? On the surface, the answer is obvious: we need to see evidence of learners' abilities to use mathematics in a distinctive and complicated situation. In other words, the challenge is to assess students' abilities to bring to bear a repertoire of ideas and skills to a specific situation, applied with good judgment and high standards. In QL, we are after something akin to the "test" faced by youthful soccer players in fluid games after they have learned some discrete moves via drills, or the "test" of the architect trying to make a design idea fit the constraints of property, location, budget, client style, and zoning laws.

Few of us can imagine such a system fully blown, never mind construct one. Our habits and our isolation—from one another, from peer review, from review by the wider world—keep mathematics assessment stuck in its ways. As with any habit, the results of design mimic the tests we experienced as students. The solu-

tion, then, depends on a team design approach, working against clear and obligatory design standards. In other words, to avoid reinventing only what we know, assessment design needs to become more public and subject to disinterested review—in a word, more professional.

This is in fact the chief recommendation for improving mathematics teaching in *The Teaching Gap,* based on a process used widely in Japanese middle schools.[12] I can report that although such an aim may at first seem threatening to academic prerogative, for the past 10 years we have trained many dozens of high school and college faculties to engage in this kind of group design and peer review against design standards, without rancor or remorse. (Academic freedom does not provide cover for assessment malpractice: a test and the grading of it are not valid simply because a teacher says that they are.)

Thus the sweeping reform needed to make QL a reality in school curriculum and assessment is as much about the reinvention of the job description of "teacher" and the norms of the educational workplace as it is about developing new tests. To honor the case statement is to end the policies and practices that make schooling more like a secretive and austere medieval guild than a profession.[13] The change would be welcome; I sketch some possibilities below.

What We Assess Depends on Why We Assess

Any discussion of assessment must begin with the question of purpose and audience: for what —and whose—purposes are we assessing? What are the standards and end results sought and by whom? What exactly do we seek evidence of and what should that evidence enable us and the learners to do?

These are not simple or inconsequential questions. As I have argued elsewhere, in education we have often sacrificed the primary client (the learner) in the name of accountability.[14] Students' needs too often have been sacrificed to teachers' need for ease of grading; teachers' needs as coach too often have been sacrificed to the cost and logistical constraints imposed by audits testing for accountability or admissions. Rather than being viewed as a key element in ongoing feedback cycles of learning to perform, testing is viewed as something that takes place *after* each bit of teaching is over to see who got it and who did not, done in the most efficient manner possible, before we move on in the linear syllabus, regardless of results.

If there is an axiom at the heart of this argument it is this: assessment should be first and foremost for the learner's sake, designed and implemented to provide useful feedback to the learner (and teacher-coach) on worthy tasks to make improved performance and ultimate mastery more likely.[15] This clearly implies that the assessment must be built on a foundation of realistic tasks, not proxies, and built to be a robust, timely, open, and user-friendly system of feedback and its use. Assessments for other purposes, (e.g., to provide efficiently gained scores for ranking decisions, using secure proxies for real performance) would thus have to be perpetually scrutinized to be sure that a secondary purpose does not override the learner's right to more educative assessment.

We understand this in the wider world. Mathematicians working for the U.S. Census Bureau are paid to work on situated problems on which their performance appraisals depend. We do not keep testing their mathematical virtuosity, using secure items, to determine whether they get a raise based merely on what they know. Athletes play many games, under many different conditions, both to test their learning and as an integral part of learning. I perform in concert once a month with my "retro" rock band the *Hazbins* to keep learning how to perform (and to feel the joy from doing so); a score from a judge on the fruits of my guitar lessons, in isolated exercises, would have little value for me. The formal challenge is not an onerous extra exercise but the raison d'être of the enterprise, providing educational focus and incentive.

Yet, most tests fail to meet this basic criterion, designed as they are for the convenience of scorekeepers not players. Consider:

- The test is typically unknown until the day of the assessment.

- We do not know how we are doing as we perform.

- Feedback after the performance is neither timely nor user friendly. We wait days, sometimes weeks, to find out how we did; and the results are often presented in terms that do not make sense to the performer or sometimes even to the teacher-coach.

- The test is usually a proxy for genuine performance, justifiable and sensible only to psychometricians.

- The test is designed to be scored quickly, with reliability, whether or not the task has intellectual value or meaning for the performer.

In mathematics, the facts are arguably far worse than this dreary general picture suggests. Few tests given today in mathematics classrooms (be they teacher, state, or test-company designed) provide students with performance goals that might provide the incentive to learn or meaning for the discrete facts and skills learned. Typical tests finesse the whole issue of purpose by relying on items that ask for discrete facts or technical skill out of context. What QL requires (and any truly defensible mathematics program

should require), however, is assessment of complex, realistic, meaningful, and creative performance.

Whether or not my particular opening quiz questions appeal to you, I hope the point of them is clear: Evidence of "realistic use," crucial to QL, requires that students confront challenges like those faced in assessment of reading literacy: Hmm, what does this mean? What kind of problem is this? What kind of response is wanted (and how might my answer be problematic)? What is assumed here, and is it a wise assumption? What feedback do I need to seek if I am to know whether I am on the right track?[16] Assessment of QL requires tasks that challenge the learner's judgment, not just exercises that cue the learner.

The same holds true for assessing students' understanding of mathematics in perspective. Students may be able to prove that there are 180 degrees in any triangle, but it does not follow that they understand what they have done. Can they explain why the proof works? Can they explain why it matters? Can they argue the crucial role played by the parallel postulate in making the theorem possible, the 2000-year controversy about that postulate (and the attempts by many mathematicians to prove or alter it), and the eventual realization growing from that controversy that there could be other geometries, as valid as Euclid's, in which the 180-degree theorem does *not* hold true?

As it stands now, almost all students graduate from college never knowing of this history, of the existence of other valid geometries, and of the intellectual implications. In other words, they lack perspective on the Euclidean geometry that they have learned. When they do not really grasp what an axiom is and why we have it, and how other systems might and do exist, can they really be said to understand geometry at all?

What is at stake here is a challenge to a long-standing habit conveyed by a system that is not based on well-thought through purposes. This custom was perhaps best summarized by Lauren Resnick and David Resnick over 15 years ago: "American students are the most tested but the least examined students in the world."[27] As the case statement and the Resnick's remark suggest, what we need is to probe more than quiz, to ask for creative solutions, not merely correct answers.[18]

What Is Realistic Assessment and Why Is It Needed?

Regardless of the nettlesome questions raised by the call for improved quantitative literacy, one implication for assessment is clear enough: QL demands evidence of students' abilities to grapple with realistic or "situated" problems. But what is unrealistic about most mathematics tests if they have content validity and tap into skills and facts actually needed in mathematics? The short answer is that typical tests are mere proxies for real performance. They amount to sideline drills as opposed to playing the game on the field.

The aims in the case statement are not new ones. Consider this enthusiastic report about a modest attempt to change college admissions testing at Harvard a few years back. Students were asked to perform a set of key physics experiments by themselves and have their high school physics teacher certify the results, while also doing some laboratory work in front of the college's professors:

> The change in the physics requirement has been more radical than that in any other subject. . . . For years the college required only such a memory knowledge of physical laws and phenomena as could be got from a . . . textbook. . . . [U]nder the best of circumstances the pupil's thinking was largely done for him. By this method of teaching . . . his memory was loaded with facts of which he might or might not have any real understanding, while he did very little real thinking. . . . This was a system of teaching hardly calculated to train his mind, or to awaken an interest in [physics].

> How different is the present attitude of the college! It now publishes a descriptive list of forty experiments, covering the elementary principles of mechanics, sound, light, heat, and electricity. These, so far as possible, are quantitative experiments; that is, they require careful measurements from which the laws and principles of physics can be reasoned out. Where, for any reason, such measurements are impossible, the experiments are merely illustrative; but even from these the student must reason carefully to arrive at the principles which they illustrate. The student must perform these experiments himself in a laboratory, under the supervision of a teacher. He must keep a record of all his observations and measurements, together with the conclusions which he draws from them. The laboratory book in which this record is kept, bearing the certificate of his instructor, must be presented for critical examination when he comes to [the admissions office]. In addition to this, he is tested by a written paper and by a laboratory examination.[19]

This account was written about Harvard in the *Atlantic Monthly*—in 1892! We know what happened later, of course. The College Board was invented to make admissions testing more streamlined and standardized (and thereby, it must be said, more equitable for students around the country, as well as less of a hassle for colleges), but at another cost, as it turns out.

Although the century-old physics test may not have been situated in a real-world challenge, it was a noble attempt to see if students could actually *do* science. This is surely where assessment for QL must begin: Can the student do mathematics? Can the student confront inherently messy and situated problems well? That is a different question from "does the student know various mathematical 'moves' and facts?"

Some folks have regretted or resented my long-time use of the word "authentic" in describing the assessments we need.[20] But the phrase remains apt, I think, if readers recall that one meaning of authentic is "realistic." Conventional mathematics test questions are not authentic because they do not represent the challenges mathematicians face routinely in their work. As noted above, a mathematics test is more like a series of sideline drills than the challenge of playing the game. In fact, mathematics tests are notoriously unrealistic, the source of unending jokes by laypersons about trains heading toward each other on the same track, and the source of the wider world's alienation from mathematics. (Research is needed, I think, to determine whether simplistic test items are so abstracted from the world as to be needlessly hard for all but the symbolically inclined.)

How should we define "realistic"?[21] An assessment task, problem, or project is realistic if it is faithful to how mathematics is actually practiced when real people are challenged by problems involving numeracy. The task(s) must reflect the ways in which a person's knowledge and abilities are tested in real-world situations. Such challenges

- *ask us to "do" the subject.* Students have to use knowledge and skills wisely and effectively to solve unstructured problems, not simply grind out an algorithm, formula, or number.

- *require judgment and innovation.* Instead of merely reciting, restating, or replicating through demonstration the lessons taught and skills learned, students have to explore projects in mathematics, using their repertoire of knowledge and skills.

- *reflect the contexts in which adults are tested in the workplace, in civic life, and in personal life.* Contexts involve specific situations that have particular constraints, purposes, and audiences.

- *allow appropriate opportunities to rehearse, practice, consult resources, solicit feedback, refine performances, and revise products.* Secrecy, enforced quiet, solitary work, and other artificial constraints imposed by large-scale testing are minimized.

Nothing new here. Benjamin Bloom and his colleagues made the same point almost 50 years ago, in their account of application and synthesis:

> [S]ituations new to the student or situations containing new elements as compared to the situation in which the abstrac-

tion was learned . . . . Ideally we are seeking a problem which will test the extent to which an individual has learned to apply the abstraction in a practical way.[22] . . . [A] type of divergent thinking [where] it is unlikely that the right solution to a problem can be set in advance.[23]

In later materials, Bloom and his colleagues characterized synthesis tasks in language that makes clearer what we must do to make the assessment more realistic:

> The problem, task, or situation involving synthesis should be new or in some way different from those used in instruction. The students . . . may have considerable freedom in redefining it. . . . The student may attack the problem with a variety of references or other available materials as they are needed. Thus synthesis problems may be open-book examinations, in which the student may use notes, the library, and other resources as appropriate. Ideally synthesis problems should be as close as possible to the situation in which a scholar (or artist, engineer, and so forth) attacks a problem he or she is interested in. The time allowed, conditions of work, and other stipulations, should be as far from the typical, controlled examination situation as possible.[24]

Researcher Fred Newmann and his colleagues at the University of Wisconsin have developed a similar set of standards for judging the authenticity of tasks in assessments and instructional work and have used those standards to study instructional and assessment practices around the country.[25] In their view, authentic tasks require:

CONSTRUCTION OF KNOWLEDGE

1. Student organization of information (higher-order skills)

2. Student consideration of alternatives

DISCIPLINED INQUIRY

3. Core disciplinary content knowledge required

4. Core disciplinary processes required

5. Elaborated written communications required to expand understanding

VALUE BEYOND SCHOOL

6. Problems are connected to the world beyond the classroom

7. An audience beyond the school is involved

What do such tasks look like? Compare Figures 1 and 2 below. Figure 1 shows various test questions on an eighth-grade state mathematics test. Six test "items" (the four below and two others) make up the entire set of questions used to assess against the state standard for the students' knowledge of volume. Figure 2 shows an example of a situated performance that requires students to use their understanding of that same knowledge effectively. (The second test does not replace the first test; it supplements it.)

Let us cast this contrast in terms of validity of inference. We are being asked to consider: what can we infer from good performance on the four test items? I would certainly grant the conventional premise that a student who gets most of these questions right is more likely to have control over the discrete skills and facts of this sub-domain than a student who gets most of them incorrect.

What about evidence of QL? Can we infer the likelihood that a student who got all the state test questions correct will likely do well on the second contextualized problem? Not a very plausible inference, I would claim, backed in part by data from a pilot mathematics portfolio project we ran for the Commission on Standards and Accountability in 15 districts that took the state test that had these test items.[26] The scores on the task in Figure 2 were low across the board—averaging 2 on a rubric scale of 6, with little range in scores within and across quite varied districts. This is not what we would expect, and it underscores the validity problems lurking in an exclusive reliance on conventional test items.

The second approach permits us to see evidence of the student's thoughtful use of knowledge and skill. It does *not* obviate the need for the traditional items. But it is simply untrue, as many people defending the status quo claim, that in light of the first test, the second is unnecessary—and especially not worth the hassle and expense.

Figure 1: State Test Items, Eighth-Grade Geometry

34. What is the surface area of the cylinder shown below?

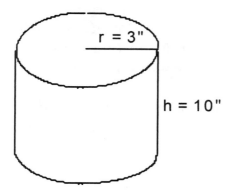

    A   13 π square inches

    B   18 π square inches

    C   60 π square inches

    D   78 π square inches

35. A can of Goofy Grape Soda has a diameter of 5 cm and a height of 10 cm. What is the volume of the can of soda?

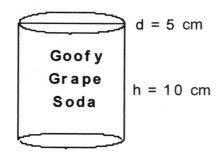

    A   78.50 cm^3

    B   157.00 cm^3

    C   196.25 cm^3

    D   392.50 cm^3

36. What is the volume of the cone?

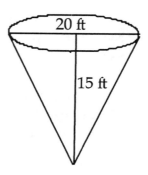

    A   4,710 cu ft

    B   1,570 cu ft

    C   942 cu ft

    D   300 cu ft

37. The area of the base of a triangular pyramid was doubled. How does the new volume compare with the old volume?

    A   one-fourth

    B   one-half

    C   two times

    D   four times

Figure 2: A More Realistic Performance Task on the Same Content

That's a Wrap. You are in charge of the gift wrapping of purchases in a large department store. On average, 24,000 customers make clothing purchases in your store each year. About 15 percent of the customers want their purchases gift wrapped. In a month, the store typically sells 65 jackets, 250 shirts, 480 pairs of pants, and 160 hats. All boxes cost the same price per square foot of flat cardboard—$1, and wrapping paper costs 26 cents per yard. Each roll of gift wrap is one yard wide and 100 yards long.

As the manager of gift wrap, you naturally want to plan for the year's gift wrapping costs and you want to save money where possible. What would be the best box shape for pants, shirts, jackets, and hats that requires the least amount of box and gift wrap?

Your task: Recommend to the purchasing agent in a written report, with graphs and models:
- What size boxes should be ordered for pants, shirts, jackets, and hats when ordered separately;
- The number of rolls of wrapping paper; and
- The approximate cost of wrapping paper for a year's worth of sales of pants, shirts, jackets, and hats.

Points to consider:
1. When the clothes are folded, how big does the box need to be? Of course, the way you fold makes a difference as to what shape box you could use without messing up the clothes.
2. Experiment with measuring, folding, and boxing clothes in the typical light-cardboard boxes clothes come in (or make boxes out of large pieces of paper for the experiment).
3. Some package shapes are easier than others to wrap, with minimal waste. Yet, some easy-to-wrap shapes require more paper to wrap, although less is wasted. Are there any rules or generalizations you can come up with about the amount of paper a box shape ideally requires versus the waste of paper that might be eliminated if a different-shaped box were used? Or are the savings in using the easier-to-wrap box offset by the increased costs in wrapping the new shape?
4. No one can wrap a package without wasting some paper. Figure in the cost of the extra paper and the unused or wasted paper on the roll required, given the needs of real-world wrappers in your sales force.

Your work will be judged against the following criteria:
- Effectiveness in meeting the challenge set
- The appropriateness of the mathematical and logical reasoning used
- The clarity of your communication
- The accuracy of your work

Four scoring guides for each of the criteria are used to judge your work.

Realism and Context

Ultimately, realism hinges on situational fidelity—context—not merely whether the task is open-ended or "hands on." QL assessment asks: Can you draw on a rich repertoire to address this complicated problem, mindful of the particular—perhaps unique—features of context? The packaging example in Figure 2 (and QL aims more generally) seek evidence of students' understanding in situations, not their technical skills in isolation. "Do you understand what to do *here,* in this new situation, and why that approach might work?" "Do you grasp the significance of both the problem and the answer?" "Can you generalize from your experience, and how might that generalization be flawed or too sweeping?" These are the kinds of questions we must ask in the assessment of QL. It is, after all, what we mean by "transfer," the Holy Grail in education.

Our failure to attend to contextualization in mathematics education can lead to humorous results. Consider the infamous National Assessment of Educational Progress (NAEP) bus problem: "An army bus holds 36 soldiers. If 1128 soldiers are being bused to their training site, how many buses are needed? Only 24 percent of eighth graders could answer it correctly. Alas, about the same percentage of the respondents answered "31 remainder 12." No story better illustrates the habits of teaching, testing, and learning whereby mathematics floats in a netherworld of unmoored abstractions.

Context matters, so it must come to matter in day in and day out assessment. Let us have unending problems that force students to ponder its impact. Consider, for example, how the particulars of the situation affect the use of mathematics in the following problem:

> Manufacturers want to spend as little as possible, not only on the product but also on packing and shipping it to stores. They want to *minimize* the cost of production of their packaging, and they want to *maximize* the amount of what is packaged inside (to keep handling and postage costs down: the more individual packages you ship the more it costs).

> Suppose you are an engineer for M&M's. The manager of the shipping department has found the perfect material for shipping (a piece of poster board you will be given). She is asking each engineering work group to help solve a problem: *What completely closed container, built out of the given materials, will hold the largest volume of M&M's for safe and economical shipping?*

> You will need to prove to company executives that the shape and dimensions of your group's container idea maximize the volume. You will need to turn in a convincing written report to the managers, making your case and supplying all important data and formulas. Build multiple models out of the material to illustrate your solution. The models are not proof; they will illustrate the claims you will offer in your report. Your group will also be asked to make a three-minute oral report at the next staff meeting. The reports will be judged for accuracy, thoroughness, and persuasiveness.

Merely providing the correct mathematical answers is beside the point here. We might say without stretching the truth too much that the seemingly correct mathematics answer (the sphere) is the wrong answer here. In fact, I have seen seventh graders provide better answers to this problem than calculus students, with more insight yet limited tools.

Realism thus is not merely about access to performance-based test questions. Realism refers more to verisimilitude of content-process-situation-task-goal constraints. Most performance-based test questions are typically unrealistic because they strip context to a bare minimum, in the service of isolating the skills to be tested. To focus on context is to do justice to the fluid, ambiguous, and ill-structured situations in which typical adult performance invariably occurs, in which the answer is often "Well, it depends . . . or "Well, if . . . then . . . else . . . then . . ."

The humor in the NAEP bus problem should not blind us to the harm of failing to assess in contexts. Decontextualized training and assessment lead to unfortunate, even fatal results. Consider this complaint, made a few years back in a federal report criticizing the testing program of a national organization: "These programs are lacking in 'real world' scenarios and result in non-thinking performance, where the ability of the student to demonstrate a mastery of complex problems, good judgment, situational awareness, . . . and leadership skills have all been removed." The sobering fact is that this is not an accrediting report about a school's program but a Federal Aviation Administration (FAA) report concerning deficiencies in the annual pilot testing and rectification program for a major U.S. airline. It is even more sobering to realize that the FAA is criticizing the airline for its use of airplane simulators in annual re-certification testing—a challenge more realistic than almost all school testing in mathematics today.[27]

How then should we proceed with our design work? Context is usefully addressed in assessment by reference to the mantra at the heart of process writing: worry about specific purpose and audience. Realistic challenges always have real (or virtual) purposes and real (or virtual) audiences. We can add other criteria and set out questions that can be used as design standards for the building of context in QL assessment:

- Is there an overriding performance goal to guide action that is obvious to the student?

- Is there a distinct audience for the work whose needs and feedback can appropriately focus the work and adjustments en route?

- Are the options and constraints in the task realistic or arbitrary?

- Are appropriate resources available? Does the task require an efficient as well as effective use of notes, materials, and repertoire of skills and concepts?

- Is secrecy concerning performance goals, possible strategy, criteria, and standards minimized?

- Is the setting realistically noisy and messy—sufficiently ill-structured and ill-defined that the learner must constantly consider what the question really is and what the key variables are?

- Are there apt opportunities to self-assess, to get lots of feedback, and to self-adjust en route as needed?

In *The Understanding by Design Handbook*, we summarize these design questions by the acronym GRASPS:

- What is the performer's *goal* in this scenario? What must he or she accomplish?

- What *role* does the performer play in this situation?

- Who is the primary *audience* for the performer's work?

- What is the *situation*? What conditions/opportunities/constraints exist?

- What are the particular *performances/products* that must be produced?

- Against what *standards* and criteria will the work be judged?[28]

We also developed a six-faceted view of how understanding (in context) manifests itself.[29] For example, when we truly understand, we

- Can *explain, make connections, offer good theories:* We can make sense of what we experience. We can "show our work" and defend it. We can provide thorough, supported, and justifiable accounts of phenomena, facts, and data. We can answer such questions as: Why is that so? What explains such

events? What accounts for such an effect? How can we prove it? To what is this connected? How does this work? What is implied? Why do you think so?

- Can *interpret:* Tell meaningful stories; offer apt translations; provide a revealing historical or personal dimension to ideas and events; make it personal or accessible through images, anecdotes, analogies, models. We can answer such questions as: What does it mean? Why does it matter? What of it? What does it illustrate or illuminate in human experience? How does it relate to me? What does and does not make sense here?

- Can *apply:* Effectively use and adapt what we know in diverse contexts. We can answer such questions as: How and where can we use this knowledge, skill, process? In what ways do people apply this understanding in the world beyond the school? How should my thinking and action be modified to meet the demands of this particular situation?

- Have *perspective:* See multiple points of view, with critical eyes and ears; see the big picture. We can answer such questions as: From whose point of view? From which vantage point? What is assumed or tacit that needs to be made explicit and considered? How is this justified or warranted? Is there adequate evidence? Is it reasonable? What are the strengths and weaknesses of the idea? Is it plausible? What are its limits?

- Can *empathize:* Get inside, find value in what others might find odd, alien, or implausible; perceive sensitively, enter the mind and heart of others. We can answer such questions as: How does it seem to you? What do they see that I do not? What do I need to experience if I am to understand? What was the artist, writer, or performer feeling, seeing, and trying to make me feel and see?

- Show *self-knowledge:* Perceive the personal style, prejudices, projections, and habits of mind that both shape and impede our own understanding; we are aware of what we do not understand, why it is so hard to understand. What are my blind spots? What am I prone to misunderstand because of prejudice, habit, style? How does who I am influence how I understand and do not understand?

As this summary suggests, the idea of "context" is inseparable from what it means to understand. Three of the six facets described above explicitly warn us to attend to context: application, perspective, and empathy. Other colloquial language also makes this clear. We want students to develop *tact* in the older sense of that term as used by William James in his *Talks to Teachers:* "sensitivity to the demands of the particular situation"[30] Thus, I would argue, understanding is a usefully ambiguous term: it properly asks us to consider both the intellectual content and the interpersonal wisdom needed here, now, in this case.

Thus the goal in assessing QL is not merely to determine whether students can use mathematical knowledge in problems but whether they can communicate with others about that understanding and be held accountable for the consequences of the use of their knowledge. Our failure to assess using real-world consequences of the work itself and to assess students' defense of their choices and results (as opposed to giving an answer and waiting for scores returned by teachers or test companies) may explain a ubiquitous phenomenon that greatly angers the general public: students' failure to take an adequate interest in work quality and results.

Here is a vivid example of the problem. A graphics design teacher at a vocational high school brought in a real potential client for design jobs, and the students were asked to bid on the work by providing mock-ups and price quotes. They listened to the man explain his product needs, they went to work (without asking questions), and they worked very hard, much harder than usual, to produce what they thought he wanted. He came back the next week, inspected the work, and politely turned down all the efforts. The students' reaction? Anger. "We worked so hard!. . ." Yes, but did they ever check with the client to make sure they were on the right track? Did they put a variety of design styles before the client to tease out his tastes, as all good designers do? No. The teacher had taught these students technical skills but not how to accomplish results in the marketplace. This illustrates the need to take seriously all six facets of contextual understanding. To find evidence of students' understanding, we need problems that *require* such understanding.

Consider the following transformations of a conventional high school unit, based on a well-known textbook, to see how assessment of course content can be approached more contextually without sacrificing rigor:

THE ORIGINAL UNIT, SUMMARIZED:

Topic: Surface Area and Volume (geometry)
Knowledge and skill sought:

- How to calculate surface area and volume for various three-dimensional figures

- Know and use Cavalieri's Principle to compare volumes

- Know and use other volume and surface area formulas to compare shapes

Assessments, all derived from the University of Chicago School Mathematics Project geometry textbook:

- Odd-numbered problems in Chapter 10 Review, pp. 516–519

- Progress self-test, p. 515

- Homework: each third question in the sub-chapter reviews

- Completion of one "exploration"

- Exploration 22, p. 482—"Containers holding small amounts can be made to appear to hold more than they do by making them long and thin. Give some examples."

- Exploration 25, p. 509—"Unlike a cone or cylinder, it is impossible to make an accurate two-dimensional net for a sphere. For this reason, maps of earth are distorted. The Mercator projection is one way to show the earth. How is this projection made?"

The assessments, **revised:**

- Consult to the United Nations on the least controversial two-dimensional map of the world, after having undertaken Exploration 22.

- Investigate the relationship of the surface areas and volume of various containers (e.g., tuna fish cans, cereal boxes, Pringles, candy packages, etc.). Do they maximize volume? Minimize cost? If not, why not? Consider what nonmathematical variables determine container shape and size.

What we are really seeking evidence of in context-bound assessment is a combination of technical skill and good judgment in its use. A "good judge," said Dewey, "has a sense of the relative values of the various features of a perplexing situation," has "horse sense," has the capacity to "estimate, appraise, and evaluate," and has "tact and discernment." Those who judge well, whether it be in matters of numeracy or human interaction, bring expertise to bear intelligently and concretely on unique and always incompletely understood events. Thus, merely "acquiring information can never develop the power of judgment. Development of judgment is in spite of, not because of, methods of instruction that emphasize simple learning. . . . [The student] cannot get power of judgment excepting as he is continually exercised in forming and testing judgments."[31]

It is noteworthy that fields with the incentive to better merge theory and praxis (engineering, medicine, business, law, etc.) have gravitated to the case- or problem-based learning method of instruction and assessment, in which context is key. Yet, it is still rare in mathematics testing to ask students to confront questions such as quiz questions 1, 3, 5, and 6 until very late in a mathematics career, if at all.

Why is this so? I believe part of the answer is a tacit (and false) learning theory that dominates mathematics education, which might be vocalized as follows: "First, you have to learn all the basics, in the logical order of the elements (thus disconnected from experiential and historical context), using only paper and pencil; *then* you can ask important questions and confront 'real' problems." By that argument, of course, we would never allow little kids to play the difficult game of soccer until years of deskbound study or let medical students make rounds to see patients. This is simply un-thought through pedagogy—a bad habit—abetted by overreliance on textbooks, built as they are on the logic of mathematics ideas instead of the logic of pedagogy to maximize the understanding of those ideas.[32]

In no area of human performance is it true that years of drills and facts must precede all attempts to perform. That view is truly premodern. And as noted above, the validity of tests that follow from this assumption is open to question: evidence of competence cannot be had from exclusive reliance on results from "sideline drills," for the same reason that ability to cite the textbook meaning of a symptom is not an accurate predictor of performance ability in medicine.

Assessment of QL requires challenges that are essentially not well structured or even well defined; problems that are, well, *problematic*. As in book literacy, evidence of students' ability to play the messy game of the discipline depends on seeing whether they can handle tasks without specific cues, prompts, or simplifying scaffolds from the teacher-coach or test designer. In QL, students confront situations that have no signs pointing to the right algorithm or solution path. This raises havoc with traditional psychometrics because it is the exact opposite of an effective test "item."

Because real problems are messy and not amenable to unequivocal final answers, we need to see how students respond to such uncertainties metacognitively. A realistic assessment would thus always ask for a self-assessment. "How well did your proposed answer or solution work? What were the strengths and weaknesses of that approach? What adjustments need to be made, based on your approach and the resultant effects?" Unless they confront such questions, students will continue to exit formal schooling with the belief that merely giving back what was taught is a sufficient indicator of numeracy, or believing that performance is a ritual response to an academic prompt. This is why Norm Frederiksen, a former senior researcher at Educational Testing Service, declared that the real bias of the SAT was not related to content but to format: the neat and clean character of test items versus the messy and uncertain character of the challenges put before us in life.[33]

Genuine fluency always demands creativity, not "plug and chug." It is worth recalling that Bloom and his colleagues (who developed the *Taxonomy of Educational Objectives*) described "synthesis" as always "creative," and "application" as requiring "novel situations or problems."[34] Fifty years on, the *Taxonomy* still has not achieved its purpose. Two generations (or more) of mathematics educators have misunderstood what Bloom meant. Understanding *why* must be part of the QL agenda, too. Usiskin speculated in *Mathematics and Democracy* that the problem is training. Most teachers think of "application" as "word problems":

> The many examples of the need for quantitative literacy offered in the case statement can easily lead us to wonder why so little has been accomplished. I believe the problem relates in part to a perception by the majority of mathematics teachers about the "word problems" or "story problems" they studied in high school. . . . These problems have little to do with real situations and they invoke fear and avoidance in many students. So it should come as no surprise that current teachers imagine that "applications" are as artificial as the word problems they encountered as students, and feel that mathematics beyond simple arithmetic has few real applications.[35]

We see the urgency of this issue more clearly now in the fallout from the disputed Florida election results. The idea of "margin of error" was made real and high stakes; the consequences of failing to consider the lessons of past, close local elections have come back to haunt us. (In retrospect, it seems amazing that there was no procedure for considering a very close election as a statistical tie that then would call forth additional means for fairly filling the office in question.) The consequences of a person's work need to be *felt in context*—in the same way they are on the playing field or in the auditorium. A challenge, then, is to engineer assessment so that students have far more direct and powerful experiences of the actual effects of their work—on themselves, on other people, and on situations, be they real or virtual. We need an intellectual Outward Bound, as I like to call it, or better assessment software that is more like *Oregon Trail* than *Reader Rabbit*.

Core Assessment Tasks

Because so few current mathematics assessments seem to pass muster, I would propose that we commission a national team of experts to develop the equivalent of the Olympic decathlon in mathematics: 100 key tasks, forming the mathematics "centalon." The parallel is apt. Around the time Harvard was trying out its new physics performance tests, the modern Olympics were being invented. One of the challenges faced was an assessment problem related to our concern. The task was to design a performance test, over a few days, for well-rounded "athleticism" in all its manifestations, with no favoritism given to speed, strength, hand-eye coordination, or stamina. Thus, the decathlon.

What would be the equivalent in mathematics? We need to know: too few teachers can today answer these questions: What are the most important and representative problems in mathematics? What types of complex challenges should we seek evidence of to deem a graduate quantitatively literate? What might be 100 performances at the heart of QL in which high school students and college underclassmen should be certified, along the 1892 Harvard model? What genres of problems (again to use the parallel with reading and writing literacy) sum up the domain of real performance that a highly literate person should be able to master? Too much of the reform debate has been cast in terms of mathematics content. In light of the bad habits and lack of imagination in mathematics assessment, we need a sage account of priority performances and situations.

Lauren Resnick and her colleagues in the New Standards project developed an answer a few years back. Beyond the mix of open-ended and constructed-response questions developed for the standardized examinations, there is a mathematics portfolio to be assembled by students locally. Each student submits evidence of work in conceptual understanding of number and operation, geometry and measurement, and functions and algebra; and exhibits in problem solving, data study, mathematical modeling, design of a physical structure, management and planning, pure mathematical investigation, and history of a mathematical idea. In addition, students provide evidence of 12 discrete skills (e.g., "know how to write a simple computer program to carry out computations to be repeated many times").[36] Apropos the issue of context, under design of a physical structure the guidelines say: "Show that you can design a physical structure that meets given specifications . . . [and] explain how your design meets its purpose and how it can be built within constraints (physical, functional, budgetary, aesthetic)."

An ironic weakness in this approach is that the evidence sought was framed by a very broad-brush and context-less set of guidelines, with no reference to any specific big ideas, core content, or key situations. For example, the guidelines under problem solving say, "Show that you can formulate a variety of meaningful problems . . . use problem-solving strategies to solve non-routine and multi-step problems . . ."—without offering any examples or criteria as to what such problems are. We also gain no sense here of the key questions that lie at the heart of thoughtful numeracy.

Questions offer a key doorway into identifying bigger ideas and more meaningful work. In *Understanding by Design,*[37] we coach faculties in developing "essential questions" for all units, courses, and programs as a way to focus their teaching on more justified intellectual priorities. Sadly and predictably, mathematics teachers have the hardest time of any group doing the work. Indeed, more than a few mathematics teachers have told me there are no big ideas in mathematics. It is a "skills" discipline, they say.[38]

Here, for example, is a draft curricular unit in algebra from a veteran teacher who was trying for the first time to organize his lessons around big ideas:

Course Title: Integrated Mathematics 1
Topics: Linear Equations, Linear Graphs
  Understandings:
    First degree equations give linear graphs.
    Intercepts are zeros.
    Slope intercept form ($y = mx + b$).
    Standard form ($Ax + By = C$).
  Essential Questions:
    What does slope measure?
    How is slope calculated?
    How do you graph a line from an equation?
    How do you write an equation of a line from a graph?

We look in vain here for meaningful issues and challenges that might stimulate student thought or inquiry. But change is occurring. Consider the following responses to a design exercise by a small group of high school mathematics teachers:

Unit goal, with reference to big idea: Students will understand measures of tendency (and other methods for grading, voting, and ranking)

Thought-provoking questions on unit goal:

1. By what mathematical method should grading and rankings be done to be most fair?

2. Should voters be allowed to rank order candidates? Are there defensible alternatives to our voting system?

3. Is the mathematically sound solution always the most objectively fair solution?

Predictable misunderstandings:

1. Computing the "average" or "majority" is the only fair method

2. Mathematics cannot help us resolve differences of opinion about fairness

Interesting investigations:

1. Saylor point system in soccer standings

2. Distributive and rank order voting

3. New grading systems for students (median/standard deviation/throw out high and low, etc.)

Or, consider these thought-provoking and perspective-providing questions generated by the mathematics department at the Tilton School, based on a multiyear effort focused on *Understanding by Design:*[39]

Do mathematical ideas exist separate from the person who understands and can communicate them?

1. What is a quantifiable idea? Is any idea quantifiable? If not, when and why not?

2. How do we determine what makes mathematical ideas true, proven, and/or usable?

3. How do we use mathematical ideas to decipher and explain the world we live in?

4. In what ways is mathematical thinking and logic applicable outside the realm of mathematics? What are the limits or dangers of that extension, if any?

5. In what ways is mathematics rigid, fixed, and systematic? In what ways is mathematics aesthetic, elegant, flexible, and ever expanding?

The Tilton mathematics faculty have committed to address these questions in all their courses. The *Understanding by Design* model requires that the questions be matched by assessments and enabling lessons to ensure that the questions are not idle but integral.

It Is Not the Problems But What We Score that Ultimately Matters

Even the most wonderful, realistic challenges are ruined by foolish scoring and grading practices. Perhaps nothing reveals the need for fundamental reform in mathematics more than the propensity of teachers to use simplistic scoring on one-time test items: the answer is either right or wrong (with partial credit sometimes granted, although with no explicit criteria for points taken off).

But if all understanding is a matter of degree, existing along a continuum and subject to disagreement (we can have different understandings of the same problem), there is much teacher baggage to throw overboard in giving grades and scores. If we seek evidence of a student's explanation of confusing data, what does a range of explanations look like—from the most simplistic to the most sophisticated on any of my 11 quiz questions? For example, what does a novice understanding of Hoops McGinty's basketball planetarium problem of scale or the retirement funds problem look like compared with a sophisticated answer?

We can ask such questions meaningfully precisely because the proposed test questions are by design not technique-unique, unlike almost all current mathematics test questions. QL questions can be asked of high school sophomores or college seniors, with profit, just as writing prompts and soccer games can be used from K–16. We find that when we assess this way, some students with less technical skill propose better solutions than students with more advanced technical knowledge, as in the M&M's problem. We would expect such results if we were assessing for QL, just as we expect and actually find some younger performers in writing whose language is less developed but more powerful than that of older students with more schooling and vocabulary under their belts.

But are teachers of mathematics ready to think this way? Consider the following two student answers to the same problem to see how even an experienced teacher of twelfth-grade mathematics can have difficulty escaping our common habits of testing and grading:

Consider an ice cream sugar cone, 8 cm in diameter and 12 cm high, capped with an 8 cm in diameter sphere of luscious rich triple-chocolate ice cream. If the ice cream melts completely, will the cone overflow or not? How do you know—explain your answer.

Answer 1: We must first find the volume of the cone and the ice cream scoop:

$$v_{cone} = (1/3)\pi r^2 h$$
$$= (1/3)\pi \, 4^2 \times 12$$
$$= 201.06 \text{ cm}^3$$

$$v_{scoop} = (4/3)\pi r^3$$
$$= (4/3)\pi \times (4)^3$$
$$= (4/3) \times 201.06 \text{ cm}^3$$
$$= 268.08 \text{ cm}^3$$

We now see that the scoop of ice cream has a volume that is well over 50 cm more than the cone's volume. Therefore it is unlikely that the melted ice cream could fit completely inside the cone. However, as all ice cream lovers like myself know, there is a certain amount of air within ice cream [therefore experiments would have to be done].

Answer 2: Obviously, the first thing to do would be to plug in the values in the equations for the volume of a cone and sphere [the student performs the same calculations as above]. From this we can see that the ice cream will not fit in the cone.

Now I will compare the two formulas:

$$(4/3)\,\pi r^3 = (1/3)\,\pi r^2 h$$
$$4\pi r^3 = \pi r^2 h$$
$$4\pi r = \pi h$$
$$4r = h$$

From this final comparison, we can see that if the height of the cone is exactly 4 times the radius, the volumes will be equal . . . [The student goes on to explain why there are numerous questions about ice cream in real life that will affect the answer, e.g., Will the ice cream's volume change as it melts? Is it possible to compress ice cream?, etc. He concludes by reminding us that we can only find out via experiment.]

The second explanation is surely more sophisticated, displaying a number of qualities we seek in QL (e.g., attention to context, comfort with numbers and data). The student's analysis is mature in part because it subsumes the particular mathematics problem under a broader one: under what conditions are the volumes of different shapes equal? In the first case, all the student has done is calculate the volumes based on the formulas and the given numbers. The second explanation is mature and indicative of understanding by showing perspective: the student has written a narrative as if he were explaining himself to his teacher—mindful, in a humorous way, of audience and purpose.

Nonetheless, the teacher in question gave these two papers the same grade. Both papers gave the correct mathematical answer, after all. Even more alarming, the second paper was given lower grades than the first paper by a slight majority of middle school mathematics teachers (who seemed to take offense at the student's flippancy) in a national mathematics workshop a few years ago.

Of course, when scoring criteria are unclear, arbitrariness sets in—usually in the form of scoring what is easiest to see or scoring based on the teacher's unexamined and semiconscious habits. That is why learning to score for inter-rater reliability (as is done

with Advanced Placement essays and in state and district tests) is such a vital part of any successful reform effort. Yet over 50 percent of teachers of mathematics in our surveys argued that rubrics are "not needed" in mathematics and that, in any event, such scoring is "too subjective."

What if mathematics teachers routinely had to use multiple criteria with related rubrics in the assessment of performance? Here are five possible criteria, with the top-level descriptor from each rubric (used in the pilot statewide performance assessments in North Carolina, mentioned above) [40]:

- *Mathematical Insight.* Shows a sophisticated understanding of the subject matter involved. The concepts, evidence, arguments, qualifications made, questions posed, and/or methods used are expertly insightful, going well beyond the grasp of the topic typically found at this level of experience. Grasps the essence of the problem and applies the most powerful tools for solving it. The work shows that the student is able to make subtle distinctions and to relate the particular problem to more significant, complex, and/or comprehensive mathematical principles, formulas, or models.

- *Mathematical Reasoning.* Shows a methodical, logical, and thorough plan for solving the problem. The approach and answers are explicitly detailed and reasonable throughout (whether or not the knowledge used is always sophisticated or accurate). The student justifies all claims with thorough argument: counterarguments, questionable data, and implicit premises are fully explicated.

- *Contextual Effectiveness of Solution.* The solution to the problem is effective and often inventive. All essential details of the problem and audience, purpose, and other contextual matters are fully addressed in a graceful and effective way. The solution may be creative in many possible ways: an unorthodox approach, unusually clever juggling of conflicting variables, the bringing in of unobvious mathematics, imaginative evidence, etc.

- *Accuracy of Work.* The work is accurate throughout. All calculations are correct, provided to the proper degree of precision/measurement error, and properly labeled.

- *Quality of Communication.* The student's performance is persuasive and unusually well presented. The essence of the research and the problems to be solved are summed up in a highly engaging and efficient manner, mindful of the audience and the purpose of the presentation. There is obvious craftsmanship in the final product(s): effective use is made of supporting material (visuals, models, overheads, videos, etc.) and of team members (when appropriate). The audience shows enthusiasm and/or confidence that the presenter understands what he/she is talking about and understands the listeners' interests.

Note that these criteria and rubrics provide more than a framework for reliable and valid scoring of student work. They also provide a blueprint for what the assessment tasks should be. Any assessment must be designed mindful of the rubrics so that the criteria are salient for the specifics of the proposed task. That compels teachers and examination designers to ground their designs in the kinds of complex and nonroutine challenges at the heart of QL. Rather than requiring a new array of secure tests with simplistic items, we should be requiring the use of such rubrics in all assessment, local and statewide.

This approach has an important parallel in literacy assessment. In miscue analysis, we make readers' strategies and renderings explicit, helping them see where they succeeded and where they did not and why, and where a misreading is plausible and sensible and where not, so that both learner and teacher come to better understand reading performance. But we rarely do such miscue analysis at higher grades in any subject, despite its power for the learner.

Here is what happened when some mathematics students were taught to self-assess their work through an error analysis after a test: "After we graded their tests, students were asked to evaluate their own performance. . . . Each student was required to submit a written assessment of test performance that contained corrections of all errors and an analysis of test performance. . . . We directed our students to pay particular attention to the *types* of errors they made. . . . They were to attempt to distinguish between conceptual errors and procedural errors." The teachers found this process extremely useful: "Student self-assessment and the resulting student-teacher dialogue were invaluable in drawing a clear picture of what students were thinking when errors were made." But they also reported that students found the task demanding. In particular, teachers in training "had difficulty weighing the seriousness of an error" and seemed "to have difficulty assigning grades to their work. . . . Many had a tendency to weigh effort heavily regardless of the quality of the product."[41]

The previously cited example from North Carolina included a rubric for assessing mathematical insight. Not only is insight vital to mathematics but it can and must be taught, hence assessed, as part of quantitative literacy.[42] This is yet another "radical" aspect of the QL agenda: even though we typically flinch from assessing insight because of fear or ignorance, we must assess what we value highly, including mathematical intuition or insight. *Of course* insight is measurable: anyone who can see through messy contexts, unfamiliar situations, or ill-structured and seemingly intractable problems to an effective solution has insight. We think insight is impossible to assess because we rarely use test items that require insight.

An article on the Third International Mathematics and Science Study (TIMSS) results by a *New York Times* reporter makes the point clearly:

> Consider one problem on the test. . . . It shows a string wound around a circular rod exactly four times, creating a spiral from one end of the rod to the other. The problem was asked only of those who had studied advanced mathematics: what is the string's length, if the circumference of the rod is 4 centimeters and its length is 12 centimeters?
>
> The problem is simply stated and simply illustrated. It also cannot be dismissed as being so theoretical or abstract as to be irrelevant. . . . It might be asked about tungsten coiled into filaments; it might come in handy in designing computer chips. . . . It seems to involve some intuition about the physical world. . . .
>
> It also turned out to be one of the hardest questions on the test. . . . [Only] 10% solved it completely. But the average for the United States was even worse: just 4 % . . . . The rate of Swedish students' success was 6 times greater than that of the Americans; Swiss students did more than four times as well. . . .
>
> What is so interesting about this particular example . . . is that it requires almost no advanced mathematics at all. It does not require memorization of an esoteric concept or the mastery of a specialty. It requires a way of thinking. If you cut the cylinder open and lay it flat, leaving the string in place, you get a series of four right triangles with pieces of string as their diagonals. The length of the string is calculated using a principle learned by every ninth grader. . . .
>
> Nothing could be a better illustration of the value of teaching a mathematical way of thinking. It requires different ways of examining objects; it might mean restating problems in other forms. It can demand a playful readiness to consider alternatives and enough insight to recognize patterns.[43]

Here are some indicators ("look-fors") of insight, derived in part from analysis of the six facets of understanding mentioned earlier. These indicators can be used as guidelines for designing tasks that require such abilities. Insight is revealed by the ability to show:

- Other plausible ways to look at and define the problem;

- A potentially more powerful principle than the one taught or on the table;

- The tacit assumptions at work that have not been made explicit;

- Inconsistency in current versus past discussion;

- Author blind spots;

- Comparison and contrast, not just description;

- Novel implications; and

- How custom and habit influence the views, discussion, or approach to the problem.

The basic blueprint for tasks that can help us assess insight was provided by a grumpy workshop participant many years ago: "You know the trouble with kids today? They don't know what to do when they don't know what to do!" But that is because our assessments are almost never *designed* to make them not know what to do.

Longitudinal Rubrics

sophistication. Of a person: free of naiveté, experienced, worldly-wise; subtle, discriminating, refined, cultured; aware of, versed in, the complexities of a subject or pursuit.[44]

As suggested in our discussion of rubrics and criteria, understandings are not right or wrong. They exist on a continuum running from naïve to expert. To find evidence of QL, we need something more than scores on new test questions. We need a whole different way of charting progress over time. We need to validly and reliably describe a student's degree of understanding of core tasks over time, just as we have done for a few decades in English literacy. QL requires that we discriminate between naïve, developing, competent, and expert performance (to suggest four key points on a continuum of ability).

Some such rubrics already exist in mathematics, with greater refinement. Consider the following from Great Britain representing what might be termed the British rubric for QL:

ATTAINMENT TARGET 1: MA1. USING AND APPLYING MATHEMATICS:

- *Level 1.* Pupils use mathematics as an integral part of classroom activities. They represent their work with objects or pictures and discuss it. They recognise and use a simple pattern or relationship.

- *Level 2.* Pupils select the mathematics they use in some classroom activities. They discuss their work using mathematical language and are beginning to represent it using symbols and simple diagrams. They explain why an answer is correct.

- *Level 3.* Pupils try different approaches and find ways of overcoming difficulties that arise when they are solving problems. They are beginning to organise their work and check results. Pupils discuss their mathematical work and are beginning to explain their thinking. They use and interpret mathematical symbols and diagrams. Pupils show that they understand a general statement by finding particular examples that match it.

- *Level 4.* Pupils are developing their own strategies for solving problems and are using these strategies both in working within mathematics and in applying mathematics to practical contexts. They present information and results in a clear and organised way. They search for a solution by trying out ideas of their own.

- *Level 5.* In order to carry through tasks and solve mathematical problems, pupils identify and obtain necessary information. They check their results, considering whether these are sensible. Pupils show understanding of situations by describing them mathematically using symbols, words and diagrams. They draw simple conclusions of their own and give an explanation of their reasoning.

- *Level 6.* Pupils carry through substantial tasks and solve quite complex problems by independently breaking them down into smaller, more manageable tasks. They interpret, discuss and synthesise information presented in a variety of mathematical forms. Pupils' writing explains and informs their use of diagrams. Pupils are beginning to give mathematical justifications.

- *Level 7.* Starting from problems or contexts that have been presented to them, pupils progressively refine or extend the mathematics used to generate fuller solutions. They give a reason for their choice of mathematical presentation, explaining features they have selected. Pupils justify their generalisations, arguments or solutions, showing some insight into the mathematical structure of the problem. They appreciate the difference between mathematical explanation and experimental evidence.

- *Level 8.* Pupils develop and follow alternative approaches. They reflect on their own lines of enquiry when exploring mathematical tasks; in doing so they introduce and use a range of mathematical techniques. Pupils convey mathematical or statistical meaning through precise and consistent use of symbols that is sustained throughout the work. They examine generalisations or solutions reached in an activity, commenting constructively on the reasoning and logic or the process employed, or the results obtained, and make further progress in the activity as a result.

- *Exceptional Performance.* Pupils give reasons for the choices they make when investigating within mathematics itself or when using mathematics to analyse tasks; these reasons explain why particular lines of enquiry or procedures are followed and others rejected. Pupils apply the mathematics they know in familiar and unfamiliar contexts. Pupils use mathematical language and symbols effectively in presenting a convincing reasoned argument. Their reports include mathematical justifications, explaining their solutions to problems involving a number of features or variables.[45]

The phrasing throughout nicely indicates that students must gain not merely more specialized knowledge of mathematics per se but also increased understanding of mathematics in use. Again, these rubrics do more than show how we should score. They properly serve as criteria for the development of tasks requiring such abilities.

A Sad Irony: Our Ignorance About How Assessment Works

Why is the problem of innumeracy so difficult to solve if many of the ideas cited above are now in use in some high schools and colleges worldwide? Because too many mathematics educators have not been forced to defend their assessments or challenge their habits. Typical tests would not pass muster if held up to the light.

Please suspend disbelief. (If you are still reading, you are *not* among the educators I worry about.) Consider such common unthinking and questionable grading habits in mathematics classes as forcing a small sample of scores to fit a bell curve or computing grades via a calculation of the mean score, as if both were the only possible or defensible practices. In fact, both practices are ironic examples of the *thoughtless use of algorithms*—in the context of classrooms and educational goals. Yet when surveyed, many mathematics teachers claim that the grades they assign are *more* valid than those in other fields because "mathematics is inherently more precise and objective," as one teacher put it. Many of the same teachers are surprisingly uninterested in relevant educational research. "That may be true in their study," is the common refrain, "but not in my class."

A more serious misconception has to do with the relation of QL to state tests. Consider the universal excuse offered by mathematics educators when many of these reform ideas are presented in work-

shops. "That's great, we would love to do this, but we cannot. We have to teach to the test." In our surveys, the argument for being unable to teach for understanding because of tests comes more from mathematics teachers than any other group. Yet this "teach to the test" mantra ironically turns out on closer inspection to be an example of a *form of innumeracy* described by John Paulos in his deservedly best-selling book on the subject: namely, the educator is often confusing causality with correlation.[46]

The extended lament makes this conflation clearer: "Well, we're told that we must get test scores up. So, clearly we cannot teach for the kind of QL and understanding being discussed here. We have no choice but to teach to the test, to use in our testing the kinds of items the state test uses. We have to cover so much content superficially. . . ." Two quick arguments will get the speaker and listeners to stop and consider the reasoning implied:

1. Let me see if I understand. Aren't you saying, then, that the way to raise test scores is to teach less competently (since you admit to being forced to use a superficial and scattered approach, as opposed to teaching for understanding)?

2. If you're right, then by analogy I should practice the physical examination all year if I want to have the best possible result on my annual medical checkup.

The bewildered looks speak volumes. They do not protest my analysis; it clearly puzzles them. Then, I march out the data: National Assessment of Educational Progress (NAEP), the Second International Mathematics and Science Study (SIMSS), the Third International Mathematics and Science Study (TIMSS), and other credible test data all suggest that mathematics instruction is not working for the vast majority of American students. More generally, in an exhaustive meta-analysis Paul Black and Dylan Wiliam have shown that improving the quality of classroom feedback offers the greatest performance gains of any single teaching approach: "There is a body of firm evidence that formative assessment is an essential component . . . and that its development can raise standards of achievement. We know of no other way of raising standards for which such a strong prima facie case can be made."[47] A score, by itself, is the least useful form of feedback; rubrics provide a great deal more, and specific comments in reference to the rubrics—*contextual* feedback—provide still more.[48]

The National Academy of Sciences recently released a set of summary findings on how people learn, in which they concluded:

> Students develop flexible understanding of when, where, why, and how to use their knowledge to solve new problems if they learn how to extract underlying principles and themes from their learning exercises. [But m]any assessments mea-

sure only propositional (factual) knowledge and never ask whether students know when, where, and why to use that knowledge.[49]

The most telling research stems from the TIMSS teaching study, summarized in *The Teaching Gap*.[50] J. Stigler and J. Hiebert present striking evidence of the benefits of teaching for understanding in optimizing performance (as measured by test scores). When correlated with test results, the data clearly show that although Japanese mathematics teachers in middle school cover fewer topics, they achieve better results. Rather than defining themselves as teachers of "skills" in which many discrete skills are covered (as American teachers identify themselves and as videos of their classes reveal), the primary aim in Japanese middle school classes is conceptual understanding. Other data confirm this view: Japanese teachers teach fewer topics in greater depth than do American teachers. They emphasize problem-based learning, in which rules and theorems are typically derived, not merely stated and reinforced through drill.

How did Japan develop such a sophisticated conception of instruction in mathematics? The authors answer: the key is a continuous-progress group professional development research process called Lesson Study. The phrase sums up a long-standing tradition in Japan whereby K–8 teachers work all year in small teams to study student performance and develop, refine, and teach exemplary lessons to improve results. The process involves constant experimentation and peer review:

1. Group defines problem and plans lesson

2. A group member teaches the lesson

3. Group evaluates and revises the lesson

4. Another member teaches revised lesson

5. Evaluation by entire faculty

6. Share results in print and at "lesson fairs"

With respect to the next to the next-to-last step, the authors note:

> *Evaluating and Reflecting, Again.* This time, it is common for all members of the school faculty to participate in a long meeting. Sometimes an outside expert will be invited to attend as well. . . . Not only is the lesson discussed with respect to what these students learned, but also with respect to more general issues raised . . . about teaching and learning.[51]

Is it any wonder, then, if this process is customary, that the typical Japanese teacher would develop more sophisticated curricular and assessment designs? Stigler and Hiebert ironically note that one reason the Japanese process works is that the teachers' research, unlike university research, is done *in their context,* i.e., research leading to "knowledge that is immediately usable."[52] Interestingly, many educators in our workshops readily admit that local faculty are not yet ready for such a system, given the American norm of individual isolationism.

An unflinching view of the situation suggests that many of the problems that have led to the current concern with QL are of the Pogo variety: we have met the enemy and it is us. But that is also good news, because it is in our power as educators to change things. Let us begin in an obvious place: with explicit design standards for assessment and curriculum to counter habit, many models of exemplary design, and policy-based incentives to honor the standards.

Who, then, might drive this reform, if we are in danger of having the blind leading the blind? My Swiftian modest proposal, based on the Pogo caution: Do not let mathematics teachers and professors dominate the discussion. If realistic assessment is what we want and school rarely offers it, let us go beyond school and college walls to the obvious source of contextual insight: people who work and live in the many QL contexts of the wider world. Such a strategy is implied in the case statement in which the "expressions of quantitative literacy" sketch out dozens of venues from which assessment could be taken.[53]

Interestingly, this is what all vocational teachers in New York State must do. They assemble a team of people in their trade, in what is termed a Consultant Committee. The group discusses the teacher's curriculum and assessments twice a year (as well as job placement issues). Why not require all academic departments to do this? In mathematics, let us assemble teams composed of engineers, mapmakers, software designers, baseball statisticians, machine workers, accountants, lab technicians, etc., to advise mathematics educators on how their subject is really used and on what persistent problems they encounter concerning their workers' abilities. Mathematics educators then could tweak draft designs based on these findings into useful assessments. Finally, to complete the process, we could turn to teams of academics and practitioners for peer review of the designers' work.

The core message of *The Teaching Gap*[54] is that ongoing teacher research and development is the key to local improvement in all facets of teaching. According to Stigler and Hiebert, the typical Japanese teacher is now far more sophisticated and focused than is the typical American teacher. Why? Because in Japan the culture of the school and the daily demands of the profession make research and development part of the job. Let us base the process of reform on this axiom: to be valid, of high quality, and credible to all key constituencies, assessment requires collaboration in design, the making public of all design work, and peer review against design standards.

Finally, let us never forget that although the issues here seem technical and political, at bottom they are moral. The aim in any realistic assessment process is to gather *appropriate* evidence and render a *considered* judgment, much like what the judge has to do in a civil trial. The analogy is useful because such a judgment is always fraught with uncertainty; it is never neat and clean; it is always in context. The evidence is weighed, considered, argued about. The standard for conviction is that there be a preponderance of evidence of the right kind. To "convict" a student of understanding similarly requires compelling and appropriate evidence and argument: the student should be considered innocent of understanding unless proven otherwise by a preponderance of evidence. That is a high standard, and appropriately so—even though impatient teachers, testers, and policymakers may wish it were otherwise. Alas, for too long we have gotten away with verdicts in mathematics education using highly circumstantial, indirect evidence. It is high time we sought justice.

Notes

1. From N. Movshovitz-Hadar and J. Webb, *One Equals Zero, and Other Mathematical Surprises* (Emeryville, CA: Key Curriculum Press, 1998).

2. *New York Times,* 13 August 2001, A35.

3. Lynn Arthur Steen, ed., *Mathematics and Democracy: The Case for Quantitative Literacy* (Princeton, NJ: National Council on Education and the Disciplines, 2001), 1–22.

4. Steen, *Mathematics and Democracy.*

5. Steen, *Mathematics and Democracy.*

6. Deborah Hughes-Hallett, "Achieving Numeracy: The Challenge of Implementation," in *Mathematics and Democracy,* Steen, ed., 93–98.

7. Hughes-Hallett, "Achieving Numeracy," in *Mathematics and Democracy,* Steen, ed.

8. Peter T. Ewell, "Numeracy, Mathematics, and General Education," in *Mathematics and Democracy,* Steen, ed., 37–48.

9. Howard Gardner, *The Unschooled Mind: How Children Think and How Schools Should Teach* (New York, NY: Basic Books, 1991), 165.

10. See, for example, the theme issue "The Mathematical Miseducation of America's Youth" in *Phi Delta Kappan* 80:6 (February 1999), and Schoenfeld, A. 1992. "Learning to Think Mathematically: Problem Solving, Metacognition, and Sense Making in Mathematics." In D. A. Grouws, ed., *Handbook of Research on Mathematics Teaching and Learning.* New York: Macmillan, 334–371.

11. Larry Cuban, "Encouraging Progressive Pedagogy," in *Mathematics and Democracy,* Steen, ed., 87–92.

12. J. Stigler and J. Hiebert, *The Teaching Gap: Best Ideas from the*

World's Teachers for Improving Education in the Classroom (New York, NY: Free Press, 1999).

13. Cf. Dan Kennedy, "The Emperor's Vanishing Clothes," in *Mathematics and Democracy,* Steen, ed., 55–60.

14. Grant Wiggins, *Assessing Student Performance* (San Francisco: Jossey-Bass, 1996).

15. See Grant Wiggins, *Educative Assessment: Assessment to Improve Performance* (San Francisco: Jossey-Bass, 1998).

16. P. T. Ewell, "Numeracy, Mathematics, and General Education," in *Mathematics and Democracy,* Steen, ed., 37:

   . . . the key area of distinction [between QL and mathematics] is signaled by the term literacy itself, which implies an integrated ability to function seamlessly within a given community of practice. Literacy as generally understood in the verbal world thus means something quite different from the kinds of skills acquired in formal English courses.

17. Daniel Resnick and Lauren Resnick, "Standards, Curriculum, and Performance: A Historical and Comparative Perspective," *Educational Researcher* 14:4 (1985): 5–21.

18. A cautionary note, then, to professional development providers: information, evidence, and reason will not change this habit, any more than large numbers of people quit abusing cigarettes, alcohol, and drugs because they read sound position papers or hear professionals explain why they should quit. Habits are changed by models, incentives, practice, feedback—if at all.

19. "The Present Requirements for Admission to Harvard College," *Atlantic Monthly* 69:415 (May 1982): 671–77.

20. See, for example, G. Cizek, "Confusion Effusion: A Rejoinder to Wiggins," *Phi Delta Kappan* 73 (1991): 150–53.

21. Earlier versions of these standards appeared in Wiggins, *Assessing Student Performance,* 228–30.

22. Benjamin Bloom, ed., *Taxonomy of Educational Objectives: Book 1: Cognitive Domain* (White Plains, NY: Longman, 1954), 125.

23. B. S. Bloom, G. F. Madaus, and J. T. Hastings, *Evaluation to Improve Learning* (New York, NY: McGraw-Hill, 1981), 265.

24. Bloom, et al., *Evaluation to Improve Learning,* 268.

25. Newmann, W. Secada, and G. Wehlage, *A Guide to Authentic Instruction and Assessment: Vision, Standards and Scoring* (Madison, WI: Wisconsin Center for Education Research, 1995).

26. Wiggins, G. & Kline, E. (1997) *3rd Report to the North Carolina Commission on Standards and Accountability,* Relearning by Design, Ewing, NJ.

27. Federal Aviation Report, as quoted in "A Question of Safety: A Special Report," *New York Times,* Sunday 13 November 1994, section 1, page 1.

28. Jay McTighe and Grant Wiggins, *The Understanding by Design*

Handbook (Alexandria, VA: Association for Supervision and Curriculum Development, 1999).

29. Grant Wiggins and Jay McTighe, *Understanding by Design* (Alexandria, VA: Association for Supervision and Curriculum Development, 1998).

30. William James, *Talks to Teachers* (New York, NY: W. W. Norton, 1899/1958).

31. John Dewey, *The Middle Works of John Dewey: 1899–1924* (vol. 15) (Carbondale, IL: Southern Illinois University Press, 1909), 290.

32. A historical irony. For it was Descartes (in *Rules for the Direction of the Mind*) who decried the learning of geometry through the organized results in theorems presented in logical order as needlessly complicating the learning of geometry and hiding the methods by which the theorems were derived. See Wiggins and McTighe, *Understanding by Design*, 149 ff.

33. Norm Frederiksen, "The Real Test Bias," *American Psychologist* 39:3 (March 1984): 193–202.

34. Bloom, *Taxonomy of Educational Objectives: Book I: Cognitive Domain.*

35. Zalman Usiskin, "Quantitative Literacy for the Next Generation," in *Mathematics and Democracy,* Steen, ed., 84.

36. National Center on Education and the Economy, *New Standards: High School Mathematics Portfolio* (Washington, DC: National Center on Education and the Economy, 1995).

37. Wiggins and McTighe, *Understanding by Design.*

38. This narrow-minded comment was echoed repeatedly by American teachers in the TIMSS teaching study, discussed below, with unfortunate results for student performance.

39. Wiggins and McTighe, *Understanding by Design.*

40. Wiggins, G. & Kline, E. (1997) *3rd Report to the North Carolina Commission on Standards and Accountability*, Relearning by Design, Ewing, NJ.

41. Stallings, Virginia and Tascione, Carol "Student Self-Assessment and Self-Evaluation." *The Mathematics Teacher.* NCTM. Reston, VA. 89:7, October 1996. pp. 548–554.

42. Cf. Hughes-Hallett, "Achieving Numeracy," in *Mathematics and Democracy,* Steen, ed., 96–97.

43. Edward Rothstein, "It's Not Just Numbers or Advanced Science, It's Also Knowing How to Think," *New York Times,* 9 March 1998, D3.

44. From the Oxford English Dictionary CD-ROM.

45. From the *National Curriculum Handbook for Secondary Teachers* in England, Department of Education and Employment, 1999. Also available on the Internet at www.nc.uk.net. Note that these rubrics are called "Attainment Targets."

46. Paulos, John Allen. 1990. *Innumeracy: Mathematical Illiteracy and Its Consequences* (New York: Vintage Books).

47. Black, P. J. and D. Wiliam. 1998. "Assessment and Classroom Learning." *Assessment in Education* 5(1) 7-74.

48. See Wiggins, *Educative Assessment*, on the importance of feedback to assessment systems and reform.

49. J. Bransford, A. Brown, and R. Cocking, eds., *How People Learn: Brain, Mind, Experience, and School* (Washington, DC: National Academy Press), 37.

50. Stigler and Hiebert, *The Teaching Gap.*

51. Stigler and Hiebert, *The Teaching Gap,* 112 ff.

52. Stigler and Hiebert, *The Teaching Gap,* 122.

53. Steen, *Mathematics and Democracy,* 9 ff.

54. Stigler and Hiebert, *The Teaching Gap.*

Statistics and Quantitative Literacy

RICHARD L. SCHEAFFER

With contributions from Beth Chance, California Polytechnic State University; Cathryn Dippo, Bureau of Labor Statistics; Thomas Moore, Grinnell College; Jerry Moreno, John Carroll University; and Jeffrey Witmer, Oberlin College.

Because much of the early work in quantitative literacy was led by statisticians—indeed, many K–12 programs in probability and statistics are named "quantitative literacy"—statistics bears a very special relation to quantitative literacy, with respect to both substance and education. This essay provides a perspective by leaders of statistics education on issues raised in the other background essays prepared for the Forum on quantitative literacy.

Setting the Stage

Who would disagree that college graduates, not to mention high school graduates, should be able to understand and correctly interpret disease or unemployment rates, the comparative costs of car or apartment rental agreements, and trends in the composition of the country's population? Yet many graduates are mystified by quantitative arguments, a mystification that ranges from minor confusion in some to functional innumeracy in others. Just as the information age is making the world more quantitative, however, the ability of people to deal with numerical issues of practical consequence is shrinking. It is past time to take seriously the challenge of improving the quantitative skills of graduates of U.S. high schools and colleges.

Before examining the role of statistics in the movement to improve quantitative literacy, it is wise to consider definitions of the key terms under discussion because there have been many different interpretations, even among enlightened readers. In fact, at the level of education under consideration here (high school and undergraduate) what some would call "statistics" might be termed "data analysis" or "statistical thinking" by others. We need to sort out the definitions of at least three different terms, all dealing with the same substance.

Statistics often is thought of as the keeper of the scientific method (although this may sound a little presumptuous to physical scientists) because it is the discipline that studies how to understand the world through the rubric of setting hypotheses, collecting data relevant to those hypotheses, analyzing the data, and drawing conclusions about the hypotheses from analysis of the data. Here "data" is to be understood broadly, because it well may include judgments of experts as in a Bayesian analysis. Although statistics has many elegant theories, its practice usually outstrips theory in the sense that many practical problems do not fit nicely into the assumptions of any theory.

This difficulty leads directly to *data analysis,* which can be thought of as following the rubric of the scientific method but with emphasis on answering real questions rather than trying to fit those questions into established theories. In data analysis, exploratory techniques stand alongside confirmatory techniques. Empirical evidence that a technique works often is taken as "proof" among data analysts who might choose to use such a technique in practice. "An approximate answer to the right question is better than an exact answer to the wrong question" is one of the mantras of the data

---

Richard L. Scheaffer is Professor Emeritus of Statistics at the University of Florida and in 2001 was President of the American Statistical Association (ASA). Scheaffer served as the first Chief Faculty Consultant for the College Board's new AP Statistics course. He has written extensively in statistical education and on sampling theory and practice. For many years Scheaffer has been active on ASA education committees where he has fostered joint work with NCTM in statistics education.

analyst, the supreme example of whom is the late John Tukey (Tukey 1962). In today's complex world, data analysis is what most statisticians actually practice, and so it is quite appropriate that the subject be referred to as data analysis in standards and guidelines.

In reality, full-bore data analysis is more than most people need to deal with the statistical issues of everyday life and work. As a result, the third term, *statistical thinking,* comes into play. Statistical thinking is essential for anyone who wants to be an informed citizen, intelligent consumer, or skilled worker. It is the backbone of the contemporary emphasis on quality improvement because all levels of employees in a firm, from the CEO to the janitor, must have some notion of statistical thinking if a firm is to operate optimally. Using a quality-improvement definition, statistical thinking involves viewing life as made up of processes and viewing all processes as having variation. Once understood, variation can be broken down into that which can be reduced and that which must be managed.

This most basic of the three statistical terms might sound the most abstract, but we must keep in mind that processes can be simple and the sources of variation fairly obvious. Figuring out the gas mileage of a car is a process subject to variation, the most obvious sources of which are perhaps the grade of gasoline used and the style of driving. A person's health is likewise subject to variation, but here the sources of variation are many and sometimes difficult to detect. It is statistical thinking that keeps people from making rash decisions when accidents increase this month over last or one school has a slightly lower test score average than another school. The inherent variation in processes must be considered to determine whether change can be attributed to any cause other than pure chance.

Some might further differentiate between statistical thinking and *statistical literacy,* giving the latter a less formal definition than one involving processes and their variation. The ability to read a newspaper critically often is used as an attribute of a statistically literate person. The books by David Moore (2001) and Jessica Utts (1999) are good references for courses on statistical literacy, as is the Web-based Chance course (see www.dartmouth.edu/~chance). Because statistical thinking and statistical literacy are so close in the larger scheme of things, this essay uses the term statistical thinking when referring to this level of statistical education (which also may reduce the confusion over the many uses of the word *literacy*).

As to the definition of *quantitative literacy* (QL), two of the many possibilities adequately cover the topic for purposes of this essay. The British report *Mathematics Counts* (Cockcroft 1982) popularized the term *numeracy* and defined it in part as "an 'at homeness' with numbers and an ability to make use of mathematical skills which enables an individual to cope with the practical demands of everyday life"(Cockcroft 1982, 11). More recently, the International Life Skills Survey, as quoted in *Mathematics and Democracy: The Case for Quantitative Literacy* (Steen 2001), offers a slightly broader definition of quantitative literacy as an "aggregate of skills, knowledge, beliefs, dispositions, habits of mind, communication capabilities, and problem-solving skills that people need in order to engage effectively in quantitative situations arising in life and work" (Steen 2001, 7).

There are strong ties between statistical thinking, data analysis, and quantitative literacy in terms of historical developments, current emphases, and prospects for the future. As pointed out in *Mathematics and Democracy* (Steen 2001), the American Statistical Association (ASA) conducted a National Science Foundation-funded project called Quantitative Literacy in the mid-1980s that produced materials and workshops to introduce mathematics teachers at the middle and high school levels to basic concepts of data analysis and probability. The project was built around a hands-on, active learning format that involved student projects and appropriate use of technology.

The ASA QL program was motivated by the Schools Project in England that had introduced statistics into the national curriculum, using the report *Mathematics Counts* (Cockcroft 1982) as one of the supporting documents. This report noted that statistics is "essentially a practical subject and its study should be based on the collection of data . . . by pupils themselves." To this end it urged "in-service training courses on the teaching of statistics not only for mathematics teachers but also for teachers of other subjects" as well as "teaching materials which will emphasize a practical approach" (Cockcroft 1982, 234). Even then, 20 years ago, the Cockcroft commission recognized that "micro-computers . . . offer opportunities to illuminate statistical ideas and techniques" (Cockcroft 1982, 235). All these points were taken to heart by the ASA QL team, and all are still valid concerns.

The emphasis on statistical thinking and data analysis that was introduced in Britain migrated to Canada and was picked up as a main theme for U.S. K–12 education by a Joint Committee of the ASA and the National Council of Teachers of Mathematics (NCTM). The ASA-NCTM QL project served as a model for the data analysis and probability strand in *Curriculum and Evaluation Standards for School Mathematics* published by NCTM (1989), a strand that is even stronger in the updated edition (NCTM 2000).

The movement to include data analysis and probability in the school mathematics curriculum thus has some of the same historical roots as the current QL movement, and has similar emphases. Properly taught, statistical thinking and data analysis emphasize mathematical knowledge and skills that enable an individual to cope with the practical demands of everyday life. They also develop knowledge, beliefs, dispositions, habits of mind, communication capabilities, and problem-solving skills that people need to engage effectively in quantitative situations arising in life and work. It is no accident that almost all of the examples given in the opening paragraphs of *Mathematics and Democracy* (Steen 2001) are statistical in nature.

Simultaneous with the K–12 effort, many statisticians began emphasizing statistical thinking at the college level. As mentioned above in the discussion of statistical literacy, excellent textbooks and other materials as well as numerous college courses have been developed around this theme. These deal with issues of quantitative literacy in much more authentic ways than almost any mathematics text seems to.

Because statistics and quantitative literacy share so much in common, we hope that statisticians and mathematics educators will work together to build a strong emphasis on QL in the school and college curriculum. Many statisticians would probably disagree with the statement in *Mathematics and Democracy* (Steen 2001) that QL is "not the same as statistics." Indeed, many think that a very large part of QL *is* statistics (statistical thinking or data analysis), just as the Cockroft commission thought that statistics was a large part of numeracy. In what follows, we take a more detailed look at the common ground between statistics and QL and suggest ways of building on that commonality for the good of all.

QL and Citizenship

Patricia Cline Cohen, quoting Josiah Quincy, notes in her essay that one of the duties of responsible government is to provide statistical knowledge about the general welfare of its citizens. Hard data "are to be sought and ought to be studied by all who aspire to regulate, or improve the state of the nation. . ." (Cohen, see p. 7). In fact, the very word "statistics" derives from its use to collect information on and about the state. A good example of the growth of statistics in government can be seen in the development and expansion of the U.S. Census Bureau over the years and the widespread uses to which its data are put. Developing an informed citizenry is one of the tasks of public education and, in light of the emphasis on data within the government, a large part of that task involves improving the quantitative literacy of all citizens. That statistics can be misused by politicians (and others) is one of the reasons citizens need some skill in statistical thinking and reasoning with data.

According to Cohen, statistics are a powerful tool of political and civic functioning, and at our peril we neglect to teach the skills required to understand them. In large measure, Cohen equates quantitative literacy with statistics and makes a strong case for including statistics in everyone's education. With this, statisticians

certainly can agree. They would not agree, however, with Cohen's statement that "statistics has become a branch of mathematics." Statistics has many roots, including business, engineering, agriculture, and the physical, social, and biological sciences; it deals with many issues that would not be considered mathematical. Emphasis on context is one such issue; emphasis on the design of studies is another. Although statistics uses mathematics, the key to statistical thinking is the context of a real problem and how data might be collected and analyzed to help solve that problem. Some would say that the greatest contributions of statistics to modern science lie in the area of design of surveys and experiments, such as the demographic and economic surveys of the Census Bureau and the Bureau of Labor Statistics and the experiments used in many health-related studies.

In fact, statistics has much broader uses than its mathematical roots might suggest, and many, including the federal government itself, are attempting to enlighten citizens about the proper collection, analysis, and interpretation of data. One example of this is the effort of the FedStats Interagency Task Force to develop a statistical literacy program for users of the Federal Statistical System. A related effort is embodied in a recent report from the National Research Council entitled *Information Technology Research for Federal Statistics,* which talks about the importance of literacy, visualization, and perception of data:

> Given the relatively low level of numerical and statistical literacy in the population at large, it becomes especially important to provide users with interfaces that give them useful, meaningful information. Providing data with a bad interface that does not allow users to interpret data sensibly may be worse than not providing the data at all, ... The goal is to provide not merely a data set but also tools that allow making sense of the data. (NRC 2000, 20)

These and other efforts by the federal government to improve statistical literacy are supported by Katherine Wallman, chief statistician of the US government, who said in a 1999 speech (Wallman 1999):

> Electronic dissemination is truly a boon to national statistical offices anxious to make their data more accessible and useful—and to user communities equipped to handle the wealth of available information. But this technology remains to a degree a bane, for while we have taken monumental strides in making our nation's statistics electronically available, attention to documentation in electronic media has lagged. And I continue to argue, as I have for almost a decade, that the gap between our citizens' computer literacy and their "statistical literacy" remains significant.

Citizens encounter statistics at every turn in their daily lives. Often, however, they are ill-equipped to evaluate the information presented to them. Fortunately, quantitative literacy initiatives show prospects of enhancing the statistical literacy of the next generation. Our ideal would be students who can use statistics to keep their fingers on the pulse of humanity, as envisioned by the great Belgian statistician and social scientist Adolph Quetelet:

> I like to think of the constant presence in any sound Republic of two guardian angels: the Statistician and the Historian of Science. The former keeps his finger on the pulse of Humanity, and gives the necessary warning when things are not as they should be. The Historian . . . will not allow humanity to forget its noblest traditions or to be ungrateful to its greatest benefactors. (Walker 1945, 10)

QL and the Workplace

Everyone agrees that business needs workers with QL skills, but according to Linda Rosen and her colleagues in their essay, it is not at all clear what those skills are or how urgently they are needed. In fact, the types of skills needed vary from business to business, and it may require some serious research to sort out the best set of skills for the workforce of tomorrow. Rosen offers sound advice, emphasizing notions of communication and cooperation that are similar to skills that often are seen as part of QL itself. In particular, she urges advocates of quantitative literacy to better document the existing level and anticipated need of QL in the workplace, to raise general awareness about the importance of QL in today's workplace, and to engage educators to help upgrade the QL skills of the workforce based on identified quantitative needs (Rosen et al., see pp. 43–52).

These recommendations fit well with current efforts in the statistics community to build bridges between the academic community and business, industry, and government to ensure an effective statistics education for the workforce of the future. Somewhat surprisingly, however, the level of skills attached to quantitative literacy varies greatly among those quoted by Rosen, ranging from merely knowing basic arithmetic to making "judgments grounded in data." If such judgments are thought of in the sense of statistical thinking and data analysis, they are much deeper than basic mathematical skills and require an educational component that is not found in traditional mathematics courses. Statistical thinking has a stochastic component (could this variation be caused by chance alone?) that is essential to intelligent study of business, industry, and government processes.

It is important to realize that data, information, and knowledge are a part of a hierarchy: an event yields observations called *data,* which are collected and processed into *information,* which is analyzed and combined with human intelligence to produce *knowledge. Wisdom* is the product of knowledge, judgment, and experi-

ence. Such taxonomies are important in new fields such as data mining—the process of discovering knowledge through data. As these fields become increasingly important to society, the statistical aspects of thinking intelligently about data and its uses (and misuses) become critical. Most often, the teaching of statistics only reaches the information stage because moving to the higher stages of knowledge and wisdom requires setting the information inside a framework in which to make intelligent judgments. If statistical thinking is a part of the framework, issues such as context (including the surrounding science) and variation are taken into account. How to go beyond the information level in understanding the world around us is one way to phrase the key intellectual challenge of QL. Statisticians surely agree with those cited by Rosen who argue that the core mathematics curriculum must be "something more than arithmetic proficiency."

Although business leaders may be confused about the details of what QL is and how much of it they want, as Rosen suggests, most enlightened leaders of business and industry see the advantages of quantitative thinking quite clearly in at least one area, that of quality control and productivity improvement. The total quality management (TQM) effort is giving way to the Six Sigma improvement initiative, which has become extremely popular in the past several years. In addition to generating a great deal of discussion within statistics and quality-control circles, it has been one of the few technically oriented initiatives to generate significant interest from business leaders, the financial community, and the popular media. Hitching the QL wagon to the Six Sigma star would be one way to move QL higher on the agenda of business leaders.

QL and Curriculum

A central theme of QL is that the meaning of "literate" must be expanded to include quantitative literacy and that the latter, like the former, must be addressed across the curriculum. This theme is clearly stated in the essay by Randall Richardson and William McCallum, who enunciate two main criteria for a QL curriculum: it must go beyond the basic ability to read and write mathematics to the development of conceptual understanding, and it must be engaged with a context, be it humanities, business, science, engineering, technology, or everyday life (Richardson and McCallum, see pp. 99–106).

Richardson and McCallum argue, along with many others, that QL cannot be regarded as the sole responsibility of teachers of mathematics, whether in high school or college. It is the responsibility of those in other disciplines to help provide basic tools and conceptual understanding and to model the use of mathematics as a way of looking at the world. In short, QL should be the focus of mathematics across the curriculum. The nurturing of QL across the curriculum, however, requires strong administrative support and significant institutional change.

Those experienced with teaching statistics suggest that one way to garner administrative support and foster institutional change is to tie much of QL to the statistics curriculum, everywhere it is housed. The very lifeblood of statistics is context, and the current teaching of statistical thinking and modern data analysis is built around conceptual understanding (calculations are done by machine). Because it is *used* across the curriculum, in most colleges and universities statistics already is *taught* across the curriculum. It would make practical as well as pedagogical sense to anchor the expansion of QL to the statistics teaching efforts of colleges and universities. Indeed, some postsecondary institutions ranging from liberal arts colleges (Mt. Holyoke) to large research universities (Ohio State) have centered much of the quantitative reasoning component of their general education requirements on statistics courses.

QL and Mathematics

Closely related to the issue of curriculum is the relationship between QL and mathematics. Deborah Hughes Hallett asserts in her essay that QL is the ability to identify and use quantitative arguments in everyday contexts, that it is more a habit of mind than a set of topics or a list of skills. QL is more about how mathematics is used than about how much mathematics a person knows. For this and other reasons, a call to increase QL is a call for a substantial increase in most students' understanding of mathematics. It is, therefore, not a dumbing down of rigor but an increase in standards. According to Hughes Hallett, this increase is essential because "the general level of quantitative literacy is currently sufficiently limited that it threatens the ability of citizens to make wise decisions at work and in public and private life" (Hughes Hallett, see p. 91).

Statisticians will find it interesting (and gratifying) that probability and statistics are the only subject areas that Hughes Hallett mentions specifically. Indeed, she finds the absence of these subjects in the education of many students remarkable given that they are so "extensively used in public and private life." Simply requiring more students to study advanced mathematics is not the answer: they actually must be taught QL by solving problems in context. Courses must demand "deeper understanding," which will require a coordinated effort to change both pedagogy and assessment.

Although there is much to agree with in Hughes Hallett's essay, statistics educators would probably disagree with the claim that ". . . the teaching of probability and statistics suffers from the fact that no one can agree on when or by whom these topics should be introduced." The statistics community played an important role in developing the NCTM standards (1989, 2000) and offers strong support for the data analysis and probability strand contained in these recommendations. Similarly, ASA has been involved in the expansion of the data analysis and probability section of the National Assessment of Educational Progress (NAEP) framework for the 2004 examination. The NCTM recommendations for all grade levels, which are reflected in the NAEP framework, call for instructional programs from prekindergarten through grade 12 that enable all students to:

> . . . formulate questions that can be addressed with data and collect, organize, and display relevant data to answer them; select and use appropriate statistical methods to analyze data; develop and evaluate inferences and predictions that are based on data; understand and apply basic concepts of probability (NCTM 2000, 48).

With NSF support, ASA has developed a series of supplemental materials for teaching modern data analysis in the elementary, middle, and high school grades called, respectively, Exploring Statistics in the Elementary Grades, Quantitative Literacy, and Data Driven Mathematics. (See the education section at www.amstat.org or the Dale Seymour section of Pearson Learning at www.pearsonlearning.com.) These materials support and enhance the NCTM recommendations, and thus also the kinds of quantitative literacy that Hughes Hallett seeks.

The Advanced Placement (AP) Statistics course has become quite popular among high school teachers and students; its course description (see http://apcentral.collegeboard.com/repository/ap01.cd_sta_4328.pdf) reflects modern trends in data analysis that now are being emulated in some college courses. Statistics educators discovered long ago that classroom activities, laboratory activities, and group projects really work. The Mathematical Association of America (MAA) publication *Teaching Statistics: Resources for Undergraduate Instructors* showcases many examples of materials and programs that support this approach (Moore 2000). That the statistics community has rallied around these ideas is evidenced by the promulgation of good resources for hands-on, active teaching of statistics at both the school and college levels.

At the college level, both ASA and MAA have prepared guidelines concerning the undergraduate teaching of statistics. The ASA "Curriculum Guidelines for Undergraduate Programs in Statistical Science" encourages a broad range of programs that offer all students useful options beyond the traditional introductory course:

> Undergraduate statistics programs should emphasize concepts and tools for working with data and provide experience in designing data collection and in analyzing real data that go beyond the content of a first course in statistical methods.

The detailed statistical content may vary, and may be accompanied by varying levels of study in computing, mathematics, and a field of application. (ASA 2001, 1)

Reports from the MAA (CUPM 1993) recommend that all undergraduate mathematical sciences majors should have a data-centered statistics course. Taken together, the standards, guidelines, and curriculum materials fashioned by the statistics community (with support from the mathematics community) give solid evidence that many pieces of the "coordinated effort" needed to improve quantitative literacy are in place. The QL reform that may be coming should make good use of the projects and related ideas already afloat within the statistics education community.

To be honest, however, many statistics courses still are taught in a manner that misses the QL point. This is partly because tension always exists between breadth of coverage and deep understanding—the latter of most importance to QL. Although the statistics education community may have reached consensus on how to deal with the tension, this consensus does not always play out easily in the classroom. Courses serve many clients, some of whom demand coverage of many specific topics in statistical inference.

Jan de Lange's paper, also about QL and mathematics, introduces two new and important ideas (de Lange, see pp. 75–89). First, it extends the definition of quantitative literacy to the term "mathematical literacy" because of the indisputable fact that much more in mathematics is useful besides numbers. Indeed, many aspects of statistical thinking (which de Lange includes under the name "uncertainty" as one of his core phenomenological categories) are not about numbers as much as about concepts and habits of mind. For example, the idea of a lurking variable upsetting an apparent bivariate relationship with observational data is a conceptual idea, part of statistical thinking but not particularly about numbers. The notion that designed experiments are more reliable than observational studies is another very important nonquantitative idea.

De Lange's second important idea is that if mathematics were properly taught, the distinction between mathematical content and mathematical literacy "would be smaller than some people suggest it is now." The issue is part of the aforementioned tension between breadth of coverage and depth of understanding, but it also suggests a resolution of the dilemma of QL courses. Separate courses in QL create serious problems. First, students are pigeonholed into those capable of taking "real mathematics" and those who will only need QL, thereby entrenching two classes of students in a structure that serves the nation poorly. Second, although all students need to be quantitatively literate, there is growing evidence that those who take regular mathematics courses (and who in a segregated system may not encounter much QL) are not learning many of the critical thinking skills they need.

QL and Articulation

Articulation of the K–16 mathematics curriculum is difficult to attain because it involves inextricably linked political and policy issues. Michael Kirst's essay (Kirst, see pp. 107–120) outlines the main areas of political tension: between professional leadership and political consensus, between flexible and specific standards, between dynamic standards and reasonable expectations for change, between professional leadership and public understanding of standards, between expectations and requirements. Progress toward improving articulation requires a clear signal up and down the line as to what is required. Part of that signal should be a clear message about QL.

As subject-matter standards and examinations have evolved in recent years, one of the widespread changes has been increased emphasis on data analysis and statistics; however, one of the main limiting factors is the quality of materials for teachers. "Any attempt to change mathematics curriculum," Kirst observes, "must involve rethinking textbook creation and adoption policies." Another limiting factor is the ever-present standardized examination. Multiple-choice basic skills tests do not adequately emphasize complex thinking skills such as statistical inference and multistep mathematical problem solving.

The statistics community would argue that an emphasis on statistics and QL in the mathematics curriculum could help alleviate some of these tensions. The movements to infuse school mathematics with data analysis and to enhance undergraduate statistics offerings owe much of their success to the fact that leaders from business and industry supported the efforts. It helped, of course, that these efforts began when quality improvement was a high national priority; that theme is still important for garnering support for statistics among business and political leaders. Another theme that allows statisticians to enter doors that might be more difficult for mathematicians to open is data: everyone is collecting tons of it and few know what to do with it. The public understands something of these issues. Indeed, many see the need for statistics education much more clearly than they see the need for mathematics education (although they might view statistics as a part of mathematics).

Will college faculty buy into an articulated program in mathematics education that includes a strong component of QL? Statistics faculty are likely to do so, if the success of the AP Statistics course and the support for the changes promoted by the NCTM standards and the NAEP framework are any indication. A QL emphasis would not look as radically new to a statistician as it might to a mathematician.

QL and Assessment

Many of the exhortations in the background essays about the importance of assessment to a successful QL program are subsumed in the comprehensive and detailed paper by Grant Wiggins (Wiggins, see pp. 121–143). In Wiggins' view, echoed by others, "we have often sacrificed the primary client (the learner) in the name of accountability." Wiggins seeks to put the interests of the learner back in the center of assessment.

Assessment plays a central role in QL reform. Wiggins argues for a realignment of assessment with QL that puts more emphasis on open-ended, messy, and "authentic" assessment tasks. Much of this realignment will require challenging changes in the focus of traditional instruction, including much more formative (diagnostic) assessment. To develop reliable examples of high-quality assessment strategies that are focused on a few big ideas will require significant collaboration. In addition, instructors will need training to design, administer, and grade these new types of assessment.

Wiggins makes much of "context" but seems to use the term in at least two different ways. One relates to determining the source of a problem (who is asking the question, how was the information gathered, who is the answer for, what are relevant issues in the discipline that may affect the solution). Another suggests a more philosophical, historical point of view (where do laws or theorems come from, are they debatable, can you understand the history and how it affects our present state of knowledge). Although historical perspective is important, Wiggins seems to overemphasize the role of this type of context for beginning students. To statisticians, the first definition of context is absolutely essential for any problem; the second, although helpful for some problems, is not nearly as essential.

Data analysis problems usually have a built-in context that may make them easier for teachers to attack (although not many such examples are found in Wiggins' essay). They have less of the baggage of the years of formalism that has accompanied mathematics instruction and that can be difficult for new teachers to break free from.

Wiggins differentiates between "meaning making" and "statistical reasoning," whereas statisticians would not see these as so different. His interpretation of "meaning making" as "what is mathematics and why does it matter" seems a bit narrow. Many levels of reasoning and conceptual understanding are important in mathematics even when historical perspective is incomplete. The focus should be on students' abilities to reason with their own knowledge and "understand how it works," even if their ability to question and debate is limited. Mathematics that is relevant to students' direct experiences is more meaningful to many beginning students than philosophical debates. The important message is that different experiences are meaningful to different students, and teachers need to be ready to provide students with a variety of contexts.

One of the main goals of mathematics education reform surely should be, as Wiggins claims, to make assessment design "more public, collaborative, and subject to ongoing peer review." This cannot be overemphasized, but teachers need more examples of how to do this, particularly for lower-level students. Although many of Wiggins' examples are quite grand, what teachers need are simpler tasks that could be assigned on a daily basis to help students learn to interpret and test their understanding. Fortunately, statistics educators have been thinking about authentic assessment for some time; B. L. Chance (1997) and J. B. Garfield (1994) give good overviews of current thinking on authentic assessment.

Conclusion

Statistics and quantitative literacy have much in common. Although few would disagree with this, statisticians would probably argue that QL is mainly statistics while mathematicians and mathematics educators tend to argue that QL is only partly statistics. Statistics emphasizes context, design of studies, and a stochastic view of the world. Although statistics is clearly not the same as mathematics, nor even a part of mathematics, it uses mathematics as one of its main tools for practical problem solving. Being one of the most widely used of the mathematical sciences, statistics is well entrenched in many places across the curriculum. At the K–14 level, statistics already has embarked on a program that emphasizes active learning, much in the spirit recommended by modern cognitive science. All this suggests that students will reap dividends if the two disciplines work together.

Although statistics education has gained acceptance (even respect) over the past 15 years as a key component of the K–12 mathematics curriculum, this acceptance does not always translate into classroom practice. The taught curriculum is far from reconciled with the recommended curriculum. In addressing this challenge, statistics and QL should be mutually reinforcing. Simply put, statistics has opened the door for quantitative literacy. In his background essay on curriculum in grades 6–12, Lynn Arthur Steen argues that in a balanced curriculum, "[D]ata analysis, geometry, and algebra would constitute three equal content components in grades 6 to 8 and in grades 9 to 11" (Steen, see p. 66). "Real work yielding real results," he emphasizes, "must begin and end in real data" (see p. 59).

On the pedagogical side, statistics educators have learned to emphasize both engagement and relevance. There is ample evidence that both teachers and students like a hands-on, activity-based approach to data analysis (the type recommended earlier in this essay), and that students learn better through this approach. Two teachers using data analysis materials in an algebra course and a teacher of AP Statistics have noticed how data analysis not only adds valuable content to the curriculum but also improves attitudes:

> The [data analysis] materials allow the students to construct knowledge based on their experiences, and these materials provide activities and experiences to guide the students to good concept-based skills. The students understand what and why they are doing things.

* * *

> Almost all of the students were amazed by the fact that some of the mathematical concepts that they study (logs and exponentials) are actually used in such situations. I must also say that I find it very exciting to engage in these topics as well!

* * *

> I would like to echo the comments about the value of an early statistics education. Yesterday, our AP Psychology teacher told me how much difference she sees between students with a stats background and students without. She said the difference was like "night and day," especially with project work. Our science teachers are saying the same thing. I guess what I am saying is what a lot of us already believe: a knowledge of statistics enriches every other discipline and life in general. Three cheers for statistics!

At the college level, statistics is one of the most widely required or recommended courses in the mathematical sciences, and the same emphasis on data analysis with hands-on activities and laboratory experiences is permeating these courses. AP Statistics is widely accepted, even emulated, by many college programs and can form one of the paths for articulating a QL message between schools and colleges. Strong ties between ASA and MAA can help cement the path.

As noted above, Adolph Quetelet emphasized the importance for science of both statisticians and historians of science. It seems appropriate, then, to end this review with a relevant observation from a historian of science, Theodore Porter:

> Statistical methods are about logic as well as numbers. For this reason, as well as on account of their pervasiveness in modern life, *statistics cannot be the business of statisticians alone,* but should enter into the schooling of every educated person. To achieve this would be a worthy goal for statistics in the coming decades. (Porter 2001, 61) (Italics added.)

References

American Statistical Association. 2001. "Curriculum Guidelines for Undergraduate Programs in Statistical Science." http://www.amstat.org/education/Curriculum_Guidelines.html.

Chance, B. L. 1997. "Experiences with Authentic Assessment Techniques in an Introductory Statistics Course" *Journal of Statistics Education,* 5(3). www.amstat.org/publications/jse/ v5n3/chance.html.

Cockcroft, W. H., ed. 1982). *Mathematics Counts.* London: Her Majesty's Stationery Office.

Garfield, J. B. 1994. "Beyond Testing and Grading: Using Assessment to Improve Student Learning." *Journal of Statistics Education* 2(1). www.amstat.org/publications/jse/v2n1/ garfield.html.

Mathematical Association of America. 1993. "Guidelines for Programs and Departments in Undergraduate Mathematical Sciences." http://www.maa.org/guidelines.html.

Moore, D. 1998. "Statistics Among the Liberal Arts." *Journal of the American Statistical Association* 93:1253–59.

Moore, D. 2001. *Statistics: Concepts and Controversies,* 5th ed. New York, NY: W. H. Freeman.

Moore, D., and G. Cobb. 2000). "Statistics and Mathematics: Tension and Cooperation." *American Mathematical Monthly,* 615–630.

Moore, T., ed. 2000. *Teaching Statistics: Resources for Undergraduate Instructors,* MAA Notes No. 52. Washington, DC: Mathematics Association of America.

National Council of Teachers of Mathematics. 1989. *Curriculum and Evaluation Standards for School Mathematics.* Reston, VA: National Council of Teachers of Mathematics.

National Council of Teachers of Mathematics. 2000. *Principles and Standards for School Mathematics.* Reston, VA: National Council of Teachers of Mathematics.

National Research Council. 2000. *Information Technology Research for Federal Statistics.* www4.nationalacademies.org/cpsma/cstb.nsf/ web/pub_federalstatistics?OpenDocument.

Porter, T. 2001. "Statistical Futures." *Amstat News* (291) (September): 61–64.

Steen, Lynn Arthur, ed. 2001. *Mathematics and Democracy: The Case for Quantitative Literacy.* Princeton, NJ: National Council of Education and the Disciplines.

Tukey, J. 1962. "The Future of Data Analysis." *Annals of Mathematical Statistics* 33: 1–67.

Utts, J. 1999. *Seeing Through Statistics,* 2nd ed. Belmont, CA: Duxbury Press.

Walker, H. 1945. "The Role of the American Statistical Association." *Journal of the American Statistical Association* 40:1–10.

Wallman, Katherine K. 1999. "At the Intersection of Official Statistics and Public Policy: Confronting the Challenges." Amsterdam: Celebrating the Centenary of the Netherlands Statistical Office.

Articulation and Quantitative Literacy: A View from Inside Mathematics

BERNARD L. MADISON

Various voices concerned with K–16 educational alignment[1] recently have called for greater coherence in U.S. education to make it easier and more efficient for students to pass from one level to the next, especially from school to college. Driven in part by demands for greater accountability, about half the states have created K–16 policy units that have produced curriculum frameworks, a plethora of standards, and high-stakes testing largely aimed at the K–12 sector (Kirst, see pp. 107–120). These K–16 efforts aim at aligning higher education expectations, placement testing, and curricula with K–12 curricula, standards, and testing.

Nonetheless, U.S. colleges and universities continue to operate as 3,000 or so independent contractors that unwittingly wield considerable influence on K–12 education—on parents and students through coveted spots in freshman classes and on curricula through the influence of the academic disciplines. In no part of U.S. education are the problems caused by disunity (or lack of articulation) greater than in mathematics. Only language and writing compete with mathematics for prominence in K–16 curricula, and no other discipline creates as many difficulties for students as mathematics.

A principal cause of the transition problems in U.S. mathematics education is the lack of an intellectually coherent vision of mathematics among professionals responsible for mathematics education. Mathematicians similarly lack a coherent vision. The sometimes heated and often public disagreements about the nature of mathematics and about effective ways to teach it have led to a bewildering variety of curricular and pedagogical approaches.[2] Much of this confusion in curricula and pedagogy occurs near the critical transition from school to college.

As the United States has moved toward universal postsecondary education, mathematics education has become more critical and complex, especially in grades 11–14 and in the transition from school to college. This change has been driven largely by a rapid increase in the need for quantitative skills. Computers have created piles of data and myriad ways of interpreting these data. Almost daily, ordinary citizens confront data and numbers they need to understand for personal decisions, at the same time as they face increasing risk of being duped by those who misinterpret and misuse data. Quantitative Literacy (QL) is the ability to understand and use numbers and data in everyday life. Education for QL falls on all disciplines in K–16 but most heavily on mathematics and statistics, which are no longer tools only for scientists and engineers; everyday living requires that everyone have them.

This requirement poses daunting new challenges to mathematics[3] education —both K–12 and higher education. Most mathematics curricula, especially in higher education, are not designed to meet this requirement. Throughout high school and college, a single sequence of courses—geometry, algebra, trigonometry, and calculus (GATC)—dominates the mathematics curriculum. For several decades, success in mathematics has meant staying in this linear and hurried sequence. Those who do not stay in, approximately three of four, leave with disappointment (or worse) and frag-

Bernard L. Madison is Professor of Mathematics at the University of Arkansas where he previously served as Chair of Mathematics and Dean of the J.W. Fulbright College of Arts and Sciences. During 1985-89, Madison directed the MS2000 project at the National Research Council, including the 1987 *Calculus for a New Century* symposium. Madison has worked in various roles for the Advanced Placement program, including serving as Chief Faculty Consultant for AP Calculus and as a member of the Commission on the Future of AP.

mented mathematics skills that are not readily useful in their everyday lives. In effect, the GATC sequence sifts through millions of students to produce thousands of mathematicians, scientists, and engineers. Not surprisingly, this system produces the world's best-educated and most creative scientists and engineers while at the same time yielding a quantitative literacy level that ranks near the bottom among industrialized nations (OECD 2001).

As the goal of the GATC sequence, calculus serves as a surrogate for a powerful force that controls much of school and college mathematics—the need to produce mathematicians, engineers, and scientists. Underwritten by large enrollments of science and engineering students, calculus has become the gateway to advanced mathematics. Its influence, conveyed mainly through the GATC sequence, reaches far down to middle school. Largely because of the Advanced Placement (AP) Calculus Program,[4] calculus has become the capstone of high school mathematics. As such, it is now a proxy for the American yearning for badges of excellence. As a consequence, calculus also has become a lightning rod for criticism of the lack of emphasis on general education in K–16 mathematics. Clearly, what is needed is a K–14 curriculum that prepares students both for advanced mathematics study and for using mathematics in the myriad ways that it now presents itself in everyday life. To achieve that goal, major changes are needed in mathematics curricula.

Changes also are needed well beyond the mathematics curriculum. The experiences of GATC dropouts in other disciplines—the sciences, social sciences, and humanities—likely will not repair the holes in their quantitative abilities; indeed, the data analyses and quantitative measures studied in various disciplines are isolated from one another by different terminologies and contexts. Discipline-dominated college curricula offer little synergism with quantitative education.

Many of the problems with mathematics and quantitative education are problems of articulation, mismatches that place unnecessary bumps in students' paths as they navigate through school and college. Some articulation issues are vertical issues—those associated with the fit of various components as students move from grade to grade; others are horizontal—those associated with interactions between components at approximately the same grade level. In addition, there are issues of environmental articulation between the curricula in school and college and the world external to the academy. Are our curricula up to date? Are students learning what they need to know to be successful in the outside world? Do curricula meet the needs of society?

Historically, vertical articulation has been given more attention because it involves moving from one major component of U.S. education (school) to another (college). Consequently, this paper is dominated by issues of vertical articulation. Nonetheless, horizontal and environmental articulation likely are more important levers in improving U.S. education, especially in quantitative literacy.

Forces that Shape Introductory College Mathematics

The cultures of the three components of grades 11 to 14 mathematics (high school, two-year colleges, and four-year colleges and universities) differ greatly. In spite of these differences, in mathematics the four-year sector wields considerable influence over the other two. In turn, the values of mathematics graduate programs, dominated by research, are imprinted on faculty throughout college mathematics. Consequently, the culture of research mathematics has considerable influence on college and university mathematics, even down to the introductory level.

THE CULTURE OF MATHEMATICS

Mathematics research is the principal activity of what Paul Halmos called the "mathematics fraternity," which he described as a "self-perpetuating priesthood." "Mistakes are forgiven and so is obscure exposition—the indispensable requisite is mathematical insight" (Halmos 1968, 381). Prestige in mathematics is gained through manifestations of mathematical insight—developing new mathematics—and those who have prestige wield the greater power over academic mathematics.

Mathematics research is a demanding taskmaster requiring dedication, concentration, even obsession. Although most mathematics research does not aim at immediate applications, the history of unanticipated uses of mathematics provides strong support for its value to society. Consequently, educating mathematicians and creating new mathematics often dominate educating people to use mathematics.

Mathematicians see great value and power in abstract mathematical structures and seek students who can master advanced mathematics. This strongly influences views of the goals of mathematics courses and curricula, and those views are reflected in school and college mathematics. Anthony Carnevale and Donna Desrochers argue that the implicit trajectory and purpose of all disciplines is "to reproduce the college professoriate at the top of each disciplinary hierarchy" (Carnevale and Desrochers, see p. 28). Mathematics, as they go on to analyze, is no exception. Lynn Arthur Steen has compared mathematics teachers' concentrated attention on the best students to hypothetical physicians who attend primarily to their healthiest patients (Steen 2002).

The efficiency of the path to calculus and advanced mathematics has led to rigid linearity of the GATC sequence. No other discipline, save perhaps foreign language, exhibits such linearity. Foreign language education is built on using the language, however, whereas students' use of mathematics is usually far in the future. Most students in the GATC sequence never get to any authentic uses for what they learn.

Fortunately, there are some signs that the mathematics fraternity is turning its attention and vast talents to issues other than its own reproduction and expansion. Among the most recent signs are three publications: *Towards Excellence: Leading a Mathematics Department in the 21st Century* from the American Mathematical Society[5] (Ewing 1999); *Adding It Up: Helping Children Learn Mathematics* from the National Research Council[6] (Kilpatrick et al. 2001); and *Mathematical Education of Teachers* from the Conference Board of the Mathematical Sciences[7] (CBMS 2001).

THE FIRST TWO YEARS OF COLLEGE MATHEMATICS

The current CBMS survey[8] reported nearly three million U.S. postsecondary mathematics enrollments in fall semester 2000. Nearly three-fourths of these were either remedial[9] (982,000) or introductory (1,123,000) enrollments. In contrast, calculus-level enrollments totaled 700,000 and advanced mathematics enrollments only 100,000. Comparable data have been reported every five years since 1980. They document that almost three-quarters of all students in college mathematics courses never take a calculus-level mathematics course and that only about 1 in 30 enrolls in a course beyond the calculus level (Lutzer et al. 2002).

Over half of the three million undergraduate mathematics enrollments are in algebra or combinations of algebra and arithmetic, trigonometry, or analytic geometry. Algebra enrollments dominate because college algebra is a prerequisite not only for calculus but also for most general education mathematics courses, casting college algebra as a general education course.

Some states, Arkansas and Mississippi for examples, have made college algebra part of state higher education policy. In Arkansas, legislation requires that mathematics courses taken for college degree credit be at least at the level of college algebra, a testament to the perceived linearity of school and college mathematics offerings. For that reason, some courses, such as mathematics for liberal arts students, were dropped from college curricula because they were judged not up to the level of college algebra. The principal criterion for judging the level of a mathematics course became the level of the mathematics taught in the course rather than the sophistication of the applications of the mathematics. That approach, of course, makes it difficult for courses aimed at the use of mathematics to measure up as college courses.

The institutionalization of college algebra as a core general education course is fraught with misconceptions. Making college alge-

bra a requirement for some majors—e.g., for prospective elementary teachers—is even more misguided. The traditional college algebra course is filled with techniques, leaving little time for contextual problems. Students, many of whom have seen this material in prior algebra courses, struggle to master the techniques; three of four never use these skills and many of the rest find that they have forgotten the techniques by the time they are needed in later courses. No wonder the course is uninspiring and ineffective. Success rates are very low—often below 50 percent—and student dissatisfaction is high. Fortunately, many faculty and administrators realize this and reform efforts are growing. The task is nonetheless monumental.

College Influences on High School Mathematics

Multiple and complex forces shape high school mathematics. Some of these forces are matters of policy, some are circumstantial, and some are cultural. Policy forces include state and district standards for curricula and testing. Circumstantial forces include textbooks, teacher preparation, and the influence of higher education. The last is the focus of interest here.

In addition to being the locus of teacher preparation, higher education has strong influence through statements of expectations for entering students, college entrance testing (primarily the SAT and ACT), college placement testing, and national college-oriented programs. The national program with the most impact on school mathematics is the College Board's AP Program. Other national programs include the International Baccalaureate (IB) and the College Board's Pacesetter program. These national programs are discussed below.

COLLEGE STATEMENTS ON EXPECTATIONS IN MATHEMATICS

Comprehensive and useful statements from higher education institutions about mathematics expectations for entering students are rare. In spring 2001, with the help of the Education Trust, I requested from a number of states whatever statements concerning mathematics content were available from colleges and universities about expectations for the mathematics knowledge and skills of entering students. I received responses from 11 states, seven of which had such statements. The other four states had processes or policies that addressed the transition from school to college mathematics, but these did not include statements on mathematics learning, content, or skills.

The seven statements of college expectations range from comprehensive documents that look very much like a set of complete standards for grades 9–12 mathematics to explanations of skills (mostly algebraic) needed to survive in entry-level courses. California's expectations are of the first type, Maryland's and Nebraska's of the second. The latter are focused on specific entry-level courses, for example, what students should be able to do if they begin with college algebra. Because the most likely entry-level courses are intermediate algebra, college algebra, or algebra and trigonometry, these statements necessarily are heavy on algebra-based skills.

College mathematics faculty are the natural source of statements on expectations for entering students. Very often, first attempts of this kind aim far too high; college mathematicians are inclined to describe the student they would prefer to teach rather than the student that is possible and practical to find within the education system. Very often, too, statements generated by mathematics faculty are not consistent with other institutional statements about expectations or requirements. For example, many colleges use ACT scores as a criterion for entry and sometimes for placement. ACT publishes a list of mathematics competencies that various levels of ACT Mathematics test scores indicate. In one state, the mathematical competencies described by a committee of college faculty as expected of all entering students contained competencies and knowledge that were not included on the ACT list until the mathematics score far surpassed the ACT score level chosen by that state as an indication of readiness for college mathematics. Obviously, inconsistencies of this kind confuse schools, teachers, and students.

The National Council of Teachers of Mathematics (NCTM)[10] Standards (NCTM 1989, 2000) have had considerable influence on school mathematics, even though they (or localized state versions) have been implemented in different schools in different ways. These various statements describe expectations for K–12 mathematics far better than any comparable statement for college mathematics. Reliable statements of college expectations would have great influence on school mathematics, and many in school mathematics would welcome such statements. There are pockets of efforts[11] to generate statements of college expectations and to align those with school standards and transitional testing, but as of now there are almost no models that have wide acceptance.

COLLEGE PLACEMENT TESTING

In recent years, college placement testing has come under increasing scrutiny as an issue in the transition from school to college mathematics. The CBMS 2000 survey reported that almost all two-year colleges (98 percent) required mathematics placement tests of first-time students. The same survey found that 70 percent of four-year colleges and universities offered placement tests and that the tests were required of first-time students by 49 percent of these institutions. Most such tests are locally written by the user departments, but some come from the Educational Testing Service (ETS), ACT, the Mathematical Association of America (MAA),[12] and other external vendors.

Critics of college placement tests argue that these tests do not measure a student's learning in high school and are too focused on algebraic skills. An analysis reported by the Education Trust showed that some nationally available placement tests do indeed focus on algebraic skills (Education Trust 1999). Further, critics point to cases in which students are not allowed to use calculators on placement tests after having used them in school. Those who defend placement tests point to the purpose of the tests: to place students in a college mathematics course that they are prepared for. The CBMS 2000 survey reported that over 85 percent of the colleges that offered placement tests periodically assessed the effectiveness of these tests. Nonetheless, some criticism is more fundamental, based on doubt that isolated examinations of isolated skills can ever be a reliable indicator of student success. Testing experts universally advise against making important judgments based only on single test scores.

Placement testing has become more controversial with widespread use of technology and the consequent potential de-emphasis on algebraic manipulation skills. Notwithstanding considerable disagreement over what manipulation skills students should possess, faculty in individual departments often decide what skills their students need to succeed in their entry-level courses. These skills then are tested on placement examinations. It turns out that, surprisingly, many students who have done well in school mathematics are weak on such skills. Add to this the timing of many placement tests (often at summer orientations), the absence of the calculator the student is accustomed to using, and the lack of any pre-test review by students, and the results may very well be both questionable and disquieting. (Of course, placement tests and placement testing conditions—e.g., with or without technology—are likely to reflect entry-level courses and teaching conditions. If so, criticisms of placement tests and testing conditions are actually criticisms of college mathematics curricula and pedagogy.)

Many colleges and universities have no systematic way of communicating their expectations about the mathematics that entering students should know and be able to do. Consequently, the content of placement tests, although narrowly aimed at basic skills for initial success in entry-level courses, takes on a broader meaning. There are, however, partial solutions to these problems. Colleges should explain clearly the purpose of placement tests, describe what material will be tested and under what conditions, and encourage students to review the material before sitting for the tests.

TEACHER PREPARATION: FROM COLLEGE TO SCHOOL

During various periods in the past, college and university mathematics faculty have played significant roles in supporting school mathematics. During the 1960s, research mathematicians were involved in developing new school curricula and in conducting workshops for in-service teachers. Shortly after, in the wake of problems with the "new math," mathematicians largely withdrew from school mathematics and the preparation of teachers. Discussions following the introduction of standards for school mathematics in 1989 by NCTM caused many mathematicians to re-engage with school mathematics. Throughout the 1990s, this re-engagement took various forms, including some rather contentious debates about fundamental approaches to mathematics education. The 2001 CBMS report on the mathematical education of teachers seemed to signal that the re-engagement is real and constructive (CBMS 2001). Further, the MAA has planned a multifaceted, multiyear effort, Preparing Mathematicians to Educate Teachers, to help implement the recommendations of the CBMS report.

For many years, stronger teacher preparation has been the head-line recommendation from several national reports on how to improve mathematics and science education (National Commission 2000). If articulation issues are to be solved, and if QL education is to be improved, teachers—elementary, middle, and secondary—will need extensive training in teaching mathematics and statistics in context. Going one step beyond that, college faculty who teach these future teachers, which means most college faculty, also will need preparation for teaching in context.

From School to College: Mismatches and Overlaps

There are two very different views on the vertical articulation between school and college mathematics. One view reveals mismatches in both curricula and pedagogy. The other reveals that the content of school mathematics and college mathematics is largely the same. From this latter perspective, the articulation problem is one of repetition and ineffectiveness, not mismatches.

THE MISMATCHES BETWEEN SCHOOL AND COLLEGE

The NCTM standards (NCTM 2000) offer a widely accepted blueprint for both curriculum and pedagogy for school mathematics. Most state standards are generally consistent with the NCTM standards, which encourage the use of technology, promote highly interactive classrooms, and outline a reasonably broad curriculum aimed at conceptual understanding. On the other hand, college mathematics is not governed by written standards and, very often, teaching methods are determined by individual instructors. The American Mathematical Association of Two-Year Colleges (AMATYC),[13] *Crossroads in Mathematics: Standards for Introductory College Mathematics Before Calculus* (AMATYC 1995) offers one set of college guidelines for mathematics before calculus, but its effect has been muted by the influence that four-year colleges have on two-year institutions, partly driven by the need for transferability of credit. Every 10 years since

1960, the MAA's Committee on the Undergraduate Program in Mathematics (CUPM) has issued guidelines for the mathematics major, but only in the revision now being drafted are guidelines offered for undergraduate mathematics outside the major courses, now about 95 percent of all enrollments.

Many college mathematics faculty disagree with parts of the NCTM standards, especially those that are characteristic of recent reform projects. For example, many do not think that technology—calculators or computers—helps in teaching introductory college mathematics. Further, many college faculty adhere to traditional lecture and testing methods and place heavy responsibility on students for their learning. This has increased variety in college mathematics, more so in pedagogy and the tools used in learning than in course content.

Introductory course content is pretty standard. Students moving from school to college are likely to find the content of courses familiar, although the material may be presented in a different way and at a faster pace; technology may be used, tolerated, or banned; and students likely will be left more on their own to learn and demonstrate that learning on traditional tests. The mismatch in the articulated curriculum between school and college consists primarily of a narrowing of broader school mathematics to a limited set of introductory college courses dominated by algebra and pre-calculus. The narrowing is most notable in the absence of geometry, data analysis, and probability in mainline introductory college mathematics.

THE DILEMMA OF SCHOOL MATHEMATICS TRACKS

The strongest cultural force shaping school mathematics is the widespread tradition of tracking, which is especially prevalent in high schools. There often is no easy way to move from the "lower" track to the college preparatory track. Unfortunately, especially for QL education in which applications of everyday mathematics can be quite challenging, the use of the adjective "consumer" or "general" as a code for second-rate courses has done general education a grave disservice.

There are some glimmers of hope. Elimination of the "general mathematics" track was one of the major goals of the 1989 NCTM standards (NCTM 1989). Data from the 1999 State Indicators of Science and Mathematics Education showed that the proportion of U.S. high school students enrolled in general or consumer mathematics dropped from about 20 percent in 1990 to about 8 percent in 1998 (CCSSO 2002). The 2000 version of the NCTM standards reinforced the 1989 standards by prescribing a "common foundation of mathematics to be learned by all students" (NCTM 2000).

About 20 years ago when I was chair of the department of mathematical sciences at the University of Arkansas, I was struggling with ways to reduce enrollments in intermediate algebra, the one remedial mathematics course we taught. The state was pressuring us to reduce remedial enrollments, but my most pressing reason was to reduce the range of courses we had to cover. We were the only doctoral and research institution in the state and our resources were stretched very thin, covering responsibilities from high school algebra to postgraduate seminars.

My local school system, which had one high school (from which both my son and daughter later graduated), was revising its mathematics offerings and I was invited to meet with the superintendent and associate superintendent to give them advice. I took the opportunity to talk about how they could help reduce our remedial enrollments.

Typically, they were offering two tracks of mathematics. One was a college preparatory track with the usual courses—geometry, Algebra I and II, trigonometry, and AP Calculus—actually a very strong offering. The second track was general or business mathematics, I don't remember the exact terminology. I asked why they offered this clearly weaker track and why they didn't keep all the students on the track that would prepare them for college-level mathematics, since at the time, any student who graduated from high school could enroll at the University of Arkansas. Because we did not require that they had followed a college preparatory track, students from this weaker track would almost surely land in remedial algebra. My superintendent and his associate were very frank: they were not going to take the heat for students failing. I noted that they were passing that heat on to us at the university and they did not disagree.

Unfortunately for QL education, the college preparatory track has preparation for calculus as its goal and does not include significant contextual uses of mathematics. Measurement, geometry, data analysis, and probability—all parts of most school mathematics curricula—have strong QL themes, but with calculus as the goal these get shortchanged. By attempting to articulate well with colleges, schools narrow the coverage of mathematics to what is needed to succeed in calculus. The majority of high school students who never make it through a calculus course—about three of four—never reap the benefits of this narrowed mathematics curriculum.

On the other hand, students who are in a noncollege preparatory mathematics track are often shortchanged by the lower level of the courses and find themselves unprepared for college mathematics. When they arrive at college, as many do, they are likely to enter the wasteland of remedial courses.

OVERLAPS: TOO MUCH OF THE SAME THING

A second way of looking at school and college mathematics shows that there is enormous overlap, especially in the content of college courses with large enrollments. As indicated above, the CBMS 2000 survey showed that approximately 60 percent of the mathematics enrollments in four-year colleges and 80 percent of those in two-year colleges were in courses whose content is taught in high school. (Although calculus is taught in high schools, it is not included in these calculations. If it were, the 80 percent would rise to 87 percent and the 60 percent to 77 percent.) On the other hand, the fastest-growing enrollment in high school mathematics is in courses for college credit. Though seemingly antithetical, these two phenomena are related, and aspects of this overlap are seriously impeding students' learning of mathematics.

The GATC topics covered in high school geometry, algebra, and trigonometry align quite well with the corresponding college sequence, especially elementary, intermediate, and college algebra. In one sense, there is too much agreement, because many if not most students repeat much mathematics in moving from high school to college. This repetition is not only inefficient, it is discouraging to many students, and learning suffers. Other students mistakenly welcome the repetition, thinking it will lead to an easy A. As described earlier, much of the repeated material is devoted to algebraic and trigonometric methods, with little time for applications because the students are already deemed to be behind schedule. Because most of this material is preparation for later study that eludes most students, such courses are often dull and depressing for both teachers and students.

Remedial mathematics in college—accounting for one of three enrollments—is often the most depressing of all. Remedial mathematics is almost always arithmetic or high school algebra. Consequently, except for returning students who have been away from school for some time, students in remedial courses are repeating material they failed to learn in earlier, possibly multiple, efforts. Having to repeat work, not making progress toward a degree, and studying uninspiring—and to students, illogical—subject matter makes remedial mathematics courses unusually dreary. The subject matter of these courses is the kind of content—much of it algebraic methods—that appears to be best learned with attentive practice the first time through. Misunderstanding and bad habits are hard to undo. Consequently, the proportion of students who are unsuccessful in remedial mathematics courses is often high, in the range of one-half to two-thirds.

In the mid-1970s, I was named director of the mathematics component of the Academic Skills Enhancement Program (ASEP) at Louisiana State University. The goal of the program was to increase the success rate of students in remedial mathematics. We instituted a moderately complex system of four courses, each a half-semester long, whereby students would progress to the next course or start over based on the results of the previous course. I taught several of these classes, including one section of the first course in which all the students had failed to progress on their first try.

Never have I had a more challenging assignment. I was helping college-age (and older) students to succeed in ninth-grade mathematics after they had all failed to do so in the previous eight weeks. It was there that I learned the many different reasons why students have trouble with elementary algebra. I also learned why remedial algebra in universities faces almost insurmountable obstacles given the levels of success expected in most academic enterprises. Perhaps 30 years later, with the use of technology, the obstacles can be overcome.

DUAL CREDIT COURSES

The enormous overlap between college and high school mathematics has fueled the recent growth of dual credit[14] courses in high schools. The expansion is typified by this common scenario: A two-year college enters into an agreement with a high school to give college credit to high school students for specific courses taken in the high school that also count for high school credit (whence the term "dual" credit). Agreements of this type have been made for college credit in most disciplines. In mathematics, dual credit is being awarded in courses from beginning algebra up through calculus. These agreements are generating considerable college credit in courses taught in high schools by high school teachers, and most dual credit programs have nothing similar to the AP Examinations to validate their quality. The CBMS 2000 survey reported that 15 percent of all sections of college algebra (or algebra and trigonometry) taught in two-year colleges in fall 2000 were for dual credit.

A recent national survey estimated that one-half of all juniors and seniors in U.S. high schools (approximately 3.5 million) are enrolled in courses that carry credit for both high school graduation and college degrees (Clark 2001). Some of these courses are in the examination-based programs of AP and IB in which college credit depends on scores on national or international examinations and not merely on high school grades. According to the data in this report,[15] however, most dual credit enrollees (57 percent) are in courses that, unlike AP and IB, have no uniform examination. Because the recent growth of dual credit has been so large, there are no good data on how students with this credit fare in college, but if nothing significant has changed except the awarding of

college credit, the knowledge gained by many of these students will be insufficient for success in subsequent college courses. Will they then re-enroll in courses for which they already have credit? Standards for this practice are urgently needed, lest we push the line between college and school mathematics—if there still is to be one—well below what it should be.

The largest examination-based dual credit program is AP,[16] a 50-year-old program of the College Board aimed at providing opportunities for advanced study in high school with the possibility of receiving credit or advanced placement in college. AP has been growing by about 10 percent per year for the past 20 years and now offers 34 courses and examinations. Approximately 1.5 million AP Examinations will be given in 2002 to over a million high school students, mostly juniors and seniors. About 200,000 of these will be in AP Calculus and about 50,000 in AP Statistics.

AP Calculus has become the goal of ambitious mathematics students because it is a hallmark of high school success. To enroll in AP Calculus by grade 12, students must take Algebra I by grade 8. The lure of AP Calculus has accelerated the high school mathematics sequence and consequently reduced the time for teaching mathematics in context. Although contextual teaching was one of the goals of calculus reform, and the AP Calculus Course Description issued in 1998 represented a consensus on a reformed calculus course, AP Calculus is still short on the kinds of contextual problems needed to develop QL.

The AP science and social science courses do offer contextual problems, but like the college disciplines they emulate, these AP Course Descriptions and examinations are developed independently with no special efforts toward synergism in learning. Because AP courses constitute a large portion of college general education core requirements for many students, AP courses need to contribute significantly to crosscutting competencies such as QL. This will clearly require closer coordination among the various AP courses.

Notwithstanding its public prominence, AP Calculus represents only a fraction of high school calculus courses. Enrollments in all kinds of high school calculus courses are approximately 600,000 each year, roughly half of which are in courses called AP Calculus, but only about 200,000 students take an AP Calculus examination and about two-thirds of these qualify for college credit. That leaves about 450,000 students with a calculus course that likely will be repeated in college. Contrary to what we might expect, a high school calculus experience that does not result in college credit or advanced placement is likely to cause the student difficulty in college mathematics.

This problem of calculus articulation was addressed years ago by a CUPM Panel on Calculus Articulation consisting of four high school teachers and three college teachers (CUPM 1987). Their report concluded that a successful high school calculus course requires a qualified teacher with high but realistic expectations, a full year of study based on something equivalent to the AP Course Description, and students who are willing and able to learn. The report described two models of high school calculus courses that are unsuccessful: one is a partial year "highlights of calculus" course and the second is a year long, watered-down version that does not deal with the concepts of calculus in any depth. One of the panelists was quoted as describing the effects in college of the highlights course as "like showing a 10-minute highlights film of a baseball game, including the final score, and then forcing the viewer to watch the entire game from the beginning—with a quiz after every inning." Reports such as this one provided background for a joint statement from the MAA and NCTM in 1986[17] recommending, in part, "that all students taking calculus in secondary school who are performing satisfactorily in the course should expect to place out of the comparable college calculus course." A 2002 National Research Council study reached a similar conclusion, recommending that "all calculus taught in high school should be at the college level" (Gollub et al. 2002, 537).

The huge overlap between school and college mathematics complicates the school-to-college transition, partly because the line between the two systems is so blurred. There is nothing inherently wrong with students learning calculus in high school or learning algebra in college. There is something very wrong with students repeating the same material, whether it is arithmetic, algebra, or calculus. Repeating and failing are the culprits in this overlap. Schools and colleges must concentrate more effort on students' learning, success, and progress. There is little value in weak courses that do not lead to progress. Moreover, repeating courses when previous experience has failed is often a barrier to success.

COLLEGE MATHEMATICS AS A FILTER

One of the headlines of the calculus reform movements was the phrase "a pump, not a filter," expressed by National Academy of Engineering President Robert White in his opening remarks to the Calculus for a New Century Colloquium in 1987 (White 1988). Unfortunately, college mathematics still is widely used as a filter.

There are two different reasons for using mathematics as a filter. Some disciplines require particular analytical and critical thinking skills that are best learned in mathematics courses. In such cases, mathematics courses are legitimate prerequisites and necessarily serve as filters. In many cases, however, mathematics is used as a filter only because the courses are difficult and only the best prepared and most dedicated survive. This type of filtering misuses mathematics and abuses students.

> When I was a new chair of the department of mathematical sciences at the University of Arkansas, I was introduced at a social event to the dean of the college of business administration. As we chatted, I mentioned the recent increase in the mathematics requirements for business majors to two courses—one in finite mathematics and one in polynomial calculus. I said that I hoped the students would do well and that we didn't want these courses to reduce his college's enrollment. He immediately said that reduction of enrollment, that is, filtering out students, was a major purpose of the requirement. So, like my school superintendent, the business dean was passing the heat on to me.
>
> Later, as dean of my college for 10 years, I learned a lot more about the role of mathematics courses as filters. I heard about it from faculty and administrators in architecture, business, engineering, agriculture, and education, and from my own faculty, including premedical advisers, science faculty, humanities faculty, and fine arts faculty. Some were for filtering and some were against it, but all recognized it as a key role played by mathematics.

Unfortunately, many mathematics faculty accept the long tradition of their discipline as a filter and expect a large number of students to fail. This expectation casts a pall that hangs over many mathematics classrooms, causes additional students to fail, and increases resentment toward mathematics.

STATISTICS ARTICULATION

In most colleges, statistics courses are spread across several departments including statistics, mathematics, engineering, social sciences, agriculture, and business. By and large, college statistics is taught to support majors in other disciplines, often by faculty whose appointments are in the disciplines served. Statistics has been viewed as a research method in agriculture and the social sciences—consistent with Richard Scheaffer's characterization of statistics as "keeper of the scientific method" (Scheaffer et al., see p. 145). In many institutions, there is little interaction or synergy among the statistics courses taught in various disciplines. Partly because of this dispersion, college statistics departments have never had sufficient enrollments to justify large departmental faculties. Measured by degree programs, statistics is largely a graduate discipline.

But now statistics is also a high school discipline. The AP Statistics course, first offered in 1997, has grown remarkably fast, with about 50,000 examinations in 2002. Ten years ago, when the College Board's AP Mathematics Development Committee was first asked to make a recommendation about developing AP Statistics, they were stymied because there was no typical first college course in statistics, which was necessary for the standard prototype of an AP course. This lack of a standard first college course was indicative of the dispersion of statistics teaching in higher education. Therefore, in a reverse of the traditional pattern, AP Statistics, which was developed by college and school faculty outside the muddled arena of college statistics, has become a model for a first college course in statistics. This history illustrates the degree of difficulty in changing college curricula without outside impetus.

The position of AP Statistics in school and college curricula differs from AP Calculus in that the former does not sit in an established sequence of prerequisite and succeeding courses. This freedom promotes access to AP Statistics and does not affect students' course choices nearly as dramatically as does AP Calculus. AP Statistics has been well served by the introduction of a strand on data analysis and probability in the K–12 mathematics standards, which has increased the visibility of statistics to students and teachers.

One explanation for the weakness of quantitative literacy at the college level is that many undergraduate degrees do not require statistics. Even when there are program requirements, they are aimed at using statistics as a research method (in the social sciences and agriculture) or are very bound up with the jargon and practices of professional education (in business and engineering). Rarely are statistics courses required for general education, where their goal would be to help students use statistics to make decisions concerning public issues or personal welfare.

A little bit of elementary statistics—perhaps a chapter or two—does appear in some introductory mathematics courses. Some appears in courses on finite mathematics that often are required for business majors and sometimes are part of a general education core. There also is some in the mathematics courses for prospective elementary school teachers; it is essential there because of the presence of the data analysis and probability strand in the K–12 mathematics standards. As we have noted, however, college courses change very slowly and college faculty are neither attuned to changes in K–12 curricula nor much inclined to be guided by forces external to their discipline or department.

In 1991, CUPM recommended that every mathematical sciences major should take at least one semester of probability and statistics at a level that requires calculus as a prerequisite (CUPM 1991), but this recommendation by mathematicians for mathematics majors is somewhat inconsistent with statisticians' data-oriented view of statistics. The CUPM report acknowledged that in one course it is difficult to cover an introduction to probability and also convey an understanding of statistics. Consequently, a mathematics graduate is likely to have very little statistics education, and many graduate programs in mathematics do not correct this deficiency. Thus both secondary school mathematics teachers and college mathematics faculty are likely to have weak training in statistics, leaving them unprepared to teach courses in data analysis and probability. These deficits in articulation, along with the virtual absence of statistics in statements of college expectations for mathematics preparation (including the content of placement tests), weaken significantly the emphasis on data analysis and probability in school mathematics. To improve statistics education in the schools, it must be strengthened in colleges and become a more prominent part of general education.

TEACHING ACROSS THE CURRICULUM: SYNERGISM IN EDUCATION

The most important area of horizontal articulation in education is teaching crosscutting competencies in all curricular components. The most notable example of this is "writing across the curriculum," a practice that has been successfully implemented in a number of colleges and universities. Many believe that a similar model will be required for effective QL education.

Teaching QL across a college curriculum will require considerably more coordination among the disciplines than currently exists at most institutions. The independence of disciplines is strong. According to Carnevale and Desroches (see p. 21), "academic specialization that creates virtually impregnable barriers between the discrete disciplinary silos of mathematics, science, and the humanities."

My experience confirms these barriers. I was a double major in college, in mathematics and physics. I took 12 or 13 mathematics courses and an equal number of physics courses. Mathematics was a part of all the physics courses, and occasionally some physics concept would emerge in a mathematics course. Aside from elementary applications of calculus concepts—mostly the derivative—I rarely recognized any of the mathematics from my mathematics courses in the mathematics I saw in physics courses. They were two parallel worlds, occasionally touching but never merging or synergistically promoting understanding.

In my Ph.D. studies in mathematics I minored in physics, taking 12 hours of graduate work. As in my undergraduate experience, physics and mathematics were still worlds apart. And physics and mathematics should be the easiest subjects to integrate. My years of college teaching tell me that my experience is not unusual; there is very little synergy in teaching mathematics across college disciplines.

ARTICULATION WITH THE ENVIRONMENT

In his paper "Mathematics for Literacy" (see pp. 75-89), Jan de Lange makes several observations about what is needed to gain mathematical or quantitative literacy:

- The mathematics that is taught should be embedded in the real world of the student.

- Mathematical literacy will lead to different curricula in different cultures.

- The content of [mathematics] curricula will have to be modernized at least every five to 10 years.

U.S. mathematics curricula, both in high school and college, fail badly in meeting de Lange's criteria. Although high school and introductory college mathematics do include some so-called real-world problems, these very often are not embedded in the world of any student. Some national needs are cited as reasons for stronger mathematics education, but the duties of citizenship in a democracy—perhaps the most fundamental need of the country—are rarely considered when teaching mathematics. The school curriculum may have been modernized once in the past 50 years, depending on the interpretation of "modernize," and introductory college mathematics currently may be undergoing some reform, but there is no systematic way to modernize college offerings. Every five to 10 years seems beyond the pale.

Beyond a lack of connection to real-world applications, there is an additional mismatch between the mathematics curriculum and available jobs. According to Carnevale and Desrochers, "too many people do not have enough basic mathematical literacy to make a decent living even while many more people take courses such as geometry, algebra, and calculus than will ever actually use the mathematical procedures taught in these courses in high school" (see p. 25).

How Did We Get Here and How Do We Get Out?

The foregoing paints a clear picture of an enormously inefficient and ineffective system of introductory college mathematics. The GATC sequence, driven by the needs of scientists and engineers, controls the system, but the system now serves—or more accurately, disserves—a much larger population. In the interest of efficiency, we have gathered together largely uninspiring algebraic methods and created courses with a singular, dominating goal of preparation for calculus, the gateway to the use and further study of mathematics. Those who do not survive are left on the side of this narrow road with fragmented and often useless methodological skills. The system produces millions of such students every year, at least three of four entering college students.

Two major corrections are needed. First, the rigid linearity of the route to advanced mathematics must be abandoned. Second, college mathematics courses must have independent value and not be only routes to somewhere else.

Similar to mathematics research, learning mathematics at the college level need not be linear. Students can learn mathematical concepts and reasoning through combinatorial mathematics, through data analysis, and through geometry, as well as through calculus. Even fundamental concepts of calculus—rate of change, approximation, accumulation—can be understood outside the infrastructure of calculus methodology. A major impetus for the calculus reform movement was a 1983 conference convened to discuss discrete mathematics as an alternative gateway to college mathematics (Douglas 1986). By developing multiple interconnecting pathways to the advanced study of mathematics, introductory college mathematics can become more appealing and more useful to students. Further, a broader view of college mathematics can support a broader school mathematics curriculum and remove much of the emphasis on a failed system of courses dominated by algebraic methodology.

Because of their easy experience learning mathematics, most mathematicians do not relate well to a student struggling with factoring quadratics or mangling the addition of algebraic fractions. We mathematicians see the larger algebraic architecture and the logic underlying the operations; however, some of us can identify with that bewildered student by reflecting on how we first use a new graphing calculator or software package. Here the architecture and underlying logic of the hardware or software are obscure. So what do we do? We begin to use the calculator or the software package and refer to the manual primarily when needed. No one would first spend days pouring over the manual trying to commit to memory procedures or keystrokes to accomplish thousands of unconnected operations. Many of our students see college algebra and trigonometry in this same illogical light. Every operation is new and independent, making retention of skills until the end of the semester unlikely and until the next year almost impossible.

Just as computer software and calculators are useful to all of us, so is algebra. For education to be effective, these uses of algebra must be given priority over techniques, not only to accomplish tasks that use algebra but also to master algebra. This approach may help break the rigid GATC verticality and can increase access to and success in both mathematics and its applications. And technology can surely help.

Much of the GATC sequence consists of learning skills that can be performed by technology. Unfortunately, mathematicians do not agree on what manual (paper-and-pencil) skills are essential or on how technology helps; some even ban technology. Mathematicians know their own algebraic skills served them well, so when they see students falter because of poor algebraic skills it reinforces the beliefs that help maintain the GATC stranglehold.

Both the NCTM Standards and AMATYC *Crossroads* have fully endorsed using technology in mathematics education. Nonetheless, the mixed attitudes of college and university mathematics faculty toward technology have created a dual system in school mathematics: first teach and test it with technology, then teach and test it without technology. The AP Calculus Examinations display this duality—one part with calculators and one part without. No doubt this model has strengths, but we can no longer afford these strengths; there is too much else to do. We can teach and test mathematical skills and concepts using graphing and computer algebra systems (CAS) technology. Computers are part of the world of our students. It is past time to use them regularly in teaching mathematics.

By focusing introductory college mathematics courses on learning by using, especially learning by using technology, these courses can extend school mathematics at the same time they fill in gaps in learning. We can stop the treadmill of repeated failures in repetitious courses. We can stop telling students that they will need algebra later, perhaps in calculus and its applications. Instead, we can show students why algebra is important and what they need to master. With wise use of technology and learning-by-doing, the GATC sequence in college can be replaced by courses that enhance the use of mathematics in other disciplines, prepare students for the quantitative demands of everyday life, and support the study of advanced mathematics. In this way, introductory college mathematics can become a pump, not a filter.

Notes

1. The Bridge Project, housed at the Stanford Institute for Higher Education Research, has as its aim "to improve opportunities for all students to enter and succeed in postsecondary education by strengthening the compatibility between higher education admissions and placement requirements and K–12 curriculum frameworks, standards, and assessments."

   The Education Trust was created to promote high academic standards for all students at all levels, kindergarten through college. The Education Trust publishes *Thinking K–16,* an occasional newsletter that contains discussions of issues in K–16 education and how they are being addressed by various coalitions. See www.EdTrust.org.

   The American Diploma Project (ADP) is aimed at aligning high school academic standards with higher education and the needs of the new economy. ADP is sponsored by Achieve, Inc., the Education Trust, the Thomas B. Fordham Foundation, and the National Alliance of Business.

2. Personal communication. Attributed to William Schmidt by Alfred Manaster.

3. Because statistics is a part of the mathematics curriculum in K–12, mathematics at this level is often interpreted to include statistics. In this paper, the more inclusive "mathematical sciences" often will be abbreviated to "mathematics."

4. Advanced Placement Calculus is a program of the College Board that provides a course description and national examinations whereby students can earn college credit or advanced placement in college courses while still in high school.

5. The American Mathematical Society (AMS) is a professional society of mathematicians that focuses on issues in research and graduate study in mathematics.

6. The National Research Council (NRC) is the operating arm of the National Academy of Science, the National Academy of Engineering, and the Institute of Medicine.

7. The Conference Board of the Mathematical Sciences (CBMS) is a confederation of presidents of 17 professional organizations in the mathematical sciences.

8. Every five years since 1965, CBMS has surveyed college and university mathematical sciences departments on curricula, enrollments, and instructional practices. The CBMS 2000 survey was conducted in fall 2000.

9. Remedial mathematics often is called developmental mathematics and consists of courses in arithmetic, beginning algebra, and intermediate algebra. "Remedial" often indicates that college degree credit is not awarded.

10. NCTM is the National Council of Teachers of Mathematics, a professional organization that focuses on K–12 mathematics education.

11. The American Diploma Project cited above is one such effort.

12. MAA is the Mathematical Association of America, a professional organization that focuses on undergraduate mathematics. The MAA Placement Test Program, established in 1977, was discontinued in 1999 but some of the tests still are being used.

13. AMATYC is the American Mathematical Association of Two-Year Colleges, a professional association primarily of two-year college faculty.

14. Other terms used to describe these courses are "dual enrollment" and "concurrent enrollment."

15. The report gave the number of students in AP as 1.2 million in 2000; however, this was the number of examinations taken. The number of students was closer to 800,000. The estimate of 300,000 U.S. students in IB also seems too large. Using these better estimates, the percentage of students in courses that do not have national examinations is probably higher than the 57 percent cited.

16. The author has considerable experience with the AP Program, including a term as Chief Faculty Consultant for AP Calculus (1995–1999) and as a member of the Commission on the Future of the Advanced Placement Program (1999–2001).

17. Reprinted as Appendix B of the Statement on Competencies in Mathematics Expected of Entering College Students, endorsed by the Intersegmental Committee of the Academic Senates, California Community Colleges, California State University, and University of California. Sacramento, California, 1997.

References

American Mathematical Association of Two-Year Colleges (AMATYC). 1995. *Crossroads in Mathematics: Standards for Introductory College Mathematics Before Calculus.* Memphis, TN: American Mathematical Association of Two-Year Colleges.

Clark, Richard W. 2001. "Dual Credit: A Report of Programs and Policies that Offer High School Students College Credits." Philadelphia, PA: Pew Charitable Trusts.

Committee on the Undergraduate Program in Mathematics (CUPM). 1987. "Report of the Panel on Calculus Articulation: Problems in the Transition from High School Calculus to College Calculus." *American Mathematical Monthly* 94: 776–85.

Committee on the Undergraduate Program in Mathematics (CUPM). 1991. "The Undergraduate Major in the Mathematical Sciences." Reprinted in *Heeding the Call for Change,* edited by Lynn Arthur Steen, 225–47. Washington, DC: Mathematical Association of America, 1992.

Conference Board of the Mathematical Sciences (CBMS). 2001. *Mathematical Education of Teachers.* Providence, RI and Washington, DC: American Mathematical Society and Mathematical Association of America.

Council of Chief State School Officers (CCSSO). 2002. *State Indicators of Science and Mathematics Education 2000.* Washington, DC: Council of Chief State School Officers.

Douglas, Ronald G. 1986. *Toward a Lean and Lively Calculus.* Washington, DC: Mathematical Association of America.

Education Trust. 1999. *Thinking K–16: Ticket to Nowhere.* Washington, DC: Education Trust.

Ewing, John, ed. 1999. *Towards Excellence: Leading a Mathematics Department in the 21st Century.* Providence, RI: American Mathematical Society. http://www.ams.org/towardsexcellence/.

Gollub, Jerry P., Meryl W. Bertenthal, Jay B. Labov, and Philip C. Curtis, eds. 2002. *Learning and Understanding: Improving Advanced Study of Mathematics and Science in U.S. High Schools.* Washington, DC: National Academy Press.

Halmos, Paul. 1968. "Mathematics as a Creative Art." *American Scientist* 56(4): 375–89.

Kilpatrick, Jeremy, Jane Swafford, Bradford Findell, eds. 2001. *Adding It Up: Helping Children Learn Mathematics.* Washington, DC: National Academy Press.

Lutzer, David, et al. 2002. *Statistical Abstract of Undergraduate Programs in the Mathematical Sciences in the United States, Fall 2000 CBMS Survey.* Washington, DC: Mathematical Association of America.

National Commission on Mathematics and Science Teaching for the 21st Century (National Commission). 2000. *Before It's Too Late.* Washington, DC: U.S. Department of Education.

National Council of Teachers of Mathematics (NCTM). 1989. *Curriculum and Evaluation Standards for School Mathematics.* Reston, VA: National Council of Teachers of Mathematics.

National Council of Teachers of Mathematics (NCTM). 2000. *Principles and Standards for School Mathematics.* Reston, VA: National Council of Teachers of Mathematics.

Organization for Economic Cooperation and Development (OECD) Center for Educational Research and Evaluation. 2001. *Education Policy Analysis 2001.* Paris: Organization for Economic Cooperation and Development.

Steen, Lynn Arthur. 2002. "Achieving Mathematical Proficiency for All." *College Board Review.* (Spring)196: 4–11.

White, Robert M. 1988. "Calculus of Reality." In *Calculus for a New Century,* edited by Lynn Arthur Steen, 6–9. Washington, DC: Mathematical Association of America.

PART II
FORUM PAPERS

Addressing Societal and Workforce Needs

DAVID F. BRAKKE

Educational landscapes are often largely disaggregated collections of units with little connection between them. Educational institutions at the same level are rarely linked to one another and articulation between different levels generally is haphazard. Although there have been some serious attempts to build bridges from secondary to postsecondary education and from community college to university, with some attention paid to alignment, poor articulation remains a concern. Even in mathematics, perhaps the most vertical of disciplines in its range from kindergarten to graduate school, the transitions are not seamless. The teaching of mathematics is often isolated. Although mathematics is a consistent part of the curriculum throughout the various educational levels, it is increasingly disconnected from other subject areas as grade levels rise. Further, with the rapid expansion of mathematics offerings in high schools, students enter community colleges and universities with widely varying backgrounds.

The relatively poor integration of mathematics with other disciplines occurs in spite of the rich context for mathematical and statistical applications in the world around us and the increasing demand for a workforce that can think, analyze, and compute. Reasoning in a world awash in numbers and data requires quantitative analysis. Using mathematics and statistics to make decisions and solve problems in real-world settings not only provides the context for mathematics but also demonstrates its essential value. Mathematics as a discipline can be examined for its own intricacy and beauty, while its societal significance lies in its application.

As someone who has been involved in scientific studies that relate to policy issues and who teaches a course on environmental science and public policy, I first want to provide a context for the kinds of quantitative approaches that are necessary to address issues we face in understanding and managing natural resources. If science is to inform policy, we must ask the right question, collect appropriate data, and conduct analysis in a decision-making framework. Such a process naturally involves design, sampling, error, estimation, and uncertainty. We might consider rates, variability, predictability, scales, and limits. We might need to evaluate actual and perceived risks and find ways to manage those risks. Ultimately, we must communicate the results. How do we best communicate the results of an assessment of risk, especially when a public comfortable with probabilities in weather forecasts expects science to have certain answers? Informed decision making in a world full of data requires quantitative reasoning.

A second example of the application of quantitative analysis comes from a consideration of science and the courts. From DNA fingerprinting, to what constitutes evidence or who is an expert, to how we interpret various acts passed by Congress, e.g., the Wilderness Act or the Endangered Species Act, the courts have not done an adequate job. Some would call the performance lousy, while others might go so far as to suggest that there is no real role for science in the courts or that scientific evidence rarely determines outcomes. If the latter is in part the case, it is likely due to the inability of the judicial process to incorporate effectively scientific and numerical information in deliberations. A broad examination of the role of numeracy in our legal and policymaking frameworks is war-

---

David F. Brakke is Dean of Science and Mathematics at James Madison University. A limnologist, Brakke has studied ecosystem assessment, lake management, and climate change in the U.S., Canada and northern Europe. He has been actively involved with professional organizations concerning science and mathematics education, teacher preparation, and undergraduate research. Brakke also writes a quarterly column on science and society for the Association of Women in Science (AWIS) Magazine.

ranted. We ask large questions as a society and should expect reasoned answers that consider evidence, recognizing that values also play an important role in setting policy.

If we look at higher education institutions, we often find students doing relatively poorly in quantitative courses regardless of the discipline in which they are offered; the problem is not limited to mathematics courses. Simply teaching statistics in a psychology department is not an answer to providing context. As I consider the reasons why student performance is not better, I can identify at least nine factors on my own campus, and they apply to quantitative courses in most areas. Some of the reasons relate to affective behavior, both with respect to the student and the instructor. We must examine the ways we can improve student performance in quantitative courses and prepare students for decision making that involves considering, analyzing, and communicating quantitative information. I suggest that greater focus on improving performance, recognizing success, and identifying rich examples of practice may prove more helpful than focusing on what is wrong. Mathematics and statistics are interesting *and* practical.

We may want to consider defining learning outcomes for students with the goal of aligning those outcomes with societal and workforce needs. For example, if I look at my own institution, James Madison University, it has large and strong programs in five areas that are vital to the future of Virginia's economy: science, mathematics, and technology; information technology; health professions; business; and teacher preparation. As we talk to employers, we find they are asking for students who are broadly educated and have a number of critical skills and desirable attitudes, including the ability to communicate and work effectively in groups. Our programs in science and mathematics are concerned with content but also with developing a way of thinking. We provide experiences, develop skills, emphasize the use of information technology and communication, and work to enhance critical thinking and quantitative reasoning. These efforts are also applicable to the other four areas mentioned above.

We can also look at changes in various disciplines that require new or different analytical and quantitative approaches. For example, in the world of biology we have become data rich, with new horizons requiring new sets of skills. We have genomics, nano-technology, biomaterials, DNA computing, neuroscience and cognition, and environmental science (or biocomplexity) in all dimensions and on all scales. This has led the National Science Foundation (NSF) to describe "The New Biology" or "Biology for the 21st Century," which is multidimensional and collaborative, multidisciplinary, information-driven, and education-oriented. Modeling, managing with information, recognizing patterns in vast amounts of data, all require sophisticated mathematical and computational skills. Mathematics, statistics, and computational

science have become essential elements of biology, determining anew what quantitative skills are needed.

We need not focus on workforce needs to design programs, but neither should we ignore them. Preparation for the twenty-first century workforce must be part of our educational agenda. We can respond by developing or modifying programs to enhance skills and foster cognitive development. We also can shape attitudes, improve habits, and develop a level of facility in the use of mathematics and statistics as a necessary part of reasoning. To achieve quantitative literacy in our students, we must enhance the ability to ask questions, including the development of healthy skepticism. We can establish learning outcomes for students as explicit, measurable goals and provide a learning experience that is rich in application in multiple settings.

Quantitative skills development must be seen in relation not only to mathematics and other disciplines but also in relation to comprehension and communication. Quantitative approaches are part of reasoning and thinking processes rather than something uncoupled and solely mathematical. Perhaps this is illustrated succinctly by the observation that often the students who struggle in statistics are not careful readers or clear writers. Their performance in statistics can be improved by attention first to critical reading, which is also essential to problem-solving skills. Quantitative reasoning involves numbers and words in a context.

As we respond to these issues across institutions, it may be necessary to focus our discussion of quantitative reasoning separately on three populations of students: the enhancement of quantitative reasoning for all students, for those students entering K–12 classrooms as future teachers, and for students in the disciplines and professional programs. I see each of these tasks as different and as requiring separate strategies. "For all students" speaks to issues of society and civic responsibility—those abilities necessary for an educated citizen to make informed decisions. Separate attention to preparing future teachers recognizes the fundamental need for quantitative approaches in all areas of the K–12 curriculum, not just in mathematics. The third area of attention, quantitative reasoning in the disciplines and professional programs, is essential if we are to move to increasing levels of sophistication in application. At least from my perspective, education in quantitative reasoning will not succeed if it is restricted to general education or limited solely to mathematics. It must be a goal of all institutions, defined as a learning outcome for all graduating students, and assessed directly as part of the evaluation of students' major programs.

Gone are the days when we required a course but did not build on it in the major programs. Why not require major programs to set explicit goals for quantitative reasoning, develop plans for enhancing quantitative skills beyond basic required mathematics and statistics courses, and then report on the results as part of their program assessments? This approach would contribute greatly to a dialogue and ultimately to significant cooperation between mathematics, statistics, and the disciplines and professional programs in achieving overall goals for students. Appealing to the disciplines for their assistance in addressing quantitative reasoning is essential. It would also be transformative, expanding what we expect in coordinated learning outcomes across an institution and in the process redefining a rich, liberal education. A true liberal education should demand the consideration of quantitative reasoning beyond the department of mathematics and recognize and celebrate the need and utility of quantitative approaches in thinking and reasoning.

Making Mathematics Meaningful

ARNOLD PACKER

The organizers of this Forum picked an opportune time to bring mathematics education to wider attention. Congress has mandated third- to eighth-grade tests in the new Elementary and Secondary Education Act, Leave No Child Behind. Students in a number of states already are facing high school exit examinations, and other states are likely to follow suit. Students who fail will be denied their high school diplomas. Unless the situation changes quickly, the failure rate and the number of denied diplomas will be too high. As a result, the entire standards movement will be put in jeopardy.

If history is any guide, many of those denied will have failed their mathematics examination. Even today, many students interested in college programs leading to degrees in a technology field are denied entrance because of weakness in mathematics. Results of the National Assessment of Educational Progress (NAEP) document the difficulty American students—especially black and Hispanic students—have in learning mathematics. Results of the National Adult Literacy Survey (NALS) document continuing difficulty beyond adolescence.

As indicated by the NAEP, the test likely to be used to calibrate state standards, current practices in mathematics education are clearly failing at least half of our students, including a majority of blacks and Hispanics. An examination of the tests and textbooks clearly shows why: they are too abstract. Moreover, when the test questions are put in context, the context is often so odd that it may make matters worse. The book *Humble Pi* (Smith 1994) lays out some of the contexts that make up the majority of algebra word problems: trains or planes crossing in the night, mixes of two different-colored jelly beans at two different prices, the age of a relative or pet as an algebraic function of another ("Aunt Jo is twice as old as Uncle John's dog. . .) and, of course, rowing a canoe upstream or downstream.

No wonder a majority of college students need extra help in mathematics and take only the easiest and required course, proclaiming after the final "Thank God I'll never have to take another math course in my life." No wonder few students, even very good ones, can apply mathematics to real problems. No wonder gatekeepers establish mathematics as the screen to engineering and medical school, and that calculus serves as an effective screen for many. It is, however, a greater wonder that mathematics educators tolerate this state of affairs and resist change with so much vehemence.

Quantitative literacy, in my judgment, can save the day, not by being added to the curriculum but by altering *required* mathematics. National Science Foundation (NSF) director Rita Colwell makes the analogy of understanding a clock (Colwell, see p. 247). Some people need to know how to make a good timepiece and some need to understand how a clock's mechanism keeps time. But everyone needs to know how to read a clock's face and tell time.

Similarly, a few—a very few—need to know mathematics well enough to be researchers in the field. A much larger number—but still only a small percentage of the nation's labor force—need to know enough mathematics to be research scientists and engineers. But the majority of those who are going

Arnold Packer is Chair of the SCANS 2000 Center at the Institute for Policy Studies, Johns Hopkins University. An economist and engineer by training, Packer has served as Assistant Secretary for Policy, Evaluation, and Research at the U.S. Department of Labor, as co-director of the Workforce 2000 study, and as executive director of the Secretary's Commission on Achieving Necessary Skills (SCANS). Currently, his work is focused on teaching, assessing and recording the SCANS competencies.

to have successful careers need to have quantitative literacy, as does everyone who is going to be a participating citizen.

"How will students know whether they want to be mathematicians or research engineers unless they are exposed to abstract mathematics early?" some will say. "Yeah," replies the quantitatively literate after looking at some data, "as if students—especially minorities and women—are beating down the doors to graduate from mathematics departments now." The current system clearly needs to be radically improved.

Adding courses in quantitative literacy will not do; formal schooling already takes too long. Instead, we must change basic mathematics education, at least until grade 14. What does that mean in practical terms? Replacing trigonometry with data analysis and statistics as the first post-algebra course is one step. De-emphasizing calculus is another.

Even more radically, eliminate the use of x's and y's as variable names until the junior year in college. Eliminate x and y in the NAEP exams. Move understanding the transferability power of mathematics to the end of the chapter—where the applied problems now languish—to be learned *after* students see how mathematics can solve relevant problems. "See, now that you understand how rates of change apply to prices to produce measures of inflation, you can use similar equations to determine the speed of tennis serves or changes in the incidence of AIDS." The hallmark of quantitative literacy (QL), in my judgment, is its emphasis on learning in a *meaningful* context. The *Humble Pi* algebra examples are not meaningful contexts, and neither are most "consumer math" problems.

I do not mean to denigrate the importance of "transferability" and the power of mathematics in this regard. The issue of transferability is quite complex but data clearly indicate that the majority of students do not transfer what they learn in mathematics class to problems in the outside world. A full conversation would bring us into the field of learning theory, which I hardly understand. I do, however, suggest *How People Learn: Brain, Mind, Experience, and School* by the Committee on Developments in the Science of Learning of the National Research Council, which reviews recent developments (Bransford et al. 2001). The authors make the following pertinent points:

1. Learners build on what they know and unfamiliar principles are difficult to learn in unfamiliar contexts.

2. What learners already know may get in the way of new learning (for example, in ordering fractions).

3. The only reason for schooling is to transfer the lessons beyond the classroom.

4. Transfer rarely occurs unless explicitly shown and too narrow a context inhibits transfer.

Our work at the Secretary's Commission on Achieving Necessary Skills (SCANS) 2000 Center at Johns Hopkins University tends to focus on education for careers. For us, meaningful contexts are jobs paying more than the median wage. Thus, Algebra I students develop marketing plans for a tourist agency. This requires that they deal with a line whose slope changes when the printing price changes from 25 cents per 100 (for quantities under 1,000) to 10 cents per 100 (for greater quantities). Algebra II students develop a business plan for a mall and deal with trade-offs through spreadsheet simulations and probability through developing an inventory strategy. It is not rocket science (where they *may* need calculus) but it is plenty rigorous, certainly more rigorous than trying to find out where the two trains meet, or than lightweight consumer mathematics.

More important, students in our programs learn the stuff, at least as compared to their peers. In schools that have graduation rates under 25 percent, students taking our courses are graduating at about a 90 percent rate. Compared with other non-dropouts, their mathematics grades are one-half grade point higher (although still only a "C"). Even more significantly, students in these programs are one-third more likely to take and pass Algebra II.

The background essay I prepared for this Forum (see p. 33) describes a "canon" of issues in mathematics education that I will not discuss at length here. But I will mention a few issues in career education that come from SCANS. The commission listed five broad problem domains; career success is likely to require competence in a few of them. One of the SCANS problem domains, for example, is planning or resource allocation. This leads to budget problems as illustrated by the business plan project mentioned above. The planning domain also includes space problems, staff assignments, and scheduling. In addition to converting from English to metric measure (still, unfortunately, rare for Americans), a quantitatively literate person should be able to convert hours and days into minutes (for example, to determine when a heat-treated part should be removed from an oven). This is a career-relevant problem using a number system based on 60 rather than 10.

Let me reiterate five points:

1. Too many students—especially minority students and young women—are poorly served by the current practices in mathematics education.

2. The standards movement, especially the adoption of high school exit examinations, makes change in this situation imperative.

3. Quantitative literacy is a way out of the current dilemma. This implies more data analysis and statistics and less trigonometry.

4. Mathematics needs to be taught in relevant contexts of real-life problems that productive workers and engaged citizens need to be able to solve.

5. One way to achieve this is to eliminate x's and y's from mathematics until the junior year in college and from the NAEP and other high school exit examinations.

The aim of the first 13 years of mathematics education should be to equip students with the tools and desire to continue learning mathematics. By this criterion, current programs clearly fail many students. There is some evidence that quantitative literacy will succeed.

References

Bransford, John D., Ann L. Brown, and Rodney R. Cocking, eds. 1999. *How People Learn: Brain, Mind, Experience, and School.* National Research Council. Washington, DC: National Academy Press.

Smith, Michael K. 1994. *Humble Pi: The Role Mathematics Should Play in American Education.* Amherst, NY: Prometheus Books.

Grounding Mathematics in Quantitative Literacy

JOHNNY W. LOTT

> We owe our children no less than a high degree of quantitative literacy and mathematical knowledge that prepares them for citizenship, work, and further study. (NCTM 2000, 289)

Quantitative literacy (QL) is a major goal of the National Council of Teachers of Mathematics (NCTM) for the teachers of mathematics in this country and in Canada. It is worth emphasizing that "our children" means *all children*. Equity is a core principle for NCTM as well: "All students, regardless of their personal characteristics, backgrounds, or physical challenges, must have opportunities to study—and support to learn—mathematics" (NCTM 2000, 12).

Equity does not mean identical instruction for all, but it does mean that all students need access each year to a coherent, challenging mathematics curriculum taught by competent and well-supported mathematics teachers. "Well-documented examples demonstrate that all children, including those who have been traditionally underserved, can learn mathematics when they have access to high-quality instructional programs that support their learning" (NCTM 2000, 14).

As we think about quantitative literacy (or more broadly mathematical literacy), we must acknowledge that the mathematics community as a whole has provided neither access to nor a "coherent challenging mathematics curriculum" for all students. In fact, underserved groups include not only students from poor communities but also those from affluent communities that are college-bound. If anything, college-bound students may have been the most ill-served. Locked into a mathematics curriculum that has calculus as a single-minded focus, these students have been denied the most elementary understanding of mathematical literacy. Only in selected schools with a selected curriculum might we find the rudiments of mathematics that lead to quantitative literacy.

Since the release of *Curriculum and Evaluation Standards for School Mathematics* (NCTM 1989), NCTM has worked to make mathematics a foremost consideration in this country whenever education is debated. The *Curriculum and Evaluation* document focused attention on the need to improve the mathematical knowledge of all students. That document and its successor, *Principles and Standards for School Mathematics* (NCTM 2000), have become magnets for criticism from certain members of the higher education mathematics community. It is my hope, and that of NCTM, that this Forum will set the stage for a common national push for mathematical literacy.

Mathematical literacy is a responsibility of precollege mathematics teachers, but it is not their responsibility alone. A mathematical literacy curriculum must begin early in students' school careers, long before high school; otherwise it is doomed to failure. Many students do not take mathematics beyond the tenth grade, and some have dropped out of school by that age. Thus, a major portion of mathematical literacy must be achieved in grade school and early high school.

Johnny W. Lott is Professor of Mathematics at the University of Montana and President of the National Council of Teachers of Mathematics (NCTM). Lott served as co-director of the SIMMS project that developed a new mathematics curriculum for grades 9–12 called *Integrated Mathematics: A Modeling Approach*. An author or co-author of several books and many articles, Lott has been chair of the editorial panels for three NCTM periodicals.

If mathematical literacy is important before students have reached grade 10, we need to examine who can teach what is needed. Many elementary teachers may not be comfortable with the necessary mathematics because of their own backgrounds. Middle school teachers have mixed mathematics backgrounds, and secondary teachers are typically more comfortable with traditional mathematics than with the mathematics presented in a quantitative literacy program. Teacher preparation programs therefore must change. Without such change, a quantitative literacy movement has little chance of success. Expecting that teachers other than mathematics teachers either know or understand what might be considered quantitative literacy is equally unrealistic.

To succeed in the schools, quantitative literacy must have the blessing of postsecondary education, organizations representing postsecondary faculty, and business interests. Without a strong common vision from above, QL will become the general mathematics of the beginning of this century. If quantitative literacy is to be a legitimate goal for education in this country, all segments of the mathematics and science communities must demonstrate that it is important. If it is truly a goal, it must be valued on a par with calculus. This means that it must be an integral part of high school expectations, college admissions tests, and university placement tests. It cannot stand apart as something for those who cannot do "real mathematics."

A central question for precollege teachers is, "How well are the tasks, discourse, and environment working to foster the development of students' mathematical literacy and power?" *Professional Standards for Teaching Mathematics* (NCTM 1991, 62). Consider the tasks. Any mathematical literacy curriculum should be more than a collection of activities: it must be coherent, focused on important mathematics, and well articulated across pre-K–16. The topics must be context-based and built around important mathematics.

Curricular topics required for an individual to be mathematically literate are well represented in the background essays prepared for this Forum (e.g., de Lange, see p. 75; Steen, see p. 53). From an NCTM standpoint, a student must be grounded in number and operations, algebra, geometry, measurement, and data analysis and probability. Can this grounding be more of the same mathematics as in the past? The answer is a resounding "no" for each of these strands.

The number strand must include, among other topics, an understanding of large and small numbers and of matrices. Large numbers can be considered in terms such as distances the space shuttle travels, the national budget and debt, and the cost of the war in Afghanistan. Small numbers can be considered by thinking about the size of an anthrax spore, the time it takes to send an e-mail message across the country, and so on. Matrices are commonly used to record inventory as it comes in and out of a warehouse or when insurance companies study the effects of claims on premiums. The primary focus is not on the mathematics of matrices but on how blocks of data are treated and operated on in real life.

The algebra strand must include an understanding of how algebra is applied outside the classroom. It must include recursive processes such as those used in spreadsheets, one of the most common computer tools employed in the business world. For example, the recursive procedure used in the Fill Down command of most spreadsheets is comprehensible to very young children. Also, when blocks of data are used as the input of a Fill Down command, a different mathematical use of variables is illustrated than what most people commonly think of. The study of recursive formulas provides an impetus for the study of interest earned on savings accounts and easily leads to more mathematics if desired.

The geometry strand must include an understanding of three dimensions. Students must learn that no maps (whether they are two-dimensional or on a globe) are accurate. Evidence of this need is seen, for example, in the common misunderstanding of most people concerning routes that planes fly and how to measure house lots when the ground is not flat.

The measurement strand must include the notions of precision, tolerance, accuracy, and approximate errors. Students should understand which digits in numbers are worth considering. In today's manufacturing processes, in which components are built all over the world, accuracy in measurement is vital. In addition, understanding the difference between "yards" of carpet and "yards" of concrete requires a basic understanding of units of measurement.

In the area of data analysis and probability, students must learn how to handle data and how to use probabilities. We do not need more generations of people who think that a lottery is the answer to all problems, from individuals' winning in order not to work, to raising money to support schools. Both the probability of winning and an understanding of the population from which a winning number is drawn are vital to quantitative literacy.

Finally, in all efforts toward mathematical literacy, we should be teaching mathematical reasoning and problem solving. These are as basic to an understanding of future mathematics and literacy as knowing when calculators or computers are necessary tools for computing.

A quantitative literacy curriculum must offer experiences that show powerful mathematical uses for modeling and predicting real-world phenomena. Knowing what is meant by a 40 percent chance of rain, a batting average of .322, or an ad for a product that is "a silly millimeter longer" requires both connections to the real world and a basic knowledge of mathematical concepts. Such curricula exist today. See, for example, SIMMS/MCTM *Integrated Mathematics: A Modeling Approach Using Technology* (Montana Council of Teachers of Mathematics 1996).

An intelligent, mathematically literate citizen should never declare, "I can't do mathematics" just as they should never say, "I can't read." The NCTM standards set the stage for mathematical literacy for all students. How can we work together to make it a reality?

References

Montana Council of Teachers of Mathematics. 1996. *SIMMS/MCTM Integrated Mathematics: A Modeling Approach Using Technology, Levels 1–6 Objectives/Content Outline*. Bozeman, MT: Montana Council of Teachers of Mathematics.

National Council of Teachers of Mathematics. 1989. *Curriculum and Evaluation Standards for School Mathematics*. Reston, VA: National Council of Teachers of Mathematics.

National Council of Teachers of Mathematics. 1991. *Professional Standards for Teaching Mathematics*. Reston, VA: National Council of Teachers of Mathematics.

National Council of Teachers of Mathematics. 2000. *Principles and Standards for School Mathematics*. Reston, VA: National Council of Teachers of Mathematics

Quantitative Literacy:
A Science Literacy Perspective

I begin with a note of personal bias: I believe that the mathematics goals of the American Association for the Advancement of Science (AAAS) are closer to the quantitative literacy (QL) goals discussed in *Mathematics and Democracy: The Case for Quantitative Literacy* (Steen 2001) than either the goals of the new National Council of Teachers of Mathematics (NCTM) standards or current school science or mathematics curricula. Indeed, *Benchmarks for Science Literacy,* published by AAAS, has many of the same QL goals—they are just not called by that name (Project 2061 1993). In one respect, therefore, QL is very much part of what we think good science teaching should be about.

On the other hand, *Principles and Standards for School Mathematics* (NCTM 2000) abandoned, for many reasons, the vision of the original standards (NCTM 1989) that described both the mathematics important for all students to learn and the mathematics that goes beyond basic literacy important for those students going on to higher education or technical careers. *Principles and Standards for School Mathematics* is a notable and useful description of the goals of school mathematics, but it goes well beyond the goals of QL (QL may be an undefined subset) and may be an unrealistic vision of the mathematics that all children can learn in 13 years. (I am willing to make the same statement about the amount of science content in the AAAS *Benchmarks* and the *National Science Education Standards* (NRC 1995).)

I also must point out that *Mathematics and Democracy* is very mathematics-centric, even as it makes the case for the interdisciplinary nature of quantitative literacy. The references are almost all from the field of mathematics and mathematics education, not from the places where QL really lives—the natural and social sciences. QL is not something new, nor is it something that exists in isolation. It exists in many places but always in specific contexts. Yet for lack of appropriate contexts, QL rarely is seen in school classes.

For example, mathematics in science classes is typically independent of mathematics in mathematics classes. In school science, there is almost no consideration of mathematics' "scope and sequence," nor is much effort made to use consistent terminology and symbols. Typical science classes make little effort to reinforce mathematical concepts or to demonstrate their application in scientific inquiry. Mathematics classes, in turn, may employ a science setting (e.g., counting whales or planets) but not science content appropriate to the local scope and sequence. Current mathematics classes abound in inappropriate, inconsistent, or unrealistic situations and data. Units, when necessary, are often absent or incorrect. QL-type applications are rare. On an optimistic note, some of the new "reform" or "standards-based" K–8 curriculum materials in mathematics do a much better job of offering realistic and appropriate examples and contexts.

The knowledge and skills that make up quantitative literacy can be defined through careful sets of learning goals, specific concepts and skills that together paint a coherent and complete picture. There are two types of goals: targets for adult knowledge and skills such as those in *Science for All Americans*

George D. Nelson is Director of the Science, Mathematics and Technology Education Center at Western Washington University. Immediately prior to assuming this position, Nelson directed Project 2061, a national initiative of the American Association for the Advancement of Science to reform K-12 science, mathematics and technology education. An astronomer by training, Nelson earlier served as a NASA astronaut and flew as a mission specialist aboard three space shuttle flights.

(AAAS 1989) *(targets),* and benchmarks to monitor progress toward the adult goals (NCTM 1989, AAAS 1993) *(steps along the way,* or *standards).* We need both. Benchmarks are especially important as a strategy to reach our targets because they define the content around which curricula can be designed and built. So far, most of what we have in QL are targets without standards. And those targets span the disciplines.

Where does QL live, or where might it thrive? School mathematics is typically formal and theoretical, thus not yet a welcoming environment for QL. In comparison with the NCTM standards, QL involves the sophisticated use of elementary mathematics more often than elementary applications of advanced mathematics. Although science can be data-rich, natural science often is taught more like what Arnold Packer and others call "*x, y* math." Because the contexts of QL are most commonly personal or social, the social sciences may offer the most natural home. Of course, this assumes that curriculum developers, teachers, and teacher educators in the social science disciplines are willing to take on the responsibility for helping students build on the prerequisite mathematics to learn QL skills and concepts and that the sum of any student's experience totals a coherent vision of QL.

Recommendations:

- QL has a strong partner and advocate in the science community. Read and criticize the mathematics in *Science for All Americans* (Project 2061 1989), *Benchmarks for Science Literacy* (Project 2061 1993), and the *Atlas of Science Literacy* (Project 2061 2001).

- Consider engaging the social sciences (let them lead or share the lead) in the quest for QL.

- Adopt detailed and specific goals with benchmarks for progress.

- Coordinate QL across disciplines by making QL part of faculty development.

- Promote the pedagogical advances that the K–12 mathematics community has made through its curriculum development work.

- Develop reliable and valid assessments of experiments in curriculum and instruction that target QL (i.e., do science). And publish the results.

References

National Council of Teachers of Mathematics. 1989. *Curriculum and Evaluation Standards for School Mathematics*. Reston, VA: National Council of Teachers of Mathematics.

National Council of Teachers of Mathematics. 2000. *Principles and Standards for School Mathematics*. Reston, VA: National Council of Teachers of Mathematics.

National Research Council (NRC). 1995. *National Science Education Standards*. Washington, DC: National Academy Press.

American Association for the Advancement of Science. 1989. Project 2061. *Science for All Americans*. Washington, DC: American Association for the Advancement of Science.

American Association for the Advancement of Science. 1993. Project 2061. *Benchmarks for Science Literacy*. Washington, DC: American Association for the Advancement of Science.

American Association for the Advancement of Science. 2001. Project 2061. *Atlas of Science Literacy*. Washington, DC: American Association for the Advancement of Science.

Steen, Lynn Arthur, ed. 2001. *Mathematics and Democracy: The Case for Quantitative Literacy*. Princeton, NJ: National Council on Education and the Disciplines.

Learning and Working in Context

WILLIAM G. STEENKEN

My formal introduction to quantitative literacy began only six months ago at a meeting of the Mathematical Sciences Education Board (MSEB) when Rikki Blair, a faculty member at Lakeland Community College was informing the board of the planning efforts that led to this Forum. At some point in her presentation, I asked her "What the hell is quantitative literacy?" I could not see the problem and she could not provide an answer that satisfied me. In frustration, she sent me a copy of *Mathematics and Democracy: The Case for Quantitative Literacy* (Steen 2001). After reading this publication, reviewing some recent events of which I was part, and reflecting on my personal progression to becoming "quantitatively literate," I can now say, "Professor Blair, I get it!"

My approach to quantitative literacy is governed by my training as an engineer who worked in the aircraft propulsion industry—a high-technology industry—for almost 35 years and by my more recent efforts to help foster systemic and sustainable improvements in pre-K–16 mathematics and science education in Ohio. My remarks address the importance I attach to learning in context and the status of quantitative literacy in a high-tech industry such as the design and manufacture of aircraft engines. I end with some rather disquieting remarks about attempts to improve the level of quantitative literacy (QL) in the pre-K–12 student pipeline in Ohio.

First, I want to establish what I mean by QL. *Mathematics and Democracy* defines being quantitatively literate as:

- *Arithmetic:* Having facility with simple mental arithmetic; estimating arithmetic calculations; reasoning with proportions; counting by indirection (combinatorics).

- *Data:* Using information conveyed as data, graphs, and charts; drawing inferences from data; recognizing disaggregation as a factor in interpreting data.

- *Computers:* Using spreadsheets, recording data, performing calculations, creating graphic displays, extrapolating, fitting lines or curves to data.

- *Modeling:* Formulating problems, seeking patterns, and drawing conclusions; recognizing interactions in complex systems; understanding linear, exponential, multivariate, and simulation models; understanding the impact of different rates of growth.

- *Statistics:* Understanding the importance of variability; recognizing the differences between correlation and causation, between randomized experiments and observational studies, between finding no effect and finding no statistically significant effect (especially with small samples), and between statistical significance and practical importance (especially with large samples).

- *Chance:* Recognizing that seemingly improbable coincidences are not uncommon; evaluating risks from available evidence; understanding the value of random samples.

William G. Steenken recently retired as a Consulting Engineer in Engine Operability from General Electric Aircraft Engines in Cincinnati, Ohio. During his career, he published thirty-four papers and reports. An elected member of school boards in Ohio for over 22 years, Steenken is president of the National Alliance of State Science and Mathematics Coalitions, past chair of the Ohio Mathematics and Science Coalition, and a member of the Mathematical Sciences Education Board.

- *Reasoning:* Using logical thinking; recognizing levels of rigor in methods of inference; checking hypotheses; exercising caution in making generalizations.

(Steen 2001, 16)

I would venture to say that the business world would be ecstatic if students graduating from secondary schools and entering the workforce possessed these skills. Unfortunately, they do not even come close.

First, a note of caution. Those of us at this Forum and those whom we represent are a very, very small percentage of the U.S. population: we talk very well to one another (or at least we think we do). Most of the population, however, is like the typical adult described by Project 2061. Paraphrasing material from this project, the typical adult is a person over 18 years of age with no mathematics or science training beyond high school. The typical adult would recognize computation beginning with whole numbers, then fractions, and integers, and later involving algebraic and possibly trigonometric formulas as mathematics (Blackwell and Henkin, 1989, 1). Thus, it is no wonder that the general population equates being quantitatively literate with being mathematically knowledgeable. Quoting from the Forum essay by Deborah Hughes Hallett, ". . . there is, therefore, an important distinction between mathematical and quantitative literacy" (Hughes Hallett, see p. 92). As we all know, one does not imply the other. On the other hand, the foundations of quantitative literacy lie in mathematical literacy.

Becoming Quantitatively Literate

I have been quantitatively literate for almost as long as I can remember. I attribute this literacy to my training as an engineer. From the moment I entered engineering school, every course I took outside of my mathematics courses required analyses that ended with a quantitative result—that is the nature of engineering. Analyze a situation; choose, modify, or develop a suitable algorithm; and produce a result that tells you whether stresses in a structure will be exceeded, whether the heat transfer rate is too little or too much, whether the thermodynamic cycle is efficient enough, whether the current-carrying capacity of wire will be exceeded, whether pipes can handle the desired flow rate, whether jet engines produce enough thrust to overcome the drag of the aircraft, and so on. Graphs, spreadsheets, extrapolation, interpolation, statistics, probability, gathering data, and modeling new situations are all tools of the engineer every day.

Becoming quantitatively literate occurred across a wide array of courses—thermodynamics, heat transfer, fluid mechanics, electrical network theory, materials science, statics and dynamics of

structures, and it goes on. It did not happen in one course or one place but slowly became a way of life that was continually honed over a long career that continues to this day. I am always looking for a better way to present complicated numerical results that can be easily understood by a broad array of audiences.

Learning in Context

I probably gained most of my mathematical literacy from the engineering courses that I took and the subsequent need for solutions to problems encountered in my daily work. I found what I call "*xyz*" mathematics difficult throughout my education—primary, secondary, undergraduate, and graduate. Now as I read works written by many of you in this audience, I am beginning to understand why. If I had had the privilege of studying under some of you when my schooling was starting, I suspect my knowledge and appreciation of "*xyz*" mathematics would be far greater. I see great beauty in how concepts are now being developed for students and I smile to myself as I read about them, thinking "Oh, if only I could have started that way." To quote Hughes Hallett again, "One of the reasons that the level of quantitative literacy is low in the U.S. is that it is difficult to teach students to identify mathematics in context, and most mathematics teachers have no experience with this" (see p. 94).

Let me illustrate context with an example from my field. Consider the following equation:

$$X + C_1 Y^2 = C_2$$

where X and Y are variables, and C_1 and C_2 are constants.

To me, this equation, showing that X must decrease in proportion to the increase in the square of Y or vice versa is quite abstract and sterile.

But if P (pressure) is substituted for X and V (velocity) for Y, and if we let $C_1 = \rho/2g_c$ where ρ is density and g_c is the gravitational constant, then the Bernoulli equation for incompressible flow is obtained:

$$P + (\rho/2g_c)V^2 = C_2$$

This says that the sum of the static pressure and the velocity head are constant along a fluid streamline. It shows that if the velocity of a fluid increases, there must be a concomitant drop in pressure. For example, if steady flow in a pipe moves from a section of large diameter to one of smaller diameter, the flow velocity in the smaller-diameter section must increase and the static pressure must decrease.

In context, the symbols come alive for me because they are associated with usually measurable and understood physical properties or quantities. They excite me intellectually, they hold my interest, and they make me think about how they relate. They are not simply "*xyz.*"

To summarize, I quote again from *Mathematics and Democracy* ". . . skills learned free of context are skills devoid of meaning and utility" (Steen 2001, 16). I could not agree more.

Quantitative Literacy in the Professional Workforce

What I have been saying may seem self-evident, namely, that quantitative literacy is an integral part of engineers' output; however, the wide use of quantitative literacy skills continues as an employee advances in a corporation and addresses administrative and personnel issues. I often found myself quite naturally using trend charts to track planned and actual income and planned and actual expenses for my projects. By watching for deviations and changes in slope of the "actual" curves, I knew more about the state of the business for which I was responsible than by trying to interpret virtually indecipherable reams of tabulations. In reality, such detailed information, although necessary, does not provide the "big-picture" overview necessary for good administration.

Similarly, and as part of a merit pay system, I tracked salaries as a function of degree and years of experience and examined the spread between high and low performers within the same labor classification. Such detail was necessary to maintain the integrity of the merit pay system and to ensure that reward was tied to contribution. If deviations occurred outside the given parameter range, it was appropriate to question and search for the reason for the deviation. Because successively higher levels of management reviewed all merit pay recommendations, possession of such analyses and trend curves helped to gain support for my rationale.

I have always been concerned that being quantitatively literate brings added responsibilities; this became especially apparent during my tenure as an elected school board member. It always seemed to me that if anything had gone wrong that could be attributed to inattention to numbers, I would have shouldered more of the burden and would have had less ability to be severed from a legal action. It would have been easy to show that "I should have known or would have been able to know" had I undertaken due diligence analysis using the skills associated with quantitative literacy. In some quarters, I was viewed as a pain in the a__ because I demanded that numbers be reduced to easy-to-follow graphs, percentages, "deltas," ratios, etc. for use in comparison with past data. In this way, deviations from trends could easily be spotted and explanations readily sought. Based on my knowledge

of cases of fraud in industry and government, had those in positions of responsibility been quantitatively literate, fraud could not have succeeded and careers would not have been ruined.

Turning from professionals to skilled craftsmen, the need for quantitative literacy has increased enormously: operators of manufacturing cells need to know when and how many parts need to be delivered to their position so they can maintain flow in their part of the production chain; watch tolerances so their parts do not fall outside the limits of variability; understand the trends in variation curves and know which tool needs to be replaced; and be responsible for self-inspecting their production and reporting the results.

One last comment about the place of quantitative literacy in the high-technology workplace. Most of you are probably aware of the Six Sigma (less that 3.4 defects per million) quality initiative originated by Motorola and instituted by many other companies. General Electric was one of the latter. Knowledge of Six Sigma technology was deemed so important that an extremely large training effort was undertaken to give almost all employees an understanding and appreciation of variability in our products and processes. Jack Welch, the chairman of our board, drove this change, for he recognized very early that to be the number one supplier in a field and be profitable, one had to drive out defects as never before and shorten the order–manufacture–delivery cycle. There was no better way to accomplish these objectives than to give every employee the tools needed to perform analyses in support of Six Sigma goals. Thus ordered bar graphs (Pareto charts) to determine which parameters had the biggest impact (you tackle them first), statistical analysis spreadsheet tools, tests for significance, flow charting to improve processes, etc., all became daily tools in our corporate lives.

Instituting Six Sigma technologies has done more than anything else to raise the overall level of quantitative literacy in corporate America. Regrettably, nothing in the school curricula gives students this type of knowledge nor do I see it happening during the next decade. This brings me to my final point.

Mathematics Standards

Ohio has been writing mathematics standards for the K–12 grades for the past two or three years. I had the opportunity to be a member of a business team that reviewed the proposed standards. None of this group of approximately 20 businessmen—representing small to very large businesses—had any problems with the content of the standards, but the discussion was dominated by comments regarding the perceived lack of required quantitative skills and demonstration of them. Businessmen wanted graduating students to be able to understand profit-loss sheets (the basis for our capitalistic economy), compound interest and mortgage rates, taxes, balancing checkbooks, and yes, to be able to do arithmetic. I thought to myself: they are asking that students be quantitatively literate. But our standards-writing people did not get it. In fact, writers on the standards team explained that it all was really right there; they could point to the underlying "*xyz*" mathematics, but they could not see the need for context. I was told that for those things, students should "take a business mathematics course."

Thus, as a businessman, I see a significant chasm between mathematical literacy and quantitative literacy. I am hoping that the discussion at this Forum will help us identify and elucidate the problems that stand in the way of having both. Identifying the problems or barriers is the first step in moving forward to produce quantitatively literate students. Only when school graduates are quantitatively literate will the public believe that students "know mathematics" and only then will we have the opportunity to benefit from the gains in mathematical literacy that we all know are necessary if our workforce is to be internationally competitive and an enduring economic asset.

References

Blackwell, David and Leon Henkin. 1989. "Mathematics–Report of the Project 2061 Phase I Mathematics Panel." Washington, DC: American Association for the Advancement of Science.

Steen, Lynn Arthur, ed. 2001. *Mathematics and Democracy: The Case for Quantitative Literacy*. Princeton, NJ: National Council on Education and the Disciplines.

Of the Teachers, by the Teachers, and for the Teachers

Mathematics for me is a means for understanding the world, and therefore quantitative literacy is an important part of mathematical activity. I believe it is so for many mathematicians. As a rule, I do not watch television, but when America started bombing in Afghanistan, I developed a temporary addiction to CNN. As part of the contemporary trend toward multitasking, CNN runs "footlines": as reporters and their guests talk on center screen, brief summaries of breaking news stories trail across the bottom of the screen as if on a ticker tape. (The *New Yorker* calls these snippets the "CNN crawl".) One day while I was watching, sandwiched between messages giving updates on ground zero and Osama bin Laden, I read a helpful hint about car theft: nearly one-third of all car thefts occur on Friday and Saturday.

Not long after, the Committee on Education of the American Mathematical Society held its annual meeting. In my opening remarks, by way of illustrating the national need for improved mathematics education, I shared the CNN story. As soon as I stated it, the whole room of 50 or so people broke out in spontaneous laughter. Although some aspects of quantitative literacy as laid out in *Mathematics and Democracy* (Steen 2001) are probably possessed fully only by a rare few, I take the reaction of my audience as evidence that mathematicians are, on average, fairly quantitatively literate. I doubt very much, however, that they have had special quantitative literacy (QL) training outside their mathematics courses. This leads me to suspect that there are certain skills that are to some extent context free and that support the ability to deal with quantitative information in a variety of contexts. Rather than deny the existence of such skills, I hope that those who wish to promote QL would try to identify them and investigate how instruction can support them. Below, I hazard guesses as to what a couple of these skills might be.

The focus of the essays in *Mathematics and Democracy* (Steen 2001) of the background essays written for this Forum, and indeed, the title of the Forum, is upper high school and early college. Although this focus is certainly worthy of some attention, I believe that, in relation to the question of how to develop a mathematically or quantitatively literate population, it is too narrow. In fact, the temptation is nearly irresistible to call it quantitatively illiterate. The first eight grades of school, over two-thirds of a student's K–12 career, are devoted to learning arithmetic. This is where we would expect the seeds of QL to be sown. Although the precise nature and extent of full-fledged QL has yet to be defined, comfort with numbers has to be a foundational skill for any type of QL that deserves the name; and comfort, or discomfort, with numbers is learned early. There is abundant evidence that for many students and many numbers, it is discomfort.

As an example, I cite a question on a recent National Assessment of Educational Progress (NAEP) examination for eighth graders (Kilpatrick et al. 2001):

Roger Howe is Professor of Mathematics at Yale University; his research focuses on symmetry and its consequences. A member of the National Academy of Sciences, Howe is chair of the Committee on Education of the American Mathematical Society. Previously, Howe served on the Mathematical Sciences Education Board and as a member of steering committees that produced two recent reports on mathematics education: *Adding It Up* (National Academy Press, 2001) and *The Mathematical Education of Teachers* (CBMS, 2001).

Which is closest to 7/8 + 12/13 ?

(a) 1   (b) 2   (c) 19   (d) 21

If you are comfortable with numbers, you notice that each of the two fractions to be added is slightly less than 1, so the sum must be close to 2, and the correct choice is answer (b). You may wonder why such outlandish answers as 19 and 21 are even offered as possibilities. Who would guess them? It turns out over half the students chose one of these answers. The majority of 13-year-olds apparently have no effective techniques for dealing with approximation of fractions, and perhaps little intuitive grasp of what a fraction means. This level of understanding provides a weak foundation for using numbers to deal with the world.

The call for quantitative literacy is part of a broader movement of mathematics education reform that has been growing since the publication of the National Council of Teachers of Mathematics (NCTM) *Curriculum and Evaluation Standards* (NCTM 1989). Certainly there are good reasons for changing the mathematics curriculum. What used to be key skills have became much less important, and a host of new capacities is required to deal with the diverse numerical data with which we are presented on a daily basis; however, a major lesson of mathematics education research during the 1990s is that, to enable significant change in mathematics instruction, we must attend closely to what teachers know and can do (Ball 1991; Kilpatrick et al. 2001; Ma 1999; Conference Board of the Mathematical Sciences (CBMS) 2001). Failure to emphasize this point was in my view a major failing of the 1989 Standards and a significant contributor to the "math wars" in California and elsewhere. Such failure is the more regrettable because it is frequently cited as a reason for the earlier failure of the "New Math" of the 1960s, and because the standards were produced by a combination of mathematics educators and teachers, who might have been presumed to know better.

I believe that calls for quantitative literacy that ignore the contribution of the elementary years, and the need for attention to capacity-building among teachers, are unlikely to be widely effective. The capacity of the teaching corps is not a peripheral issue, to be resolved after formulation of the ideal curriculum. It is a central issue.

To illustrate some of the challenges to building a QL-friendly curriculum, I call attention to number skills that I believe are important to support numeracy. Three very important skills are:

1. Understanding order of magnitude.

2. The habitual tendency to round off (i.e., estimation).

3. Understanding of error (both absolute and relative).

(I should be clear that, although here I am emphasizing estimation as a key skill, I do not want to downgrade exact arithmetic. I suspect that confidence in estimation is based on a sure understanding of exact arithmetic. We must, however, go beyond exact arithmetic to achieve numeracy.)

Especially important in this connection is the understanding that, in most circumstances, if you care about more than the leftmost three or four digits of a decimal number, you are probably a number theorist. At four-decimal-place accuracy, the "radius of the earth" does not make sense because the earth cannot be treated as a sphere to this degree of accuracy. Even seemingly clearly defined whole number quantities such as the population of a town are difficult to pin down to four decimal places of accuracy, and five is nearly impossible.

Consider a town of 100,000 people. Between 1,000 and 2,000 babies should be born there each year and a comparable number will die. People will move in and move away. The population numbers are fluctuating on a daily basis. In the world as a whole, with its six billion or so people, about 100 million are being born each year, which makes several each second; however, it takes several minutes for each to be born. When do you add a baby to the count?

Attention to the appropriate level of accuracy is a poorly developed habit, even among curriculum developers, mathematics educators, and professional purveyors of data. Here are several examples illustrating this point. The first example is from the National Science Foundation (NSF) sponsored middle school curriculum "Connected Mathematics." I do not offer it to condemn the curriculum, but simply to show the difficulties that exist:

> In 1980, the town of Rio Rancho, located on a mesa outside Santa Fe, New Mexico, was destined for obscurity. But as a result of hard work by its city officials, it began adding manufacturing jobs at a fast rate. As a result, the city's population grew 239 percent from 1980 to 1990, making Rio Rancho the fastest-growing "small city" in the United States. The population of Rio Rancho in 1990 was 37,000.
>
> a) What was the population of Rio Rancho in 1980?
>
> b) If the same rate of population increase continues, what will be the population in the year 2000?

In the first Teacher's Edition for the series, the answer to a) was given as follows:

> Let P be the population in 1980. Then $2.39P = 37,000$, so $P = 16,481$ people in 1980.

The first remark is that this calculation is for a population that is 239 percent of its original population, not a population that has increased by 239 percent, so there is a misuse or misunderstanding of terminology in this answer. (It may, of course, have been inadvertent. We mention also that Rio Rancho is a suburb of Albuquerque, not Santa Fe.) Someone pointed out the error and a correction was made, as follows:

Let P be the population in 1980. Then $2.39P + P = 37,000$, so $P = 10,914.45428$, or approximately 10,914 people in 1980.

I would say that "approximately" 10,914 people is an unreasonable answer. The indicated population growth entails an annual growth of about 13 percent, which even in the first year when the population was smallest means an increase of about 1,400 for the year, or three or four people per day. It makes no sense to report population figures accurate to single persons—the nearest thousand would be more reasonable, especially because it appears that the reported 1990 population is rounded to the nearest thousand. Giving the answer as a nearest integer rounded off from a number with five places to the right of the decimal point makes clear that mindless calculator use went on here. Reviewing the problem in light of these considerations, we also are led to question the appropriateness of stating 239 percent as the amount of growth: a better choice would have been 240 percent. The difference is only about 100 persons, considerably less than the uncertainty in the 1990 population.

Such misleading accuracy is not restricted to curriculum developers. Professional data handlers sometimes indulge in similar practices. For example, here are selected population data for California and Washington, according to the Bureau of the Census:

Population	California	Washington
1890	1,213,398	357,232
1940	6,907,387	1,736,191
1990	29,785,857	4,866,669

For the reasons described above, and others connected simply with the counting and recording process, it is absurd to imagine, and absurd of the Census Bureau to pretend, that they have found the exact number of people living in either of these states in any one of the years. Determination even to the nearest 10,000 would have been a remarkable achievement. We would guess from the recent debates about the use of statistical sampling methods to improve the accuracy of the census that we are very lucky if these numbers are accurate even to three significant figures. This would mean that, in California, a small city could be lost or be counted without affecting the figures.

As became clear in the 2000 presidential election, even in such a seemingly cut-and-dried, closely controlled, and well-defined process such as an election, accurate counting is difficult to achieve. (And beyond the counting, there is considerable evidence that in some Florida counties, the ballots were sufficiently confusing that the recorded vote may not always have reflected the actual preference of the voter.) Even if the Census Bureau reports unrealistically accurate numbers, this does not justify the uncritical use of these figures by others, especially mathematicians and mathematics educators. My source for these numbers is not the Census Bureau itself, however, but a data analysis exercise in a draft of a text intended for teacher development. The "data" could have served as a pretext for discussion of reasonable degrees of accuracy, but they were presented without comment, as grist for a number-crunching exercise.

These simple examples of inattention to appropriate accuracy in various real-world contexts may seem more like peccadilloes than mortal sins, but they illustrate inattention to the issue of accuracy. If the same insensitivity to appropriate accuracy affects computations done with these numbers, errors can get magnified to the point where they dominate information, and reported numbers become meaningless, not in their rightmost decimal places but in their entirety.

These examples show the pervasiveness of insensitivity to the limits of accuracy, even among curriculum developers, teacher educators, and professional purveyors of data. How then can we expect our teachers to inculcate appropriately skeptical thinking habits? The evidence suggests that the teaching corps reaches its limits of numeracy long before these issues are addressed (Ball 1991; Kilpatrick et al. 2001; Ma 1999; CBMS 2001; Post, et al. 1991). To a considerable extent, today's curriculum is more or less what today's teachers can deliver. If you want major changes, you have to work with teachers to improve their capacity to deal with mathematics. Having a teaching corps, especially at the elementary level, with low numeracy and quantitative literacy skills means mathematics and QL achievement below what might be possible under better learning conditions. The costs include extensive remediation, low achievement, inadequate skilled labor, and impoverished political discourse. I would guess that these costs are huge.

It is possible to substantially improve the situation, but doing so will require major changes in the current education system as well as significant resources to support sustained effort. The most direct action would be to raise QL expectations for teachers through a system of requirements and incentives. Features of a stronger system for QL would include mathematics specialists in all grades, at least as support for elementary teachers but preferably as the main deliverers of mathematics instruction; increased mathematics requirements and more effective courses for pre-service teachers; expectations of continuing mathematics and QL development for in-service teachers both through formal course work and collegial interaction; and appropriate incentives to make the expectations feasible (CBMS 2001).

These actions would require both resources and changes in practice. Perhaps the most effective way of marshalling support for these efforts would be to develop convincing estimates of the costs of not implementing them. The case has to be made that it is not cost effective to have a teaching corps, including an elementary teaching corps, without strong mathematics and QL skills.

References

Ball, Deborah L. 1991. "Research on Teaching Mathematics: Making Subject Matter Understanding Part of the Equation." In Brophy, J., ed. *Advances in Research on Teaching, Vol. 2: Teachers' Knowledge of Subject Matter as it Relates to their Teaching Practice*. Greenwich, CT: JAI Press, 1–48.

Conference Board of the Mathematical Sciences. 2001. *Issues in Mathematics Education, Vol. 11: The Mathematical Education of Teachers*. Providence, RI: American Mathematical Society.

Kilpatrick, Jeremy, Jane Swafford, and Bradford Findell, eds. 2001. *Adding It Up: Helping Children Learn Mathematics*. Washington, DC: National Academy Press.

Ma, Liping. 1999. *Knowing and Teaching Elementary Mathematics: Teachers' Understanding of Fundamental Mathematics in China and the United States*. Mahwah, NJ: Erlbaum Associates.

National Council of Teachers of Mathematics. 1989. *Curriculum and Evaluation Standards for School Mathematics*. Reston, VA: National Council of Teachers of Mathematics.

Post, T. R., G. Harel, M. J. Behr, and R. Lesh. 1991. "Intermediate Teachers' Knowledge of Rational Number Concepts." In *Integrating Research on Teaching and Learning Mathematics*, edited by E. Fennema, T. P. Carpenter, and S. J. Lamon. Albany, NY: State University of New York Press, 194–217.

Steen, Lynn Arthur, ed. 2001. *Mathematics and Democracy: The Case for Quantitative Literacy*. Princeton, NJ: National Council on Education and the Disciplines.

Impediments to and Potentials for Quantitative Literacy

J. T. SUTCLIFFE

We can all agree that we want students to be productive citizens, well prepared for the world of work. Whether we wear the hat of mathematician, scientist, business person, or educator, we can also all agree that we want students to understand numbers in context and be able to interpret information presented in a wide variety of modes of representation (words, tables, charts, graphs, etc.). In contrast, there appears to be little agreement when discussions turn to the specifics of what a student should know or be able to do. This lack of agreement is exacerbated by the fact that there is no clear understanding of what is meant by "numeracy" or "quantitative literacy" (QL).

Many at this Forum spoke eloquently about specific mathematical competencies valued, even required, by their profession; however, high school students generally are oblivious to or unrealistic about what their future careers might be. If students entered school already preprogrammed for career choices, it would be much easier to develop a personalized high school experience that helped them develop the specific competencies required for their future career. But students do not come preprogrammed. Thus a responsible high school teacher must try to meet more general goals, namely, to help his or her students develop:

- General mathematical competencies that will allow them to successfully learn more specific competencies as, later, their career goals come more clearly into focus; and

- An appreciation for the power of mathematics coupled with a confidence that they are capable of learning and applying it.

Teachers who are not well trained in their content area (true of a significant percentage of middle and high school teachers of mathematics) tend to teach what they feel most comfortable with (usually skills) and what the end-of-course test assesses (usually skills and procedures, with some concepts). They are least likely to use multiple representations or mathematics in context or to help students gain the confidence with numbers and graphs and charts that seems to be a shared vision at this Forum.

Many teachers of mathematics are currently doing a truly outstanding job, sometimes under extremely difficult circumstances, of preparing their students for the world of work or advanced studies beyond school. These teachers are well-trained in mathematics and use a variety of pedagogical approaches to make mathematics accessible to their students. They supplement the textbook and course syllabus with rich explorations that make use of multiple approaches to mathematics. Students of teachers like these receive sufficient mathematical grounding to know what questions to ask and to have the confidence to seek and find answers in new numerical settings. They become mathematically competent, thus quantitatively literate. Although they may not have been taught Bayes' theorem or other specific applications they might require in the future, they are confident and competent learners who will be able to pick up new concepts or skills as needed.

J. T. Sutcliffe holds the Founders Master Teaching Chair at St. Mark's School of Texas in Dallas. A recipient of the Presidential Award for mathematics teaching, as well as Siemens and Tandy Technology Scholars awards, Sutcliffe has served as a member of the AP Calculus Test Development Committee and as an AP Calculus Exam Leader. Sutcliffe also helped develop *Pacesetter: Mathematics with Meaning*, a teacher professional development project for the College Board.

The real question we face, therefore, is not how to make a bulleted list of skills students must have or specific questions they should be able to answer, but how to help teachers help students understand numbers in context. Our goal may be to produce well-prepared, mathematically literate students, but we will not succeed if we do not first reach K–12 teachers.

Several Forum participants offered a different approach: eliminate courses such as Advanced Placement (AP) Calculus that, in their view, do not sufficiently support QL. I believe such action would be disastrous. When schools make a serious attempt to provide AP or International Baccalaureate (IB) courses for their students (whether for sound educational motives or politically prompted ones), it generates some wonderful repercussions that directly affect the outcomes we seek:

- Money and time are invested in AP teacher training; countless teachers will attest to the value of this training. AP training helps teachers develop both a new level of conceptual understanding and effective pedagogical approaches to implement in their classrooms. AP training also contains a strong equity component.

- Teachers have a variety of venues for AP training. They can select from one- or two-day institutes throughout the year and from weeklong institutes over the summer. Many teachers attend multiple institutes over a period of several years. In these institutes, they meet with other teachers to discuss mathematics and to share frustrations as well as success stories. These collegial contacts benefit all aspects of their teaching.

- Although AP mathematics institutes focus on specific courses (calculus or statistics), teachers find that much of what they have learned applies to other courses as well. They become better teachers of mathematics for all students and they affect positively the entire mathematics program at their school.

Eliminate AP and you eliminate more than just a high-standards mathematics course. You also eliminate a nationally recognized professional development program that offers mathematics teachers an opportunity to gain both content training that takes them to high standards and pedagogical training that extends to all students they teach. The training teachers receive from AP thus promotes this Forum's vision of quantitative literacy.

Notwithstanding the potential benefits of AP training, many hurdles stand in the way of preparing quantitatively literate students under the guidance of teachers who understand content and practice sound pedagogical techniques:

- Many teachers come to the mathematics classroom with no background in mathematics. Moreover, few students in either high school or university plan to teach mathematics. Thus few well-trained teachers will be available to fill the teacher vacancies that are being generated at an extraordinary rate.

- Teachers tend to teach what they were taught, imitating the way they were taught. Those who are less confident with mathematics tend to focus on skills, which are too frequently separated from a meaningful context that would support quantitative literacy.

- Most states have standards (to which end-of-course assessments are tied) that resemble the table of contents from a typical textbook. State end-of-course assessments that determine whether students are able to clear a minimum bar are often very high stakes for teachers and for students.

- Many teachers teach only what will be assessed on high-stakes examinations. Because problem solving and reasoning are seldom assessed on such examinations, it stands to reason that problem solving and reasoning are seldom taught.

The challenge of preparing citizens who are more quantitatively literate will not be accomplished easily, especially in the face of the above realities; however, the situation is not entirely hopeless. We can do some things that will leverage the realities of our current situation:

1. Because many teachers do not have strong content and pedagogical training in mathematics, they tend to rely heavily on a page-by-page textbook–driven pedagogy. Stronger leadership from textbook publishers to incorporate QL as a standard and a goal therefore would help bring QL ideas and problems to many more students.

2. Teachers are both guided and restricted by standards set by local districts and states; thus local and state departments of education must accept some responsibility for setting standards to increase students' quantitative literacy. As standards tilt in the direction of QL, so will classroom instruction.

3. Teachers teach according to what will be assessed on high-stakes tests. If those in charge of designing the blueprint for such tests increase the proportion of QL-like items, more QL will be taught in the schools.

4. Most mathematics educators acknowledge the importance for learning of using multiple representations, student communication, group learning, and technology. Nevertheless, although students are often seated in groups, they seldom engage in rich mathematical conversations; although they are

encouraged to "do mathematics" with their calculator, they often have little sense of what the mathematics means; although they are often asked to speak and write, they are seldom asked to speak or write about effective ways to approach or apply the mathematics they are studying. These disconnects between belief and effective action could be reduced by offering more teacher professional development opportunities, similar to AP workshops, that emphasize strategies for building quantitative literacy, conceptual understanding, and applications of mathematics.

Although QL does not have a clear definition with consensus agreement, its goal is widely shared: to prepare students with the ability to think quantitatively in a variety of contexts. To accomplish this goal, we clearly need better and more uniformly trained teachers . This will take time, money, and sustained leadership, especially from K–12 and university educators, professional societies, policymakers, and leaders in the business world.

Say What You Mean
(and Mean What You Say)

JANIS I. SOMERVILLE

Much of the discussion at this Forum has focused on the importance of quantitative literacy (QL) together with various strategies for elevating the place of QL in education. I am no expert on curricular issues, but I do bring to this conversation a certain degree of experience with an issue of arguably equal importance: the policy implications of different curricular options.

I speak from the perspective of a long-time college administrator responsible for undergraduate education who is currently facilitating a network of state education systems through which leaders of K–12 and higher education (both two- and four-year institutions) are developing more powerful collaborations to raise achievement and close gaps among students from K–16.

So I look at the question of how and where to place QL in the undergraduate curriculum—within mathematics, across the curriculum, in place of college algebra—through a special lens. I ask: Which of the options will bring about greater alignment in content and instruction between K–12 and college expectations for students? Which option will best help smooth the transition from high school to college for all students? Which may increase turbulence in this crucial passage?

From this perspective, what I have heard at this Forum is confusing. I must say, I would love to take the kinds of QL courses described and taught by many speakers. Further, the case presented for QL is compelling. But as we all know, QL is not part of current policy priorities, either at K–12 or in higher education. Therefore, the question confronting this panel—What are the policy implications?—is clearly the key to the success or failure of the QL initiative.

The dominant strategies discussed so far have been about spreading the adoption of QL in disciplines across the institution, to avoid having QL seen as "simply mathematics" (or worse, "simple mathematics"). This makes sense as one part of a strategy. But frankly, I am puzzled by the relative silence in these discussions about first making clear the place of QL in mathematics departments. Here is why: A perspective that gives priority to the impact of policies on students must take into account the expectations concerning mathematics that are currently in place for students entering college. Simply put, what mathematics faculty determine is important for students to know and be able to do to begin college-level study exerts a very powerful influence on K–12 curriculum and instruction.

To see why this is so important, consider some data that provides a national perspective on the flow of students from secondary school to higher education. A lot has changed in the years since most of us finished high school. Today, three of every four high school graduates go on to postsecondary education within two years—45 percent to four-year colleges, 26 percent to two-year colleges, and 4 percent to other postsecondary institutions.

But as we all know, many first-year college students are not fully prepared for higher education. Nearly 30 percent must take remedial courses when they enter college, and most of those (24

Janis I. Somerville is staff officer at the National Association of College and University System Heads (NASH) and directs the State K–16 Network that is jointly sponsored by NASH and Education Trust. Previously, Somerville led Maryland's Partnership for Teaching and Learning K–16, helped found the Philadelphia Schools Collaborative, and served as the senior academic officer for undergraduate education at Temple University and at the University of Pennsylvania.

percent) are in mathematics. Moreover, remediation is most heavily concentrated in colleges with high minority enrollments: in these institutions, 43 percent of entering students require some remediation, 35 percent in mathematics. Not surprisingly, students who require extensive remediation graduate at significantly lower rates than other students. In fact, those needing three or more remedial courses graduate at one-third the rate of students who enter college fully prepared.

Clearly, students and parents have understood that in today's world virtually all students need to graduate from high school prepared to go on to postsecondary education. Indeed, as these data show, students are entering college in ever larger numbers, but they are clearly not mathematically prepared at an appropriate level. I would argue that the human and financial costs of the disconnect between standards for high school graduation and what we require for college readiness are no longer tolerable.

Especially powerful for students, and for the high school teachers who teach them, are expectations in mathematics and English language arts for college admission, credit, and placement. I am not talking just about test scores, but about the expectations of knowledge and skills that we choose to measure and on which we base decisions about student achievement.

The Education Trust has gathered panels of faculty from K–16—both nationally and in several states—to look at high school exit and college admissions expectations. These include the major assessments being used for both high school graduation and college admissions and placement. Here is what we found:

- State assessments of high school mathematics focus primarily on elementary algebra and geometry, but increasingly include also at least some data analysis.

- At the same time, admissions assessments (the SAT-II and ACT) emphasize a more rigorous pre-calculus sequence (Algebra I, Algebra II, Trigonometry/Precalculus) and little, if any, geometry or data analysis.

- Placement assessments are almost universally administered by colleges once students have enrolled. Whether campuses use commercial tests (e.g., Accuplacer or Compass) or locally developed tests, the content is remarkably consistent: the standard pre-calculus sequence. Most often the missing link between state K–12 graduation standards and college-level placement is Algebra II.

Perhaps the content of these placement tests reflects a time when their intended use was simply to determine where to place students on the way to calculus. In many states now, however, public four-year and community college systems use performance on these assessments to determine whether students can begin credit-bearing versus remedial courses or even whether they can enter a four-year college at all. And as national transcript studies indicate, the more remedial courses students have to take the less likely they will even make it to the sophomore year, much less complete a college degree. High stakes indeed.

In addition to tests, many states also specify Carnegie unit requirements that students must complete to meet college admissions requirements. Once again, whenever specific courses are named, these requirements are all about algebra and geometry.

The obvious conclusion is that higher education—more specifically, the higher education mathematics community—is sending very clear and consistent messages about the important mathematical knowledge and skills that students should have to succeed in college, and this message is not at all about QL. For those of us who are particularly concerned about closing achievement gaps among poor and minority students who are especially vulnerable to weak or mixed signals, the clarity of this message is especially important. To be ready for college, you need Algebra II.

Thus as a matter of policy, school districts must focus curriculum and instruction on courses that ensure that high school graduates are prepared to meet these "college-ready" algebra requirements. Needless to say, enabling all students to achieve levels of performance previously reserved only for a few requires intensive teacher development as well as instructional support for teachers and students, support that is not focused in the direction of QL.

So my first recommendation is to think very hard about what represents college-ready mathematics and where, or if, QL fits in. If you really believe that QL is essential for all students, that it is more than just an add-on elective for some, then you cannot duck this issue. It is not enough to say "by the way, here is something new that you might like to add if there is time." QL advocates must be very clear about what all students need to know and be able to do, starting with where QL fits in the mathematics program.

Related to this is the issue of high school students who meet the minimum college-ready standard early. Right now we rush students to Advanced Placement (AP) Calculus, a course that has become the universal answer to rigorous school mathematics. For many politicians, enrollment in AP Calculus is thought of as a measure of the quality of school mathematics.

Of course, we all know better. Paradoxically, the fastest-growing part of the high school curriculum is college-level study, while the biggest part of our college mathematics program is remedial, that is, high school course work. And it is not clear that either of us does the other's work particularly well. More important, in high schools across the country, the scarce resource of experienced, qualified teachers is being distracted to teach AP Calculus when we need our strongest teachers in the core high school curriculum. In informal discussion, several of the mathematicians at this Forum have told me that calculus should be left to the colleges. If that is what you mean, say it loudly so that all can hear.

And that leads to my final observation. My K–16 work has taught me anew that the commitment of participants at this Forum to build a consensus for action is very important. Our K–12 colleagues have been able to muster substantial consensus at the state level about core knowledge and skills. Whether or not we agree on the specifics of these recommendations, mathematics and English language arts are at the core of state K–12 expectations. And there is little question that higher education can, and does, exert considerable leverage on K–12. We should recognize this and act on it. By the seemingly simple act of agreeing on what we mean by college ready, we can strongly influence both K–12 mathematics education and our own undergraduate mathematics programs.

Educational Policy and Decision Making

MARGARET B. COZZENS

Quantitative literacy (QL) is not just about mathematics and should not be viewed as such. Quantitative literacy is a much more inclusive term than mathematics and specifically includes working and reasoning with numbers and data in a contextual framework. Most people would argue that our society needs to be quantitatively literate, but because QL is generally undefined, each person has a different notion of what it may mean. Similarly, mathematics as a discipline is viewed differently by those who use it in occupations, those who study it, and those who simply use calculation skills often associated with school mathematics. To look at policy issues in the context of these ill-defined goals, I pose and partially answer three key questions.

How do we create an environment that supports quantitative literacy education in a way that does not recreate the "math wars" at another level?

Part of the answer comes from Zalman Usiskin in *Mathematics and Democracy: The Case for Quantitative Literacy,* "We may be able to obtain public support for attention to quantitative literacy if we emphasize that quantitative literacy is an essential part of literacy itself" (Usiskin 2001, 85). Literacy, of course, is the responsibility of many others besides mathematics teachers and mathematicians; so too is quantitative literacy. (If this looks like the new, new, new mathematics, we are doomed before we start.)

How do we provide for quantitative literacy education in an already full curriculum in high schools and colleges, both in mathematics and in other courses?

The answer to this question, I believe, is different if you are talking about high school students than if you are talking about college students. For high school students, to say that quantitative literacy education goes beyond mathematics education does not imply any neglect of quantitative literacy in mathematics curricula. Most of the topics suggested for quantitative literacy are topics listed in the National Council of Teachers of Mathematics (NCTM) *Principles and Standards for School Mathematics* (NCTM 2000). Newer instructional materials all include extensive treatment of data analysis and provide for mathematical problem solving using real-world problems (that is, mathematics in context).

To engage teachers in particular, we need to build on what we have. Fortunately, the NCTM standards and newer curricular materials provide this foundation, as do some very good quantitative literacy materials produced by the American Statistical Association. Teachers should not be expected to launch into new professional development efforts for quantitative literacy, especially since many have just begun to understand how to implement the standards through professional development opportunities. Teaching quantitative literacy across the high school curriculum is not possible in an already full curriculum in which teachers traditionally know little about anything but their major discipline. Reinvention takes too long and is too costly; however, universities and colleges directly control expectations for students through their admissions and placement activities.

Margaret B. Cozzens is Vice Chancellor for Academic and Student Affairs and Professor of Mathematics at the University of Colorado at Denver. Previously Cozzens served as director of the Division of Elementary, Secondary and Informal Science Education at the National Science Foundation and as Chair of the Department of Mathematics at Northeastern University. She is a member of the American Council on Education's Task Force on Teacher Preparation, and served as co-chair of the Technical Review Panel for TIMSS-R, the recent repeat of TIMSS.

College students select the courses they take to complete major, minor, and general education requirements. Quantitative literacy is not currently a part of the common core in most higher education institutions. A few liberal arts colleges do have such a requirement and some, such as Dartmouth, and Trinity in Connecticut, operate Quantitative Literacy Centers. When there is a college mathematics requirement it is most often satisfied by college algebra, a repeat of second-year high school algebra. Statistics is usually allowed, but it is typically taken only by those who are required to complete a statistics course for their major.

Thus, an opportunity exists in higher education to institute quantitative literacy across the curriculum, similar to writing across the curriculum. Better yet, quantitative literacy can become part of the core or general education requirements, satisfied by courses in numerous departments. Faculty in the social, natural, and applied sciences will have less difficulty defining quantitative literacy in their courses than those in the arts and humanities and will need less help. But even these latter fields offer some opportunities. Students will then see their course work in many areas through a quantitative lens. Mathematics and statistics departments usually will have to take the lead in such an endeavor, but development of such a program should include faculty from many departments.

How do we engage the stakeholders: teachers, faculty, other disciplines, administrators, business and industry, and parents?

Engaging stakeholders is the hardest and most critical step in developing a quantitative literacy initiative, and it must begin now. We live in an increasingly quantitative world but quantitative literacy, as important as it is, will still be competing with other areas of the curriculum in both high schools and colleges. Even with teachers, faculty, and administrators aligned on the goals of quantitative literacy, if parents and political figures are not on the same page nothing will happen, or worse, if it does, it will be stopped dead never to be revived.

It is critical for this latter group that we define quantitative literacy well and show what it is and what it is not, why it is necessary, and how it can be accomplished without diminishing other valuable parts of the curriculum. Parents in particular, when confronted by something they do not understand, revert to what they themselves learned in school.

Business and industry leaders are our greatest allies. They do not like what education systems currently provide to students at all levels in the areas of problem solving and working with data, and most are very willing to get behind a campaign to change the paradigms. Clear, concise messages are essential. To create a shared definition and vision is going to require the best minds in the country working together with representatives of the stakeholder groups to test this definition and vision.

This Forum moves in the right direction but we are a long way from even getting the definition right. It will require a small group of people working long hours and on many weekends before we can begin to have the type of national discourse necessary to effect change.

References

National Council of Teachers of Mathematics. 2000. *Principles and Standards for School Mathematics.* Reston, VA: National Council of Teachers of Mathematics.

Usiskin, Zalman. 2001. "Quantitative Literacy for the Next Generation." In *Mathematics and Democracy: The Case for Quantitative Literacy,* edited by Lynn Arthur Steen, 79–86. Princeton, NJ: National Council on Education and the Disciplines.

Policies on Placement and Proficiency Tests: A Community College's Role

SADIE BRAGG

Many U.S. students leave high school with quantitative skills far below what they need to function well in a postsecondary institution or in the workforce. It is these students who most often enter community colleges. Coley (2000) noted that in 1995–96, the U.S. Department of Education reported that only 40 percent of community college entrants took either the SAT or ACT examinations whereas nearly 90 percent of entrants to four-year institutions took one of these college entrance tests. Not surprisingly, community college students were more likely than their four-year counterparts to score in the bottom quartile on these tests.

The mission of community colleges is often described as providing access to postsecondary education programs and services that lead to stronger, more vital communities. In general, these institutions give students, regardless of their high school achievement or college placement scores, the opportunity to attend college. In many cases, community colleges give some students a chance to transfer into four-year colleges that are more selective than those they could have enrolled in directly. Hence, based on their mission, community colleges play a significant role in democratizing education (Coley 2000).

Because community colleges are positioned between the last two years of secondary education and the last two years of postsecondary education, articulation with grades 11 to 12 and grades 15 to 16 is imperative. This paper addresses how Borough of Manhattan Community College (BMCC), a community college within the City University of New York (CUNY), collaborates with New York City public schools and senior colleges within CUNY to facilitate the transition to and from community colleges and in the process enhances students' quantitative skills.

Basic Skills Requirements

With some exceptions, all students entering CUNY must take the CUNY/ACT Basic Skills Tests in reading and writing and a locally developed CUNY mathematics test. The Reading Skills Test, the COMPASS, measures reading comprehension as a combination of referring and reasoning skills. The CUNY/ACT Basic Skills Test in writing includes two parts: the ASSET Writing Skills Test, a 36-item, 25-minute objective test, and the Writing Sample, a 60-minute essay test. The CUNY Mathematics Skills Assessment Test consists of 80 multiple-choice questions and is divided into five parts: arithmetic, elementary algebra, intermediate algebra, trigonometry, and pre-calculus. Placement into required basic mathematics courses is based on the results of the arithmetic (20 questions) and elementary algebra (20 questions) sections. At CUNY, the maximum score for these two parts is 40 and the minimum passing score is a composite score of 25. Some colleges set their own minimum passing score in elementary algebra. For example, at BMCC, the minimum passing score is 15 out of 20. Placement into more advanced mathematics courses is based on the results of the CUNY intermediate algebra, trigonometry, and pre-calculus tests, as well as campus-based mathematics tests.

Sadie Bragg is Senior Vice President of Academic Affairs and Professor of Mathematics at Borough of Manhattan Community College. A former president of the American Mathematical Association of Two-Year Colleges (AMATYC), Bragg has served as a member of the Mathematical Sciences Education Board, the Advisory Board to the Education and Human Resources Directorate of the National Science Foundation, and the Academic Assembly of the College Board. Bragg is co-author of many mathematics textbooks for grades K–12.

According to recent CUNY policy, students who do not meet the university's basic skills standards are redirected to community colleges such as BMCC, which has over 16,000 students. At BMCC, about 60 percent of its freshmen with high school averages ranging from 43 to 96 come from the New York City public schools. As with many community colleges, BMCC offers basic skills courses to these students in the areas of reading, writing, arithmetic, and elementary algebra. In a given year, 87 percent of the students at BMCC take one or more basic skills courses. Approximately 13 percent of BMCC students graduate and transfer to a senior college within CUNY.

Part of BMCC's response to the university's policy on basic skills was to develop collaborative programs, one reaching students while they are still in high school, the other helping students make the transition to two CUNY senior colleges. Both programs address the need to improve the literacy and quantitative skills of potential students who plan to enroll in a community college or a senior college in the university.

BMCC's College Now program, based on a partnership between CUNY and the New York City Board of Education, is designed to prepare high school students for the college experience and to enhance their self-esteem by offering them college-level work in high school. College faculty teach special courses in mathematics and social sciences for high school students, who must meet the college's requirements to take these courses. Faculty also conduct workshops to help prepare students to pass their New York State Regents' examinations. In addition, the faculty conduct workshops for high school juniors who do not meet the CUNY/ACT Basic Skills requirements in reading, writing, and mathematics. The purpose of each workshop is to improve the writing skills and the quantitative literacy skills of the participants.

The Prelude to Success program allows first-time freshmen who wish to enter a CUNY senior college and who have passed at least one of the three CUNY/ACT Basic Skills Tests to earn college credits in introductory courses through BMCC. At the same time, students are improving their basic skills in reading, writing, and/or mathematics. BMCC collaborates with Hunter College and with the City College of New York to offer the Prelude to Success program on each of the participating campuses. Most courses in the program are taught by BMCC faculty. On completion of the one-semester program, students are retested on the CUNY/ACT Basic Skills Tests in reading and writing and the CUNY Mathematics Skills Assessment Test in arithmetic and in elementary algebra. Because of BMCC articulation agreements with Hunter College and City College, all credit-bearing courses are transferred to the senior college.

Proficiency Requirement

In addition to the university's policy on basic skills, CUNY also requires students to pass a proficiency examination. This test, the CUNY Proficiency Examination (CPE), was developed in response to a 1997 board of trustee's resolution and is required of students who are completing associate degree programs or beginning junior-level work. The CPE tests students' ability to understand and think critically about ideas and information and to write clearly, logically, and correctly at a level associated with success in upper-division courses.

The CPE consists of two tasks: Task I: Analytical Reading and Writing, and Task II: Analyzing and Integrating Material from Graphs and Texts. In Task I, students write a focused essay, drawing a relationship between specified elements of two readings and extending it, as directed, to their own experiences, understanding, or ideas. In Task II, students are given a set of materials (two charts and a brief reading passage) on similar topics. In a short written response, they must state the major claim(s) of the reading selection and discuss the extent to which the data support and/or challenge the major claim(s).

All senior college students must pass the CPE by the time they have completed 60 credits. All community college students must pass the CPE, which is a requirement for the associate degree, before they graduate. The examination also affects the ability of community college students to transfer to the senior colleges. This high-stakes examination demands that faculty within a college and faculty across the CUNY colleges throughout the system work together to find ways to prepare the students for the demands of the CPE.

Like other community colleges, BMCC has the responsibility for preparing students to enter the workforce and/or to transfer to a four-year institution. With the advent of high-stakes testing, many community college students may find it difficult to get jobs or transfer to a four-year institution. Hence, the community colleges' role in preparing students to write well and think quantitatively is imperative.

References

Coley, Richard J. The American Community College Turns 100: A Look at its Students, Programs, and Prospects. Princeton, NJ: Educational Testing Service, 2000.

Office of Academic Affairs, Test Development Program, The City University of New York. Spring 2001. "*A Description of the CUNY Proficiency Examination.*" New York: The City University of New York.

Standards Are Not Enough: Challenges of Urban Education

Background

The New York City public schools have published mathematics performance standards that clearly define what students need to know and be able to do in mathematics. These standards were developed through a careful process of review and alignment and within the context of major instructional reform in all content areas.

In 1996, the New York City Board of Education adopted a plan to introduce and implement learning standards in all major content areas. The board recognized that the process of becoming a standards-driven system would be a multiyear effort, requiring us to reexamine policies and practices, with special emphasis on aligning assessments, redirecting resources, and improving professional development. Board members understood that we would need to work closely with the New York State Education Department (SED) to ensure that our standards and assessments would align with those at the state level.

Because we believed that performance standards in the New York City public schools should reflect the best thinking of practitioners and researchers nationally in each of the content areas, we chose to work with the New Standards project codirected by the National Council on Education and the Economy and the Institute for Learning at the University of Pittsburgh. In the area of mathematics, the New Standards reflect the recommendations of the National Council of Teachers of Mathematics (NCTM).

Although our belief in the need to align our city standards with state and national ones was paramount, we also understood that for our schools and communities to accept the standards and feel a sense of ownership, they needed to be directly involved in the process. To accomplish this, we began the work of customizing the standards. The customization process brought together teachers, principals, and other pedagogical staff to review the New Standards, the NCTM standards, and the New York State learning standards to ensure alignment. The customizers also were engaged in a very important effort that would directly connect the standards with the New York City teachers and students. The customizers returned to their districts, schools, and classrooms to find evidence of student work that reflected the standards. The discussions about which work samples met the standards were very rich and provided an excellent model of professional development. This experience resulted in a standards document that included student work as a critical component and that influenced the process of professional development in our districts and schools.

Progress to Date

The New York City public school system published the first set of standards in 1997: for English language arts, Spanish language arts, and English as a second language. In 1998, we produced the

Judith A. Rizzo is Executive Director of the James B. Hunt Institute for Educational Leadership and Policy in Chapel Hill, NC. Until 2002, Rizzo was Deputy Chancellor for Instruction for the New York City public schools. Previously, Rizzo served as a K–12 teacher, principal, and central administrator, and as adjunct professor at Columbia University. Rizzo was a member of the blue-ribbon New York City Commission on Mathematics Education, chaired by Matthew Goldstein, Chancellor of The City University of New York.

first edition of the New York City Performance Standards in Mathematics for grades 4, 8, and 10. During the customization process, we worked with the SED to revamp its testing program and to realign our own assessment program and protocols. We wanted to move from using only multiple-choice tests to a more performance-based assessment system.

Our joint work produced a comprehensive assessment program for grades 3 to 8. It resulted in a change in the targeted grades tested by the SED and by the New York City school system. The state currently tests students in grades 4 and 8. The state also raised high school graduation requirements to include five Regent examinations for all students. The New York City school system tests students in grades 3, 5, 6, and 7. Both city and state assessments are published by CTB McGraw-Hill. Because of the alignment of both these assessment systems, we now have multiyear longitudinal data that allow us to track student progress from grade 3 through high school.

To supplement the New York City performance standards calibrated at grades 4 and 8, we subsequently developed and disseminated content standards for kindergarten through grade 8. The content standards are available on The New York City public schools' Web site[1] and are also published in a variety of sources: in our parent guides, *What Every Student Should Know . . . And Be Able To Do,* in our curriculum scope and sequence documents, and in the instructional guides that provide teachers with sequential teaching units. New York City recently designed a new student report card that reflects the specificity of the content standards at every grade level.

Quantitative Literacy in the Mathematics Standards

We have organized our mathematics standards into five major groups:

- Arithmetic and Numeration Concepts

- Geometry and Measurement Concepts

- Function and Algebra Concepts

- Statistics and Probability Concepts

- Mathematical Process

Our groupings reflect the NCTM standards:

- Number and Operations

- Geometry; Measurement

- Algebra

- Data Analysis and Probability

- Problem Solving; Reasoning and Proof; Communication; Connections

- Representation

A close examination of our performance standards reveals our commitment to quantitative literacy. For instance, our middle-grade mathematics standards include sample activities whereby students demonstrate their understanding of statistics and probability through real-life applications. Here is an example:

> From a sample news headline, and article, and a table of data, select and construct appropriate graphs or other visual representations of the data. Decide whether or not the headline seems appropriate. Write a letter to the editor.

Each of the five major groups includes opportunities for real-world application of the mathematics standards. In addition, to further emphasize the importance of a student's ability to apply mathematics to other disciplines, we have designed specific sections of the standards document to provide students with cross-content area applications. These sections are "Mathematical Communication" and "Putting Mathematics to Work." Suggested activities include a data study based on civic, economic, or social issues, in which students:

- Select an issue to investigate;

- Make a hypothesis on an expected finding, if appropriate;

- Gather data;

- Analyze the data using concepts such as mean and median, frequency and distribution;

- Show how the study's results compare with the hypothesis;

- Use pertinent statistics to summarize; and

- Prepare a presentation or report that includes the question investigated, a detailed description of how the project was carried out, and an explanation of the findings.

Other suggested activities include asking students to design mathematical models of physical phenomena such as those used in science studies; design and plan a physical structure, including a presentation or report on how the project was carried out; or manage and plan an event with cost estimates, supplies, and scheduling.

Each section of the performance standards is followed by student work samples demonstrating the activities and including teacher commentary assessing the degree to which the student work meets the standards. The commentary section includes an assessment of the student's writing by judging the degree to which it:

- Engages the reader by establishing a context;

- Creates expectations through predictable structures, e.g., headings;

- Makes use of appropriate writing strategies such as creating a visual hierarchy and using white space and graphics as appropriate; and

- Includes relevant information.

This section also includes suggested extension activities that provide students with real-world, practical applications of mathematics.

Policy and Strategies for Instructional Reform

The New York City public school mathematics standards emphasize that students need mathematical or quantitative literacy in their daily lives and that mathematics should be taught in a multidisciplinary manner. This does not mean that our approach shortcuts basic numeracy and computational skills. We have worked to strike a balance between the "constructivist" mathematics that has been labeled "fuzzy math" by some and the demand by others for a back-to-basics approach that focuses on memorizing tables and formulas.

A similar division existed in language arts between proponents of phonics and those who believed in a whole language approach. We believe that division has been largely eliminated in language arts thanks to our performance standards and we hope for similar success in mathematics.

Our language arts standards emphasize a balanced approach to literacy instruction. They include phonics as well as literature and writing, speaking and listening. Our primary literacy standards make it clear that neither the phonics nor the whole language approach alone prepares all children to be truly literate; used together they provide students with a more complete learning experience.

We have introduced the concept of a balanced approach to mathematics instruction as well. It may prove more difficult to institutionalize this approach among mathematics teachers, however. To succeed on the mathematics assessments students now have to apply mathematical solutions to everyday problems and explain their thinking about those solutions.

The Dilemma of What Versus How

Our efforts in New York City so far necessarily have been focused on clearly identifying performance and content standards for all grades and on aligning assessments, scope and sequence, and instructional guides. These are the "what" that students need to know and be able to do and the "what" teachers need to teach. "How" teachers teach this content depends on two other critical ingredients: curricula and instructional programs at the district and school levels and professional development for all instructional and supervisory staff.

No single instructional program can possibly meet the needs of all teachers and learners in New York City. Indeed, there is no national consensus on the superiority of one curriculum or program for teaching mathematics. Experience dictates and research corroborates that the most effective instructional programs are those developed or selected by staff whose direct responsibility it is to teach our students and lead our schools. The role of a central office is to set standards and provide guidelines and technical assistance to support district and school-based decisions about how to reach the standards.

The performance and content standards are sufficiently clear to guide those decisions and the assessments evaluate student acquisition of the skills and knowledge contained in the standards. The standards provide the basis for selecting appropriate programs, texts, and materials. A survey conducted by the National Science Foundation (NSF) two years ago found that all New York City school districts were using either NSF-validated curricula or instructional programs that were standards-based and aligned with the NCTM standards. These had all been chosen at the school or district level.

The schools therefore are not lacking an appropriate curriculum. So why are our students not consistently achieving at high levels? Why have the clearly defined student performance and content standards, aligned assessments, scope and sequence documents, and instructional guides not resulted in improved student performance.

Why have not the clearly defined student performance and content standards, aligned assessments, scope and sequence documents and instructional guides not resulted in increasing student performance?

Challenges Ahead

A nationally validated mathematics curriculum does not teach students, nor does a standards document. Common sense supported by research tells us that the single most important factor affecting student learning is a well-qualified teacher.

The major challenge we face in New York City, along with many urban school systems throughout the country, is the dearth of qualified mathematics teachers. We simply do not have enough well-trained teachers of mathematics to teach to the standards. One partial response to this problem is quality professional development.

There are two broad categories of teachers with different professional development needs: those who are certified to teach mathematics but lack the skills and knowledge to teach to the new standards and those, particularly at the elementary and middle school levels, who do not have a solid base of content knowledge in mathematics.

A one-size-fits-all approach to professional development will not meet the needs of these two categories of teachers. Clearly, professional development as we generally understand it will not suffice for the second category. These teachers need to have more in-depth training similar to course work rather than traditional workshops in mathematics pedagogy. Even the best instructional strategies are virtually useless in the hands of teachers lacking content knowledge.

Even within the first category, there is a continuum of professional development needs. Some of the teachers in this category are novice teachers. Like other school systems, New York City has begun to recruit teachers who are changing careers from mathematics-related fields. These novice teachers require very different professional development opportunities from veteran teachers.

The challenge is to provide professional development opportunities that are tailored to the needs of individual teachers but that also reflect what we know about the learning needs of the students in their particular schools and districts. The concept of differentiated approaches to teaching students is now commonplace; it should be applied to adult learning as well. We do have some tools in New York City to assist us in determining individual teacher needs and they are, coincidentally, the same tools that we use to diagnose student needs: the item analyses from our assessment results.

We began to generate item analyses a few years ago to assist teachers in identifying the learning needs of their students. The results were intended to provide teachers with useful data that would inform their instructional planning and help them address the needs of individual and small groups of students. This information was intended to be used in completing report cards, progress reports, and student portfolios and in parent conferences, and as an integral ingredient in making promotion decisions.

These test item analyses, when disaggregated by district, school, grade, or classroom, also can be used to plan focused professional development. When used appropriately, they can help to reveal areas within the mathematics curriculum that are weak or not addressed.

We now generate reports that go beyond the item analyses; these provide suggested teaching activities to address those weaknesses. The instructional guides in mathematics provide another source for designing professional development opportunities.

We also have developed guidelines and standards for designing professional development programs. These describe the essential elements of effective professional development and share successful models currently in place in our system. In addition, we have developed opportunities for teachers to participate in rigorous, credit-bearing course work in mathematics.

All these efforts combined, however, will not completely solve the problem. We need a sufficient pool of qualified mathematics staff developers and coaches who can work with teachers in their classrooms. We need deeper collaboration with our universities both to train mathematics teachers differently and to provide several levels of mathematics professional development to current teachers and supervisory staff. We need incentives to attract future graduates into teaching. And we need increased opportunities to recruit mathematically trained career changers into the teaching profession.

Conclusion

The New York City public schools have clearly defined content and performance standards and a variety of instruments to support implementation at the district and school levels. We believe that our standards and supporting materials begin to address the issue of quantitative literacy, but we need to continue to work on increasing and deepening quantitative literacy experiences for students.

We have come a long way toward improving the alignment of our assessments with our standards and collecting good data from those assessments. We are putting into operation the recommendations of a mathematics commission formed last year to improve our programs and support systems. We have begun to co-design and co-teach mathematics courses for staff in collaboration with some of our universities.

We must expand the number and variety of training opportunities for current teachers of mathematics at every level. Ultimately, we must ensure that all students are provided with solid mathematics instruction that will prepare them to use mathematics comfortably and expertly beyond their school careers or to continue their study of mathematics at the highest levels.

Notes

1. http://www.wnycenet.edu/dis/standards/Math/index.html.

Creating Networks as a Vehicle for Change

SUSAN L. GANTER

A critical feature of the national movement for quantitative literacy (QL) is the development of a strong networking component supported by common vision and direction. To this end, much can be learned from the role of networking in the national movement during the past two decades to change the undergraduate curriculum in mathematics. In particular, aspects of calculus reform and subsequent efforts to improve other areas of undergraduate mathematics can be helpful in assessing possible strategies for improving quantitative literacy.

Learning from Calculus Reform

The calculus reform efforts that the National Science Foundation (NSF) encouraged through awards from 1988 to 1994 set the direction for much of the undergraduate reform that has followed. Reflection on these efforts can aid institutions that now are working to make QL a part of every college graduate's repertoire of knowledge and skills. As part of an NSF-funded study (Ganter 2001), 18 national objectives of calculus reform were formulated based on several publications that discussed the development of the reform movement (Roberts 1996; Schoenfeld 1996; Steen 1987; Tucker 1990; Tucker and Leitzel 1995). In reviewing data collected between 1988 and 1998, several objectives clearly stand out as major thrusts of the reform efforts. The most prominent themes were:

- The development of original curricular materials;

- The use of alternative learning environments, such as computer laboratory experiences, discovery learning, and technical writing; and

- An emphasis on a variety of student skills, such as computer use, the use of applications, and a focus on conceptual understanding (Ganter 2001).

When reviewing data by institution type, the results are fairly consistent with those from the total population. A few exceptions are worth noting, however:

- Research and comprehensive universities were more likely to involve high schools in their efforts than liberal arts and two-year colleges. In fact, only 36.3 percent of the two-year colleges with NSF-funded calculus projects reported the involvement of high schools, while 57.8 percent of the comprehensive universities and 49.3 percent of the research institutions reported such involvement.

- Minority student involvement was significantly more prevalent at two-year colleges than at any other type of institution. This was perhaps because of the different composition of the student population at two-year colleges, but is certainly a noteworthy observation.

Susan L. Ganter is Associate Professor of Mathematical Sciences at Clemson University. Earlier, Ganter served as Director of the Program for Institutional Change at the American Association for Higher Education and as Senior Research Fellow of the American Educational Research Association at the National Science Foundation. Ganter is Chair of the Committee on Curriculum Renewal and the First Two Years of the Mathematical Association of America and editor of two recently published books analyzing the impact of undergraduate mathematics reform.

- Concerted efforts to involve women in the reform movement were infrequent. This result was primarily because of the absence of such a focus at research institutions. As might be expected, the primary efforts in calculus reform that focused on women occurred at women's colleges. Two-year colleges also made a significant effort to target women (Ganter 2001).

Creating Undergraduate Standards

The Mathematical Association of America (MAA) is currently engaged in a once-a-decade study of the undergraduate program in the mathematical sciences. This effort, unlike those of previous decades, is occurring in an environment informed by lessons from the calculus reform movement. In addition, also for the first time, discussions have been informed by workshops with partner disciplines in addition to focus groups of mathematicians. The goal is a set of recommendations that will have a broad impact on mathematics departments as they plan their future undergraduate curricula.

The new MAA recommendations build on an unprecedented amount of first-hand information on the mathematics needs of other disciplines, information that is being obtained through a series of disciplinary-based workshops known as the Curriculum Foundations (CF) Project. To ensure that the recommendations and subsequent reports accurately represent the views of other disciplines, the predominant participants in these workshops were faculty from disciplines other than mathematics. A curriculum conference held in November 2001 brought together pairs of disciplinary representatives from each workshop to consider similarities and differences among the reports and to compile the most important recommendations for the mathematics community (Ganter and Barker 2002). This kind of networking—both within the mathematics community and with colleagues in partner disciplines—is critical to the success of any curricular movement in the mathematical sciences. QL therefore can learn much from the Curriculum Foundations model.

Networking with other disciplines enabled the Curriculum Foundations Project to influence the MAA recommendations by encouraging an approach to mathematics that is directly supportive of QL programs in undergraduate institutions, including:

- A flexible mathematics degree program designed to fit the students, mission, and resources of individual departments;

- Ongoing cooperation and collaboration with other disciplines to work on curriculum development;

- Emphasis on developing analytical thinking and careful reasoning in all courses and for all students; and

- Emphasis on reading, writing, and speaking for the purpose of communicating and learning mathematics as well as for assessing student learning.

An important aspect of the new recommendations is strong encouragement to mathematics departments to work with students of a broad range of abilities. Increasing the number of students with quantitative experiences holds promise for increasing the overall quality of our scientific workforce and creating a general appreciation for the importance of QL.

Influencing Student Achievement and Attitudes

One of the most important, yet least-often investigated, outcomes of education innovation is the impact on student learning and achievement. Unfortunately, student achievement is not a clearly defined concept. Arguments about what a student should know and understand after one or two years of college mathematics are heated and have yet to be resolved. Also widely debated are the basic mathematical skills that provide the foundation for conceptual understanding.

Data suggest that calculus reform has had a positive impact on student achievement. Less clear are the magnitude of this impact and the appropriate mixture of reform ideas to achieve the greatest positive impact. Even less studied is the influence of reform methodologies on student skills that are difficult to quantify, such as the ability to communicate mathematics, understanding when and how to apply mathematics to real problems, and effectiveness when working in teams. Because these skills are so critical to QL, the question of their relative importance compared with other possible learning outcomes as goals for mathematics courses could affect the introduction of QL in these courses.

Student attitudes about mathematics directly affect their ability and motivation to complete the mathematics courses in which they enroll. Attitudes also can affect the number of mathematics courses students elect to take—especially courses that are not required in their major area of study. Students who do not understand the relevance of mathematics to their future will not believe it is important to learn or continue to study the subject. Introductory college mathematics courses—including those focusing on QL—are an ideal setting in which to excite students about studying quantitative ideas.

One of the most profound impacts of reform calculus is the significant positive improvement in students' attitudes about their capacity to think mathematically and to contribute valuable insights to problem-solving endeavors (Bookman and Friedman 1998; Ganter and Jiroutek 2000). This shows that, given adequate support, students can develop quantitative thinking skills in ways not often achieved in traditional classrooms. This personalization of mathematics also enables students to exhibit greater confidence and satisfaction in their quantitative abilities. Such attitudes can lead to a greater likelihood that they will enroll in more quantitative courses (Ganter 2001). Clearly, student success and enrollment in further courses will have an enormous impact on the success of quantitative courses—and on the faculty who develop and teach them.

Enhancing Learning Environments

The existence of common elements shared by the majority of the projects in the calculus reform movement suggests that the degree of success or failure depends less on what is implemented than on how, by whom, and in what setting implementation occurs. The consistent reactions of students from a wide variety of institutions point to several key components in the success of a reform environment (Ganter 2001). For example, instructors must communicate to students (and other faculty) the purpose of the changes being made. This perhaps is not as easy as it seems because the reasons for change must be understood as relevant and important to students' future success. For QL, connections with real problems and issues are a core component; thus faculty can more readily dispel the widespread belief among students that mathematics is simply a barrier to be overcome. Perhaps the most important role of courses focusing on QL is to enable students to see the many uses of mathematics.

The level of personal attention available to students also greatly affects their attitude and level of commitment. This is especially true when the elements that define a course are ones that students have never experienced, requiring additional support as students adjust their learning styles (Ganter 2001). A primary goal of QL is the creation of quantitative courses that make mathematics real and interesting for *all* students, both those for whom it has always been interesting and those for whom it has not. By fostering a collaborative spirit that encourages new ways of teaching and learning, networks of faculty both within mathematics departments and across campuses can create the supportive environment necessary for change—both for students and faculty.

Encouraging Faculty Networks

The nature and extent of faculty networks is a critical component of the QL movement and will ultimately determine its long-term sustainability. As previously suggested, an examination of the issues faced by faculty when pioneering change (such as those faced in the campaign to reform calculus) can offer insight about the potential for similar network development for QL.

Interestingly, one of the most important statements that can be made about any reform effort is that there has in fact been change. Although this may seem an obvious outcome, in reality it can be a major breakthrough in a college environment. Change was clearly observable as a result of calculus reform efforts in many departments at a wide variety of institutions (Ganter 2001). Some specific changes were directly related to faculty networking, including:

- Increased conversations within departments about undergraduate education;

- Increased recognition of the need for (and often actual) conversations with faculty in other disciplines;

- Increased understanding of the domino effect that changes in one course have on the teaching of other courses; and

- Increased interest and participation in educational issues by faculty (Ganter 2001).

In the case of calculus, reform has encouraged networking and collaborations among mathematics faculty and with faculty in other departments. These networks often result from the changes implied by the different problem types that are the focus of the newly developed curricular materials (Keynes et al. 2000; Mumford 1997). For example, the increase in applications has made necessary a closer tie between calculus and related topics in other disciplines.

The changes in calculus also have made it difficult to ignore the structure of other mathematics courses, especially those that are often taken just before and after calculus. This means that faculty who have traditionally taught these courses now are discussing topics and issues that reach across course boundaries, resulting in further networking. Consequently, the structure of the entire undergraduate mathematics curriculum, including requirements for the mathematics major, are being reviewed in numerous departments (Buccino 2000; Dossey 1998; Keynes et al. 2000).

The activities of many mathematics faculty, both within their departments and in the larger professional community, thus have changed dramatically over the past decade. Within departments, faculty now struggle with traditional structures that often do not encourage professional activities in mathematics education. Many involved in reform, especially untenured faculty, are anxious to learn how the mathematics community will respond to the changing professional roles that are implied within departments committed to curricular innovation.

Specifically, faculty who enjoy financial and collegial support—both within their institution and through external networking—

report that reform methodologies have had a positive impact on their teaching and professional development (Eiseman et al. 1996; Keynes et al. 2000). On the other hand, a lack of support from administration and minimal opportunities to network with fellow faculty members often lead to the demise of new curricula. Teaching in a more collaborative environment (both with students and other faculty) and opportunities to network through professional development offerings often are cited as the aspects of change that faculty find most valuable, rewarding, and essential to ultimate success (Eiseman et al. 1996; Keynes et al. 2000; Mathews 1995).

Workshops that allow faculty to collaborate directly with colleagues who have experience with the proposed changes—while also interacting with others who are just beginning to make changes—help them avoid the mistakes made by others and to build a network of colleagues with whom they can continue to work and talk after returning to their home campuses. Faculty involved in curricular change say that they need even more professional development opportunities, suggesting that small workshops and conferences—especially those that encourage continued networking—are perhaps the most effective means of disseminating ideas and encouraging change across campuses.

Supporting QL Through Networking

Experiences from curricular reforms in calculus and other disciplines reveal that a supportive network can be used to promote buy-in by all affected individuals and groups. Therefore, an important part of the QL movement is the design and formation of the National Numeracy Network (NNN) to assist locales in which efforts are underway to translate QL from aspiration into educational practice, to disseminate promising practices, and to exchange information among existing and potential network sites. (Details of NNN, which change regularly, can be found on-line at www.woodrow.org/nced/national_numeracy_network.html.)

Planned activities of the network include professional development experiences and opportunities to learn about QL for educators and others and a Web site through which resources, information, and exchange of ideas regarding QL will be made accessible to the broadest possible audience. Critical to NNN are local projects and meetings that bring together schools, colleges, civic groups, the media, business, and industry. Additional outreach efforts include research, reports, and publications that increase understanding of QL and its significance in education, work, and private and civic life.

One part of NNN is a QL Resource Library that provides the opportunity for faculty to share ideas by developing an extensive collection of QL materials across a variety of disciplines. The resource library includes program descriptions, course syllabi, examinations, activities, laboratories, projects, readings, publications, and examples of student work. Such a collection of materials is very important to the work of NNN, serving as a resource for outreach efforts and as a means of teaching interested individuals and organizations about QL. In addition, the QL Resource Library soon will include a database of individuals, projects, and institutions involved in the development of QL curricula.

By focusing on different aspects of policy, practice, professional development, dissemination, and assessment, the National Numeracy Network will provide a catalyst for quantitative literacy, especially in grades 10 to 14. Quantitative Literacy programs participating in the network already are working with organizations that can directly influence a wider audience to create public pressure for QL. NNN institutions and organizations are developing QL course materials and programs to share through professional development opportunities, the QL Resource Library, and the QL Web site (www.woodrow.org/nced/quantitative-literacy.html). Through networking, QL education is becoming a reality at many institutions.

References

Bookman, J., and C. P. Friedman. 1998. "Student Attitudes and Calculus Reform." *School Science and Mathematics* (March): 117–22.

Buccino, Al. 2000. "Politics and Professional Beliefs in Evaluation: The Case of Calculus Renewal." In *Calculus Renewal: Issues for Undergraduate Mathematics Education in the Next Decade,* edited by S. L. Ganter, 121–45. New York, NY: Kluwer Academic/Plenum.

Dossey, John, ed. 1998. *Confronting the Core Curriculum: Considering Change in the Undergraduate Mathematics Major.* MAA Notes No. 45. Washington, DC: Mathematical Association of America.

Eiseman, J. W., J. S. Fairweather, S. Rosenblum, and E. Britton. 1996. *Evaluation of the Division of Undergraduate Education's Course and Curriculum Development Program: Case Study Summaries.* (Prepared under contract for the National Science Foundation.) Andover, MA: The Network, Inc.

Ganter, Susan L. 2001. *Changing Calculus: A Report on Evaluation Efforts and National Impact from 1988 to 1998.* MAA Notes No. 56. Washington, DC: Mathematical Association of America.

Ganter, Susan L., and William Barker, eds. 2002. *A Collective Vision: Voices of the Partner Disciplines.* MAA Notes Series. Washington, DC: Mathematical Association of America.

Ganter, Susan L., and M. R. Jiroutek. 2000. "The Need for Evaluation in the Calculus Reform Movement: A Comparison of Two Calculus Teaching Methods." In *Research in Collegiate Mathematics Education, IV,* edited by E. Dubinsky, A. Schoenfeld, and J. Kaput, 42–62. Providence, RI: American Mathematical Society.

Keynes, Harvey B., Andrea M. Olson, D. J. O'Loughlin, and D. Shaw. 2000. "Redesigning the Calculus Sequence at a Research University:

Faculty, Professional Development, and Institutional Issues." In *Calculus Renewal: Issues for Undergraduate Mathematics Education in the Next Decade,* edited by S. L. Ganter, 103–20. New York, NY: Kluwer Academic/Plenum.

Mathews, D. M. 1995. "Time to Study: The C⁴L Experience." Undergraduate Mathematics Education (*UME) Trends*. Washington, DC: Mathematical Association of America.

Mumford, David. 1997. "Calculus Reform for the Millions." *Notices of the American Mathematical Society* 44(5):559–563.

Roberts, A. Wayne, ed. 1996. *Calculus: The Dynamics of Change*. Washington, DC: Mathematical Association of America.

Schoenfeld, Alan. H. 1996. *Student Assessment in Calculus*. Report of the NSF Working Group on Assessment in Calculus. Arlington, VA: National Science Foundation.

Steen, Lynn A., ed. 1987. *Calculus for a New Century*. Washington, DC: Mathematical Association of America.

Tucker, Alan C., and James R. C. Leitzel, eds. 1995. *Assessing Calculus Reform Efforts: A Report to the Community*. Washington, DC: Mathematical Association of America.

Tucker, Thomas W., ed. 1990. *Priming the Calculus Pump: Innovations and Resources*. Washington, DC: Mathematical Association of America.

Numeracy in an International Context

LYNN ARTHUR STEEN

As the recent intrusion of computer-generated data has transformed the way Americans live, work, and learn, so has it influenced countries around the world. The inevitable questions about appropriate new goals for mathematics education that are suggested by the transforming impact of computers are not confined to the United States. These issues arise in every country, although the responses vary greatly because of the different historical and cultural roles played by mathematics in different nations.

Several papers in this volume cite the two-decade-old report *Mathematics Counts* (Cockcroft 1982) as the source for the term "numeracy," described there as an educational goal with two attributes. First is an "at homeness" with numbers, by which is meant "an ability to make use of mathematical skills to cope with the practical demands of everyday life." Second is an ability "to understand information that is presented in mathematical terms." Although the term numeracy predates this reference, the Cockcroft report is widely regarded as the first major document to urge that numeracy—what we call quantitative literacy—be a priority for mathematics education.

More recently, the Organization for Economic Cooperation and Development (OECD) has undertaken through its Program for International Student Assessment (PISA) to define and assess student knowledge and skills in reading, mathematical, and scientific literacy (see www.pisa.oecd.org). PISA defines mathematical literacy as "the capacity to identify and understand the role that mathematics plays in the world, to make well-founded mathematical judgments, and to engage in mathematics in ways that meet the needs of an individual's current and future life as a constructive, concerned, and reflective citizen" (OECD 1999, 41). The PISA literacy tests were administered for the first time in 2000 (NCES 2002).

Some years earlier, the International Adult Literacy Survey (IALS) began using a three-part definition of literacy encompassing prose, document, and quantitative elements (OECD 1995). A follow-up study known as ALL (Adult Literacy and Lifeskills survey; see nces.ed.gov./surveys/all) is being administered internationally during 2002 and 2003. ALL focuses on numeracy not as a portfolio of passive skills but as an active pattern of behavior, such as managing situations, solving problems, and responding to quantitative information, which could be said to characterize numerate adults (Gal et al. 1999).

Those in the United States who pay attention to mathematics education have heard much in recent years about TIMSS, the Third International Mathematics and Science Study, which has recently been repeated under the name TIMSS-R (see nces.ed.gov/timss). These aforementioned studies—PISA and ALL—illustrate that international concern about mathematics is not limited to the traditional mathematics curriculum that is assessed, more or less, through the TIMSS studies. Concern about numeracy and literacy also are very much present in other countries.

Indeed, there is quite active international interest in defining and assessing students' quantitative and mathematical skills, especially at the school-leaving level, because quantitative competence influ-

Lynn Arthur Steen is Professor of Mathematics at St. Olaf College, and an advisor to the Mathematics Achievement Partnership (MAP) of Achieve, Inc. Earlier, Steen served as executive director of the Mathematical Sciences Education Board and as president of the Mathematical Association of America. Steen is the editor or author of many books and articles, including *Mathematics and Democracy* (2001), *Why Numbers Count* (1997), *On the Shoulders of Giants* (1991), and *Everybody Counts* (1989).

ences to a great extent the effective preparation of each nation's workforce and university students. For most of the past century, mathematics educators around the world have worked together through the International Commission on Mathematical Instruction (ICMI) to learn from each other both about effective approaches to mathematics education and about the different roles that mathematics plays in different societies (see elib.zib.de/IMU/ICMI/). Both mathematics and mathematics education are truly international subjects, although in the latter, cultural influences necessarily play a much larger role.

It should come as no surprise, therefore, that just as the rise of a data-driven culture has forced the United States to rethink decades-old traditions of school mathematics, so similarly motivated changes are underway in other countries. It is enlightening and sometimes empowering to see how differently mathematics can be viewed from the perspective of other traditions. We realize, after such study, that certain things we take for granted are largely arbitrary, whereas approaches we can hardly imagine are, in some nations, routine.

It is for these reasons that we invited contributions to this Forum from several mathematics educators in other nations, especially those closely associated with the international work of ICMI, PISA, and ALL. The papers in this section offer a wide variety of international perspectives that, although failing to fairly represent everything of significance in mathematics education around the world, at least illustrate forcefully the wide variety of issues, approaches, and concerns.

Mogens Niss of Denmark, secretary of ICMI during the 1990s, addresses the issues directly in a paper entitled "Quantitative Literacy and Mathematical Competencies." Niss argues for a broad PISA-like definition of "mathematical" literacy that would encompass most of what other authors in this volume refer to as "quantitative" literacy. In particular, Niss argues, if the objectives of mathematics education were organized around competencies such as reasoning, modeling, and communicating mathematically—rather than, for example, around content such as algebra, geometry, and calculus—school graduates would be far better able to navigate thoughtfully the turbulent waters of democratic debate and decision making. (See pp. 217–222.)

Michel Merle, in "Defining Mathematical Literacy in France," writes about the current work of a national commission on the teaching of mathematics in France that is chaired by former ICMI President Jean-Pierre Kahane. The charge to the commission, motivated by the same forces that led to this Forum on quantitative literacy, is how to restructure school mathematics in ways that take into account the impact of computers. The Kahane commission (Kahane 2002), as Merle describes, argues for a mathematics

syllabus dominated by four content areas: geometry ("the education of vision"); computation (both approximate and exact, including its relation to reason); statistics ("stochastic literacy"), and computers (especially data structures and algorithms). (See pp. 223–225.)

A. Geoffrey Howson, also a former secretary of ICMI, in "What Mathematics for All?," takes on what he and many others see as a disastrous decline in the mathematical competence of British school-leavers. He attributes this undisputed decline to many causes, among which is the "piece of tape" curricular philosophy in which all students study ("snip off") a certain length of a subject (a piece of tape) whose courses and examinations are designed for a university goal they never reach. Howson suggests that for most, a (QL-like) curriculum deliberately designed to focus on "the mathematics of citizenship, culture, personal finance, health, . . ." would yield greater success. (See pp. 227–230.)

Mieke van Groenestijn of the Netherlands writes about the ALL literacy assessment project, focusing in particular on the ALL characterization of numerate behavior in adults. Using ALL's rather detailed description as a foundation, van Groenestijn examines the problem of educating adults for numerate behavior, which is far different from passive (or worse, inert) knowledge. She notes that because adults learn principally through action, a predisposition to numerate behavior can best be learned in real-life situations. (See pp. 231–236.)

Ubiratan D'Ambrosio of Brazil, a former vice president of ICMI, takes note of the political and cultural roles played by mathematics in all countries and at all ages, especially the recent role of "data control and management" as a tool for excluding "cultures of the periphery." D'Ambrosio, who years ago introduced "ethnomathematics" as a way to "restore cultural dignity" in societies whose mathematics was invisible in school, here advocates a three-part endeavor he calls "literacy, numeracy, and technocracy" as a means of providing access to full citizenship. (See pp. 237–240.)

These glimpses of how mathematics educators in other nations are coming to terms with the new demands of numeracy, mathematics, and citizenship open a window on approaches that move well beyond those normally considered in U.S. curriculum discussions. In addition, by revealing great differences in fundamental assumptions and objectives concerning mathematics education, they suggest important limitations on the inferences that can safely be drawn from comparative international assessments. To the degree that numeracy and mathematics are important features of our culture, differences in national traditions will necessarily create significant differences in both the objectives and outcomes of mathematics education.

References

Cockcroft, Wilfred H. 1982. *Mathematics Counts*. London: Her Majesty's Stationery Office.

Gal, Iddo, Mieke van Groenestijn, Myrna Manly, Mary Jane Schmitt, and Dave Tout. 1999. *Numeracy Framework for the International Adult Literacy and Lifeskills Survey (ALL)*. Ottawa, Canada: Statistics Canada.

Kahane, Jean-Pierre, et al. 2002. *Commission de réflexion sur l'enseignement des mathématiques: Présentation des rapports et recommandations*. Retrieved January 25, 2002, at: http://smf.emath.fr/Enseignements/CommissionKahane/RapportsCommissionKahane.pdf.

National Center for Education Statistics (NCES). 2002. *Outcomes of Learning: Results from the 2000 PISA Assessment of 15-Year-Olds in Reading, Mathematics, and Science Literacy*. Washington, DC: Office of Educational Research and Improvement, U.S. Department of Education.

Organization for Economic Cooperation and Development (OECD). 1995. *Literacy, Economy, and Society: Results of the First International Adult Literacy Survey*. Paris: OECD.

Organization for Economic Cooperation and Development (OECD). 1999. *Measuring Student Knowledge and Skills: A New Framework for Assessment*. Paris: OECD.

Quantitative Literacy and Mathematical Competencies

MOGENS NISS

Quantitative Literacy and Its Relatives

When reading the material made available to Forum participants, in particular *Mathematics and Democracy: The Case for Quantitative Literacy* (Steen 2001) and the background essays prepared for the Forum, three observations came to my mind.

First, the authors all seem to be speaking of roughly the same "animal," but they give it a variety of different names such as quantitative literacy, numeracy, mathematical literacy, and mathematical competencies. We also could add the term "mathemacy" coined by Ole Skovsmose (1994). Irrespective of the labels used, what people have in mind is something other than proficiency in pure, theoretical mathematics, something that goes beyond such knowledge and skills.

Second, the same term, "quantitative literacy," is given a variety of different interpretations by different authors. The variation is mainly a matter of how narrowly the word "quantitative" is to be understood, vis à vis the involvement of numbers and numerical data. Some use the word in a much broader sense than numbers and data only.

Third, finally, and most significantly, there seems to be general consensus about the importance of making a case for the "animal," whatever it is going to be called. That consensus certainly includes me.

The first two observations suggest that we are short of a one-to-one correspondence between the terms used and the ideas these terms refer to. At best this may cause some terminological confusion in the discourse, at worst it may compromise the case itself. In other words, although terminological clarification is often tedious, dry swimming, I think some effort ought to be invested in clarifying the notions.

From my standpoint, and for a number of reasons, I prefer the term "mathematical literacy," roughly as it is defined in the Organization for Economic Cooperation and Development (OECD) Programme for International Student Assessment (PISA) project, in which I happen to be involved. In this enterprise, mathematical literacy is:

> The capacity to identify, to understand, and to engage in mathematics and to make well-founded judgments about the role that mathematics plays, as needed for an individual's current and future life, occupational life, social life with peers and relatives, and life as a constructive, concerned and reflective citizen. (OECD 2000)

Mogens Niss is Professor of Mathematics and Mathematics Education at the innovative Roskilde University in Denmark at which studies are based on project work. From 1987 to 1999, Niss served as a member of the Executive Committee of the International Commission on Mathematical Instruction (ICMI), the last eight years as Secretary. He is currently Chair of the International Program Committee for ICME-10, a member of the Mathematics Expert Group for OECD's PISA project, and director of a Danish national project on mathematics curriculum.

The main reason I prefer mathematical literacy is that the broadness of the term "mathematical" captures better than the somewhat narrower term "quantitative" what we actually seem to be after, for instance, when providing examples. Of course, we could argue on the basis of the history and epistemology of mathematics that many aspects of those mathematical topics that are of particular importance to real life, such as geometry, functions, probability, and mathematical statistics, among others, were in fact "arithmetised" in the nineteenth and twentieth centuries, so that we are not restricting the animal greatly by referring to it as quantitative literacy rather than as mathematical literacy. To see that, however, a person has to possess a fairly solid knowledge of modern mathematics and its genesis, and that is most certainly a prerequisite that we cannot and should not expect of all those with whom we want to be in dialogue.

Now, how is mathematical literacy related to mathematical knowledge and skills? Evidently, that depends on what we mean by mathematics. If we define mathematics in a restrictive way, as a pure, theoretical scientific discipline—whether perceived as a unified, structurally defined discipline or as a compound consisting of a number of subdisciplines such as algebra, geometry, analysis, topology, probability, etc.—it is quite clear that mathematical literacy cannot be reduced to mathematical knowledge and skills. Such knowledge and skills are necessary prerequisites to mathematical literacy but they are not sufficient.

This is not the only way to define mathematics, however. We may adopt a broader—partly sociological, partly epistemological—perspective and perceive mathematics as a field possessing a five-fold nature: as a pure, fundamental science; as an applied science; as a system of tools for societal and technological practice ("cultural techniques"); as an educational subject; and as a field of aesthetics (Niss 1994). Here, being a pure, fundamental science is just one of five "natures" of mathematics. If this is how we see mathematics, the mastery of mathematics goes far beyond the ability to operate within the theoretical edifice of purely mathematical topics. And then, I submit, mathematical literacy is more or less the same as the mastery of mathematics. By no means, however, does this imply that mathematical literacy can or should be cultivated only in classrooms with the label "mathematics" on their doors. There are hosts of other important sources and platforms for the fostering of mathematical literacy, including other subjects in schools and universities.

All this leaves us with a choice between two different strategies. Either we accept a restrictive definition of mathematics as being a pure, fundamental science and then establish mathematical literacy as something else, either a cross-curricular ether or a new subject. Or we insist (as I do) on perceiving mathematics as a multi-natured field of endeavor and activity. If we agree to use such a perception to define the subject to be taught and learned,

that subject would have the fostering of mathematical literacy, including its narrower quantitative sense, as a major responsibility from kindergarten through to the Ph.D.

Once again, this being said, the fostering of mathematical literacy also should be the responsibility of other subjects, whenever this is appropriate, which it is much more often than agents in other subjects bother to realize or accept. Mathematical literacy is far too important to be left to mathematics educators and mathematicians (in a wide sense), but it also is far too important to be left to the users of mathematics. Mathematics educators and mathematicians have to assume a fair part of the responsibility for providing our youths and citizens with mathematical literacy.

Mathematical Literacy and Democracy

Traditionally, we tend to see the role of mathematical literacy in the shaping and maintenance of democracy as being to equip citizens with the prerequisites needed to involve themselves in issues of immediate societal significance. Such issues could be political, economic, or environmental, or they could deal with infra-structure, transportation, population forecasts, choosing locations for schools or sports facilities, and so forth. They also could deal with matters closer to the individual, such as wages and salaries, rents and mortgages, child care, insurance and pension schemes, housing and building regulations, bank rates and charges, etc.

Although all this is indeed essential to life in a democratic society, I believe that we should not confine the notion of democracy, or the role of mathematical literacy in democracy, to matters such as the ones just outlined. For democracy to prosper and flourish, we need citizens who not only are able to seek and judge information, to take a stance, to make a decision, and to act in such contexts. Democracy also needs citizens who can come to grips with how mankind perceives and understands the carrying constructions of the world, i.e., nature, society, culture, and technology, and who have insight into the foundation and justification of those perceptions and that understanding. It is a problem for democracy if large groups of people are unable to distinguish between astronomy and astrology, between scientific medicine and crystal healing, between psychology and spiritism, between descriptive and normative statements, between facts and hypotheses, between exactness and approximation, or do not know the beginnings and the ends of rationality, and so forth and so on. The ability to navigate in such waters in a thoughtful, knowledgeable, and reflective way has sometimes been termed "liberating literacy" or "popular enlightenment." As mathematical literacy often is at the center of the ways in which mankind perceives and understands the world, mathematical literacy is also an essential component in liberating literacy and popular enlightenment. We should keep that in mind when shaping education for the pursuit of mathematical literacy in service of democracy.

The Danish KOM Project

If we decide to adopt a broad, multi-natured notion of mathematics, and set out to foster mathematical literacy within mathematics education, it becomes a crucial task to find and employ new ways to define and describe mathematics curricula that focus on mathematical competence rather than on facts and techniques. I give here a brief account of current attempts in that direction being made in the Danish so-called "KOM" project. The thinking behind and underpinning of that project also has exerted some influence on the OECD PISA project, as can be seen in Jan de Lange's background essay for the Forum (de Lange, see pp. 75–89).

Traditionally, in Denmark and in many other countries, a mathematics curriculum is specified by means of three types of components:

1. Statements of the *purposes and goals* that are to be pursued in teaching and learning.

2. Determination of mathematics *content*, given in the form of a *syllabus*, i.e., lists of the mathematical topics, concepts, theories, methods, and results to be covered.

3. Forms and instruments of *assessment and testing* to judge to what extent students have achieved the goals set for the syllabus as established under (2).

Serious objections can be raised against this way of specifying a curriculum. First, on such a basis, it is very difficult to describe and explain in overarching, nontautological terms what mathematics education at a given level is all about, without relying on circular descriptions such as "the teaching and learning of mathematics at this level consist in studying the topics listed in the syllabus," which is just another way of saying that the teaching and learning of mathematics are about teaching and learning (a particular segment) of mathematics.

Second, a syllabus-based curriculum specification easily leads to identifying mathematical competence with the mastery of a syllabus, i.e., knowing the facts and being able to perform the skills tied to the topics of the syllabus. Although such mastery is certainly important, this identification tends to trivialize mathematics, reduce the notion of mathematical competence, and lead to too low a level of ambition for teaching and learning. In Denmark we often refer to this reduction as the "syllabusitis trap."

Third, if we have only syllabus-based curriculum specifications at our disposal in mathematics education, we can only make inessential, trivial comparisons between different mathematics curricula, i.e., we can only identify the differences between curricula X and Y by listing the syllabus components in X∩Y, X\Y, and Y\X, respectively; however, the differences between two kinds of mathematics teaching and learning are typically both much more fundamental and more subtle than the differences reflected in the syllabi.

This leaves us with the following challenges and a resulting task. We wish to create a general means to specify mathematics curricula that allows us to adequately:

- Identify and characterize, in a noncircular manner, what it means to *master* (i.e., know, understand, do, use) *mathematics,* in and of itself and in contexts, irrespective of what specific mathematical content (including a syllabus) is involved;

- Validly describe *development and progression* within and between mathematics curricula;

- Characterise *different levels of mastery* to allow for describing development and progression in the individual student's mathematical competence; and

- Validly *compare* different mathematics curricula and different kinds of mathematics education at different levels or in different places.

The general idea is to deal with this task by identifying and making use of a number of overarching mathematical competencies.

This gave the stimulus (and the most important part of the brief) for the Danish KOM project, directed by the author of this paper. KOM stands for "Kompetencer Og Matematiklæring," Danish for "Competencies and Mathematical Learning." (More information is available at http://imfufa.ruc.dk/kom. By the end of August 2002 an English version of the full report of the project can be found at this site.) The project was established jointly by the Ministry of Education and the National Council for Science Education. It is not a research project but a development project to pave the way for fundamental curriculum reform in Denmark, from kindergarten to university. In fact it is a spearhead project in that similar projects are now being undertaken in Danish, physics and chemistry, and foreign languages; the natural sciences are soon to be addressed.

More specifically, the project is intended to provide inspiration by discussing and analyzing the possibility of dealing with the task just presented by means of the notion of mathematical competencies, and accordingly to propose measures and guidelines for curriculum reform. It is not the intention that the project itself shall propose detailed new curricula at all the different educational levels it addresses. Specific curriculum implementation is up to the curriculum authorities responsible for each of these levels; however, it is more than likely that the collaborators in the project will be asked to take part in that implementation in the sectors in which they work.

Mathematical Competencies and Insights

Let us begin by suggesting working definitions for two of the key words, competence and competency. It goes without saying that it is human beings that may possess competence and competencies.

To possess competence (to be competent) in some domain of personal, professional, or social life is to master (to a fair degree, appropriate to the conditions and circumstances) essential aspects of life in that domain. In some languages (such as Danish), there are two facets of the notion of competence. The first is formal competence, which is roughly the same as authorization or license, i.e., the right to do something. The second is real competence, roughly equivalent to expertise, i.e. the actual ability to do something. Here, the focus is on the latter facet. This leads us to define "mathematical competence" as the ability to understand, judge, do, and use mathematics in a variety of intra- and extra-mathematical contexts. Necessary, but certainly not sufficient, prerequisites for mathematical competence are extensive factual knowledge and technical skills.

A "mathematical competency" is a clearly recognizable and distinct, major constituent in mathematical competence. Competencies need be neither independent nor disjoint. Thus, the question we have to address is, What are the competencies in mathematical competence? To answer this question, let us begin by noting that mathematical competence includes two overarching sorts of capabilities. The first is to ask and answer questions about, within, and by means of mathematics. The second consists of understanding and using mathematical language and tools. A closer analysis has given rise to the following eight competencies:

1. *Thinking mathematically* (mastering mathematical modes of thought), such as:

   - Posing questions that are characteristic of mathematics and knowing the kinds of answers (not necessarily the answers themselves) that mathematics may offer;

   - Extending the scope of a concept by abstracting some of its properties and generalizing results to larger classes of objects;

   - Distinguishing between different kinds of mathematical statements (including conditioned assertions (if-then), quantifier-laden statements, assumptions, definitions, theorems, conjectures and special cases); and

   - Understanding and handling the scope and limitations of a given concept.

2. *Posing and solving mathematical problems*, such as:

   - Identifying, posing, and specifying different kinds of mathematical problems (pure or applied, open-ended or closed); and

   - Solving different kinds of mathematical problems (pure or applied, open-ended or closed), whether posed by others or by oneself, and, if appropriate, in different ways.

3. *Modelling mathematically* (i.e., analyzing and building models), such as:

   - Analysing the foundations and properties of existing models, including assessing their range and validity;

   - Decoding existing models, i.e., translating and interpreting model elements in terms of the reality modelled; and

   - Performing active modelling in a given context, i.e., structuring the field, mathematizing, working with(in) the model (including solving the problems the model gives rise to); validating the model, internally and externally; analyzing and criticizing the model (in itself and vis-à-vis possible alternatives); communicating about the model and its results; monitoring and controlling the entire modelling process.

4. *Reasoning mathematically* such as:

   - Following and assessing chains of arguments put forward by others;

   - Knowing what a mathematical proof is (is not) and how it differs from other kinds of mathematical reasoning, e.g., heuristics;

   - Uncovering the basic ideas in a given line of argument (especially a proof), including distinguishing main lines from details, and ideas from technicalities; and

   - Devising formal and informal mathematical arguments and transforming heuristic arguments to valid proofs, i.e., proving statements.

5. *Representing mathematical entities,* such as:

- Understanding and utilizing (decoding, interpreting, and distinguishing between) different sorts of representations of mathematical objects, phenomena, and situations;

- Understanding and utilizing the relations between different representations of the same entity, including knowing about their relative strengths and limitations; and

- Choosing and switching between representations.

6. *Handling mathematical symbols and formalisms,* such as:

- Decoding and interpreting symbolic and formal mathematical language and understanding its relations to natural language;

- Understanding the nature and rules of formal mathematical systems (both syntax and semantics);

- Translating from natural language to formal/symbolic language; and

- Handling and manipulating statements and expressions containing symbols and formulas.

7. *Communicating in, with, and about mathematics,* such as:

- Understanding others' written, visual, or oral "texts" (in a variety of linguistic registers) about matters having a mathematical content; and

- Expressing oneself, at different levels of theoretical and technical precision, in oral, visual, or written form, about such matters.

8. *Making use of aids and tools* (including information technology), such as:

- Knowing the existence and properties of various tools and aids for mathematical activity and their scope and limitations; and

- Being able to reflectively use such aids and tools.

The first four competencies are the ones involved in asking and answering questions about, within, and by means of mathematics, whereas the last four are the ones that pertain to understanding and using mathematical language and tools. It should be kept in mind, however, that these eight competencies are meant neither to establish a partitioning of mathematical competence into dis-

jointed segments nor to constitute independent dimensions of it. The competencies just listed are very close but not completely identical to the ones that appear in the OECD PISA framework for mathematical literacy (OECD 2000). As mentioned above, this is no accident.

These eight competencies all have to do with mental or physical processes, activities, and behavior. In other words, the focus is on what individuals can do. This makes the competencies behavioral (not to be mistaken for behavioristic).

In addition to competencies, we also have identified three important insights concerning mathematics as a discipline. These are insights into:

- The actual application of mathematics in other subjects and fields of practice that are of scientific or social significance;

- The historical development of mathematics, internally as well as externally; and

- The special nature of mathematics as a discipline.

Needless to say, these insights are closely related to the possession of the eight mathematical competencies, but they cannot be derived from them. The competencies deal with different kinds of singular mathematical activities whereas the insights deal with mathematics as a whole.

Both the competencies and the insights are comprehensive, over-arching, independent of specific content, and independent of educational level. In other words, they are general to mathematics. But they are also specific to mathematics, i.e., even if other subjects come up with similar sets of competencies using similar words, those words will be interpreted completely differently from how they are interpreted in mathematics. Even though the competencies and the insights are general, they manifest themselves and play out differently at different educational levels, in different contexts, and with different kinds of mathematics subject matter.

The competencies and insights can be employed both for normative purposes, with respect to specification of a curriculum or of desired outcomes of student learning, and for descriptive purposes to describe and characterize actual teaching practice or actual student learning, or to compare curricula, and so forth.

In this paper there is room only to describe the core ideas of the KOM project. It is also a key intention of the project to specify in some detail how these competencies will actually be developed at different educational levels in schools and universities, to specify and characterize the relationships between competencies and mathematics subject matter at different levels, and to devise ways to validly and reliably assess students' possession of the mathematical competencies in a manner that allows us to describe and characterize development and progression in those competencies.

In conclusion, if we are able to meet the challenges stated above, and to complete the tasks they lead to, we will not only have done good service for mathematics education and mathematical literacy but we also may hope to be in a better position than today to engage in dialogues with quarters outside of mathematics and mathematics education about mathematical literacy and its importance for democracy.

References

Niss, Mogens. 1994. "Mathematics and Society." In *Didactics of Mathematics as a Scientific Discipline,* edited by R. Biehler, R. Scholz, R. Straesser, and B. Winkelmann, 367–78. Dordrecht: Kluwer Academic Publishers.

Organization for Economic Cooperation and Development (OECD). 2000. *Measuring Student Knowledge and Skills: The PISA 2000 Assessment of Reading, Mathematical and Scientific Literacy.* Paris: OECD. Retrieved January 25, 2002, at *http://www.pisa.oecd.org/.*

Skovsmose, Ole. 1994. *Toward a Philosophy for critical Mathematics Education.* Dordrecht: Kluwer Academic Publishers.

Steen, Lynn Arthur, et al. 2001. "The Case for Quantitative Literacy." In *Mathematics and Democracy: The Case for Quantitative Literacy,* edited by Lynn Arthur Steen, 1–22. Princeton, NJ: National Council on Education and the Disciplines.

Defining Mathematical Literacy in France

MICHEL MERLE

Two major reforms of mathematics curricula were undertaken in France during the twentieth century. The first, in 1902, viewed mathematics as an experimental science next to physics (two hours a week were dedicated to *dessin graphique*). Until 1960, no further reform occurred, for various reasons. The slogan of the 1960 reform was "mathematics for all." In that sense, democracy was a main concern for the reformers, because mathematics was supposed to carry universal values. But its results were not those expected.

In April 1999, at a time when there were a lot of controversies about mathematics, the French Minister of Education created a commission to undertake a study of the mathematics curricula from elementary school to teacher training in university. This *Commission de réflexion sur l'enseignement des mathématiques* was chaired by Jean-Pierre Kahane, member of the French Académie des sciences and former President of the International Commission on Mathematical Instruction (ICMI). I was one of the members of the commission.

This commission was neither the first nor will it be the last committee in France to think about mathematics and its teaching, but I believe it was the first time such a committee was asked, among other requests, to focus on the impact of computers on the mathematics syllabus; however, computers were not the only topic that the commission had in hand. We addressed four issues, namely: geometry, computation (or numeracy), statistics, and computers. After considerable consultation, we produced a report (Kahane 2002), available on the Internet, that is directed to teachers and to decision makers involved in all aspects of education.

Geometry

Teaching geometry from elementary to high school levels is still necessary today. We first showed the importance of geometry in order to "grasp space," to develop the vision of space, a vision that plays an essential role in our image-oriented society. Second, the report emphasized the fact that geometry is a fundamental subject for the learning of reasoning. Finally, the report recalled how important geometry is in the training of all scientists (technicians, engineers, researchers, and teachers).

We proposed to develop space geometry as an education in vision. For plane geometry, we suggested reinforcing the use of elementary invariants (such as angle and area) and reintroducing criteria for congruence and similarity of triangles. To avoid too dogmatic a teaching approach, the report also proposed to favor open problems (research on geometric loci and construction problems) and to make room for some "rich" geometries. For instance, at the end of high school, circular geometry could be taught together with complex numbers.

As regards methods, the commission focused on two main goals: teaching pupils and students to see and to think geometrically and teaching them to reason. Among the other important suggestions included in the report was to establish strong links with other disciplines, in particular with the sciences.

Michel Merle is Professor of Mathematics at the University of Nice in France. His mathematical research is mainly focused on algebraic geometry, including applications of this theory to computer vision. Merle is currently a member of the national "Commission de réflexion sur l'enseignement des Mathématiques" and of the "Conseil national des programmes", a committee involved in the elaboration of the curriculum for French primary and secondary schools.

Computation

The commission tried to intertwine epistemological and didactical issues by questioning the nature and role of computation in the mathematical sciences and their evolution, the cultural and educational representations of the theme, and the current curriculum from elementary to university levels. In the epistemological dimension of the report, we were especially sensitive to:

- The increasing diversity of the objects and practices that computations involve;

- The dependence of computation on computational tools;

- The relationships between exact and approximate computation, and between computation and reasoning; and

- The fundamental role that computations play in the building of mathematical concepts and theories.

We then pointed out that these epistemological characteristics of computation are deeply misunderstood in the cultural and educational representations of the theme, at least as regards three main points: the relationships between computation and reasoning, between approximate and exact computation, and between computation and computational tools.

Taking this discrepancy into account, we then developed a didactic analysis structured in three main parts: meeting with the world of computation: numbers, magnitudes, measures, and dimensions; from arithmetic computations to algebraic computations; and from algebraic computations to calculus and analysis. In each of these parts, we focused on reconstructions and breaches involved in mathematical learning processes, because these are often underestimated in teaching practices. We emphasized mental arithmetic, estimation of magnitudes, and better links between computation and reasoning and between approximate and exact computations. Finding an appropriate place for current technology is seen as a crucial transversal aim of teaching. We addressed how the curriculum can contribute to achieve these aims, from the beginning of elementary school to university. Outcomes from innovative work and educational research were used to support the analysis.

Statistics

Developing stochastic literacy for professional or individual purposes is widely understood to be part of obligatory education; nonetheless, it is surrounded by controversies and many questions set out in the commission's report are under investigation in many European countries.

We first give a brief account of the close connections between statistics (designed for analyzing, visualizing, and modeling data in contexts), probability theory, and other aspects of mathematics (such as geometry and multivariate analysis). Many statistical rules rely on common sense and specific skills (such as designing experiments). Although statistical understanding does not systematically involve probability theory or mathematical reasoning, probability and other mathematical background is required to move beyond purely descriptive statistics. We then dealt with the impact on statistical practice of the widespread use of computers and the availability of powerful statistical packages. For teaching purposes, computer random simulation yields a rapid understanding of many basic points (such as properties of sampling distributions).

Statistics are involved in other parts of the high school curricula, such as biology, social sciences, economics, and physics. All teachers in those subjects (and also in mathematics) need training because stochastic reasoning is new to them. Such training is a main theme in developing statistical literacy in any country. Teachers of different subjects start learning together in order to speak a common language and use common notations. Because statistics and probability concepts cannot be restricted to dice games or oversimplified questions, interdisciplinary working sessions have to be organized.

Teaching statistics and probability theory will also provide students with a true experience in modeling, which now is used in many professions.

Computers

In 1992, UNESCO published a report on *The Influence of Computers and Informatics on Mathematics and Its Teaching* (Cornu and Ralston 1992). (Some of the contributors to this report were participants in the Forum.) Reflecting ideas from this report, our commission examined three issues created by computers:

- Changes in life, in society, and in sciences and mathematics;

- Choices to be made for the mathematics syllabus; and

- Consequences for teacher training and for schools.

With respect to the mathematics syllabus, we wanted to focus on elementary and fundamental aspects: data structures, programs and algorithms, loops and iterations, conditional structures, and cost and complexity. These aim to define another kind of literacy. For example, data structures are crucial to understand fully algorithms and their complexity and to organize statistical data. We can expect that these topics will give meaning and reality to certain fundamental abstract notions such as variable, number, iteration, evaluation, and approximation. As a consequence, the commission report revisited some notions of classical mathematics.

We proposed that, in every lycée, there should be created a "math lab" or, better said, a "mathematical sciences lab" where pupils and teachers could meet, discuss, experiment, practice, and receive visitors.

Teacher-training issues are addressed throughout the report. We were highly concerned by the following questions: What can our teachers do? and What will they be able to do? We were convinced that the content of their training and the content of mathematics curricula for schools and high schools must evolve at the same time.

References

Cornu, Bernard and Anthony Ralston, eds. 1992. *The Influence of Computers and Informatics on Mathematics and Its Teaching.* 2nd edition. Science and Technology Education No. 44. Paris: UNESCO.

Kahane, Jean-Pierre, et al. 2002. *L'enseignement des sciences mathématiques* (Rapport au ministre de l'Education nationale de la Commission de réflexion sur l'enseignement des mathématiques.) CNDP–Odile Jacob: Paris. Retrieved January 25, 2002, at: http://smf.emath.fr/Enseignements/CommissionKahane/RapportsCommissionKahane.pdf .

What Mathematics for All?

A. GEOFFREY HOWSON

Does "Mathematics for all" mean "No mathematics for all"?
—*Title of a lecture given by Jan de Lange in 1983*

A calculator, . . . a friend, or an independent financial advisor can substitute for an education in mathematics for instrumental purposes.
—*S. Bramall in S. Bramall and J. White (2000)*

Q: I would like to know the rate of inflation for the years since 1987 to the present time to work out the true value of my savings. Can you help?

A: Certainly. Since 1987 the cost of living has gone up by 70 percent. So £1 today is worth the equivalent of only 30p then.
—*Reader's question and financial expert's answer in "Your money,"* Saga Magazine, April 2001

The teaching of mathematics in English secondary schools is far from satisfactory. Concerns arise regarding how the needs of different types of students are being met, the standards attained, the manner in which students' attainments are assessed, and the provision of adequately qualified teachers. In the longer paper from which this extract is adapted (Howson 2002), we look at each of these aspects and propose possible ways ahead. Here we focus on one issue—the curricular implications of "mathematics for all."

The coming of comprehensive education in many western countries raised important issues concerning curriculum design. Just what did "mathematics for all" mean? Nowadays the phrase often is taken to mean that "mathematics" was not to be found in the old English secondary modern schools—that only arithmetic was taught in them. Although this view is perhaps a caricature, there were clear distinctions between the aims of mathematics teaching in the grammar schools and in the bulk of technical and secondary modern schools. Put baldly, in the former, students were prepared for further academic study, in other schools, for taking their place within society. This was perhaps most clearly typified in the teaching of geometry. For the academic students there was Euclid-style "theorem and proof," for the others "practical geometry," the classification of shapes and solids, mensuration and, to varying extents (depending on the nature of the school), elementary scale and technical drawing.

The introduction in 1965 of a Certificate of Secondary Education (CSE) intended for those within the fortieth to eightieth percentiles of the ability range was not intended to threaten this dichotomy of aims. The comprehensive schools introduced just after that time, however, contained all types of students and their early differentiation would have defeated the aims of comprehensive schooling and produced only multilateral schools—those in which students are separated into different curricular streams within the same school. Yet postponing differentiation meant postponing streaming for CSE or the traditional GCE O-level (intended for the top 25 percent of students) and this, in turn, resulted in the former becoming a "watered-down" version of the latter.

A. Geoffrey Howson is Professor Emeritus of Mathematical Curriculum Studies at the University of Southhampton in England. A former Dean of Mathematical Studies at the university, Howson served from 1982 through 1990 as secretary of the International Commission on Mathematical Instruction (ICMI). He is author of several books on mathematics and mathematics education, most recently the TIMSS monograph *Mathematics Textbooks: A Comparative Study of Grade 8 Texts*.

The Cockcroft report (Cockcroft 1982), the outcome of a government committee established to counter criticisms of current school mathematics standards, proposed to rectify this by a "bottom-up" approach to curriculum design that concentrated first on the needs of the lower attainers. Accordingly, it drew up a "foundation list": what the report saw as a basic mathematical kit for all school leavers. That, in its turn, was supplanted in the late 1980s by the National Curriculum, which appeared to be designed not so much to meet the needs of students but rather those of an untried and ambitious assessment scheme. All students now were to follow the same curriculum, but at their own rates. A hierarchy of levels was defined that was to be followed by students at varying speeds, but the question of depth of treatment within a level was ignored. No one, apart from the highest attainers, had any fixed curriculum goal: students had simply to swallow as much of the curriculum as they could before the age of 16. No heed was taken of the wise words of the 1947 Hamilton Fyfe report:

> Whatever be the values of the "subject" carried to its full term in university study, they cannot be achieved for the child of 16 by simply snipping off a certain length of the "subject" like a piece of tape. . . . Every course must have its own unity and completeness and a proper realism requires that content and methods alike be so regulated as to reach their objective within the time available (Fyfe 1947).

The "piece of tape" mentality still persists and, for example, forces weaker students to learn algebraic techniques that they will never develop into usable knowledge. Of course, such students are no longer being "denied" the opportunity to learn algebra, but instead are simply forced to learn techniques that might conceivably (but with a fairly low probability) lead to something more useful and valuable. It is difficult to see exactly what the aims of the present curriculum are. There is an attempt to please everyone and do everything, at the expense of a focus on clear aims and the provision of sound and secure learning. That after 11 years of compulsory mathematics it should be felt necessary to institute post-16 courses and tests in "key skills" for sixth-formers (16- to 18-year-olds) illustrates the problems.

Such curricular considerations led recently to the publication of a collection of essays entitled *"Why Learn Maths?"*, edited by two philosophers of education, S. Bramall and J. White, which questioned the arguments put forward in the defense of teaching mathematics and its status as a compulsory subject within the national pre-16 curriculum (Bramall and White 2000). Although reported in newspapers as a polemic, the monograph contained contributions that genuinely merit consideration. The present mathematics curriculum cannot be justified solely by the repetition of pious clichés or such foolishness as the National Curriculum's claims of mathematics' promoting "spiritual development through . . . helping pupils obtain an insight into the infinite," or

"moral development through . . . helping them learn the value of mathematical truth."

Essentially, all the contributors to Bramall and White accepted that every student should learn the mathematics that is "commonly useful"—basic arithmetic and mensuration—but "beyond that the case for inclusion is not so clear-cut." Some contributors still argued for the teaching of mathematics for nonutilitarian reasons, e.g., training of the mind or the intrinsic delights of the subject and its place in human culture, but the editors themselves saw no justification for compulsory mathematics post-14. Indeed, White argued, "by the year 2002, 75% of British children will have reached Level 4 . . . by the age of 11 . . . that will provide them with the basic arithmetic they need to get by."

This is hardly believable, because it is not until Level 5 that students are expected to "multiply and divide whole numbers and decimals by 10, 100, and 1000, . . . solve simple problems involving ratio and proportion, . . . or calculate fractional or percentage parts of quantities." Clearly Level 4 plus a few odds and ends of "civic arithmetic" will not suffice for an educated citizen.

On the other hand, are the needs of the future mathematician being met? Certainly the percentage of the age cohort opting to study mathematics post-16 remains disappointingly small, as does that which goes on to read mathematics at university. And what of the standards attained? Here we need only quote from a recent report, *Measuring the Mathematics Problem* (Institute of Mathematics and its Applications 2000), which presented evidence of a marked decline in university entrants' mathematical skills: "This decline is well established and affects students at all levels."

What Mathematics for All?

Clearly, a prime aim of school mathematics must be to provide all students with that mathematics required by today's thinking citizen. What exactly, though, is that? Two recent attempts to define this merit a mention. One was in a section of the Third International Mathematics and Science Study (TIMSS) in which England did not participate. It was a test on mathematical and scientific literacy set to students in their last year of secondary school whether or not they were still studying mathematics. The items were all posed in "real-life" contexts and covered topics on arithmetic (including estimation), data handling (including graphic representation), geometry (including mensuration), and (informal) probability. The resulting data were of considerable interest in indicating the extent to which countries had prepared their students to deal with the kind of mathematics they would meet in the street or the press. (More recently the Organization for Economic Cooperation and Development (OECD) carried out a somewhat similar study on 15-year-olds. This was very much in the nature of a pilot study, however, and did not test all aspects of mathematical literacy.)

Another, significant offering is a report, *Mathematics and Democracy: The Case for Quantitative Literacy,* published by the National Council on Education and the Disciplines (NCED) (Steen 2001), that seeks a complete reorientation of the traditional U.S. school mathematics syllabus. This report distinguishes between what it terms *quantitative literacy,* which stresses the use of those mathematical and logical tools needed to solve common problems (e.g., percentages and mensuration), and *mathematical literacy,* which emphasizes the traditional tools and vocabulary of mathematics (e.g., formal algebra and, later, calculus).

Change Also Is Underway in Other Countries

In the 1990s, Japan's upper secondary school (USS) offered two mathematics courses stressing, respectively, mathematical literacy and mathematical thought. ("Mathematical literacy" had the meaning ascribed to it in the NCED report.) All students had to take mathematical literacy in their first year in USS; students hoping to study mathematics, engineering, or physics at university were encouraged to take both. In the latest revision of the Japanese curriculum, all students still must continue to study mathematics in the first year of USS, but now they may take a one-year "Fundamentals of Mathematics" option, which is very much like quantitative literacy, that is, mathematics for citizenship. Alternatively, they may begin a three-year "Science Mathematics" course (i.e., mathematical literacy leading to calculus) or a three-year "Mathematics" course (including, for example, formal Euclidean geometry).

The distinction between a traditional mathematical focus and some form of quantitative literacy seen in Japan is the subject of much debate in the NCED report. As we might expect, there is some variation in what the contributors to *Mathematics and Democracy* believe "quantitative literacy" to mean. At one extreme we find "mathematics and quantitative literacy are not the same thing . . . mathematics is more formal, more abstract, more symbolic than quantitative literacy, which is contextual, intuitive and integrated." Another view, however, is that there is no essential dichotomy between formal mathematics and context-rich quantitative literacy. This latter view is one I share—provided that the need for an increased emphasis on reasoning and the ability to deal with complex problems is recognized.

I have no doubt, for example, that the correspondent and adviser in the *Saga Magazine* exchange quoted earlier happily would have tackled the questions on percentages to be found in the national 16-plus examination papers. It was the extra complexity of having to determine which figure had risen by 70 percent that threw them. Teaching and examinations must prepare students to answer complex as well as one-step, so-called, real-life problems. That ability to reason, which can be built up on percentages just as well as on circles, chords, and tangents, is what both users of mathematics and budding mathematicians require.

I believe that it would be possible to develop a GCSE course (the national certificate intended for students from the whole of the ability range, which replaced the "divisive" O-levels and CSE) for all students that would prove more valuable and would motivate more students than the present one if it were focused more specifically on the mathematics of citizenship, culture, personal finance, health, and other curricular subjects. This still would leave us with a fund of worthwhile mathematics to teach in arithmetic, geometry, data handling, simple probability, and the use of algebraic formulas. Of course, when appropriate (not merely when there is an opportunity), computer software and calculators would be used. Moreover, providing that emphasis were given to extended reasoning, coping with complexity, and arousing students' involvement and interest, such a course could prove to be a firm foundation for the further study of mathematics.

Nonetheless, the high-attaining young mathematician would benefit from a course that offered more than this and concentrated less on mathematics' role as a "servant." I see, then, the need for both a compulsory "literacy-oriented" mathematics GCSE course that need not necessarily be examined in different tiers and also an optional two-year course (for 14- to 16-year-olds) that introduces students more explicitly to proof and rigorous mathematical thought. The two would have a relationship similar to that between "English" and "English Literature." The great aim of the new course would be to introduce students to a wider view of mathematics and provide the intellectual challenges that are so frequently missing in today's GCSEs.

Although this paper has concentrated on the situation in England, it would be wrong to leave the impression that ours is the only country with problems. Other countries, too, frequently experience difficulties relating to teacher quality and recruitment. Also, a study of the TIMSS data on specialist final-year secondary school students of mathematics from various western countries (see Howson, forthcoming) has revealed problems similar to those experienced in England. In particular, much mathematics teaching appears to be centered on getting students to jump through technical hoops. Sometimes this is done with considerable success; however, when students are tested on an understanding of fundamental concepts or on their ability to deal with multistep problems and problems in which the mathematics to be employed is not obvious, there is often an alarming dropping off in the success rate.

Paradoxically, students are being trained to perform those operations that can now be dealt with using suitably chosen software, but all too often students share the computer's inability to analyze a problem and to reason. I wonder to what extent students have been empowered to use the mathematics they have been taught in new contexts, rather than merely to answer stock examination questions on it. There would, then, appear to be a requirement in many countries for a clearer definition of goals for school mathematics linked more closely to the differing needs and aspirations of students.

References

Bramall, S., and J. White, eds. 2000. *Why Learn Maths?* London: Institute of Education.

Cockcroft, Wilfred H. 1982. *Mathematics Counts.* London: Her Majesty's Stationery Office.

Fyfe, Hamilton. 1947. *Secondary Education.* Edinburgh: Her Majesty's Stationery Office.

Howson, A. Geoffrey. 2002. "Yet More Maths Problems," *National Institute Economic Review,* January 2002.

Howson, A. Geoffrey. Forthcoming. "Advanced Mathematics: Curricula and Student Performance." In *Secondary Analysis of the TIMSS Results: A Synthesis of Current Research,* edited by D. F. Robitaille and A. E. Beaton. Dordrecht: Kluwer Academic.

Institute of Mathematics and its Applications, Engineering Council, and London Mathematical Society. 2000. *Measuring the Mathematics Problem.* Southend-on-Sea, UK: Institute of Mathematics and Its Applications.

Steen, Lynn Arthur, ed. 2001. *Mathematics and Democracy: The Case for Quantitative Literacy.* Princeton, NJ: National Council on Education and the Disciplines.

Numeracy: A Challenge for Adult Education

MIEKE VAN GROENESTIJN

In adult education, we are often confronted with adults who once learned mathematics in school but who have developed insufficient skills to use mathematics efficiently in real-life situations. This problem is seen very clearly in surveys such as YALS, NALS, and IALS,[1] and PISA.[2] Although awareness of the importance of mathematics is increasing because of technological developments in western societies, numeracy has not yet received the priority it requires in educational settings. One reason for this may be that it is not yet clear what kinds of knowledge and skills are necessary to become numerate and what should be taught in school to help learners develop numerate behavior.

The first part of this paper addresses the concept of numeracy in general and the way in which it was operationalized in the Adult Literacy and Lifeskills (ALL) survey to develop items for numeracy assessment.[3] In the second part I make a few suggestions for implementation of numeracy in educational settings based on my own study of numeracy in adult basic education (van Groenestijn 2002).

What's in the Name?

The initial problem we encounter is confusion about the definitions of quantitative literacy, numeracy, and mathematical literacy. The three terms originally came from different perspectives but today have the same intention and cover almost the same areas.

The YALS, NALS, and IALS are based on three components of literacy: prose, document, and quantitative literacy. In these surveys, familiarity with numbers and quantities has been defined as part of literacy because it is often embedded in spoken words and written texts in real-life situations. In this context, the original definition of quantitative literacy was:

> The knowledge and skills required to apply arithmetic operations, either alone or sequentially, to numbers embedded in printed materials, such as balancing a checkbook, figuring out a tip, completing an order form, or determining the amount of interest on a loan from an advertisement. (OECD 1997; Dossey 1997; Houtkoop 1999)

In this original definition, quantitative literacy covered only a small part of mathematics. In *document* literacy, however, we also find some mathematical aspects that we now consider to be part of numeracy, such as reading and understanding tables, graphs, and charts and understanding and interpreting data.

As a follow-up to the IALS, the ALL project is planned for the years 2002 and 2003.[4] In the ALL study, the term "quantitative literacy" has been replaced by numeracy. An international numeracy team[5] was established to develop numeracy assessment items. The ALL numeracy team has ex-

---

Mieke van Groenestijn is a researcher at Utrecht University of Professional Education in the Netherlands. Her main research interests concern the mathematical knowledge and problem- solving strategies of adults in Adult Basic Education (ABE) programs. She is a member of the international numeracy team of the Adult Literacy and Lifeskills survey (ALL), a trustee of Adults Learning Mathematics (ALM) and a board member of the Dutch National Organization for the Development of Mathematics Education.

panded the original quantitative literacy (QL) definition to a broader concept of numeracy: "The knowledge and skills required to effectively manage the mathematical demands of diverse situations."

The word "manage" indicates that being numerate encompasses more than just knowing mathematics. It implies that to organize their lives as individuals, as workers, and as citizens, adults need to feel confident of their own mathematical capacities and be able to make effective decisions in mathematical situations in real life. The word *numeracy* was chosen for the ALL study because this concept was originally introduced as a parallel for literacy (Cockcroft 1982), whereas quantitative literacy is seen as part of literacy. Further, numeracy is more commonly used in adult education in English-speaking countries. It signals a difference from school mathematics, which often reminds adult learners of negative school experiences. Numeracy courses focus on the use of mathematics in real-life situations.

In the PISA study, a closer link was created between school mathematics and the application of mathematics in real life by introducing the concept of mathematical literacy:

> Mathematical literacy is an individual's capacity to identify and understand the role that mathematics plays in the world, to make well-founded judgments, and to engage in mathematics in ways that meet the needs of that individual's current and future life as a constructive, concerned, and reflective citizen" (OECD 1999, 41; de Lange, see p. 76).

According to de Lange, "ML is less formal and more intuitive, less abstract and more contextual, less symbolic and more concrete. ML also focuses more attention and emphasis on reasoning, thinking, and interpreting as well as on other very mathematical competencies or skills" (see p. 77).

Although there are differences in wording, these definitions have a common intention. All three focus on the competencies of individuals to make sensible use in real-life situations of the mathematics they learned in school. Attention to this need is based on the alarming results of, in particular, the YALS, NALS, and IALS surveys (Dossey 1997; OECD 1997). The IALS results, for example, showed that on average about 40 percent of the adult population of the participating western countries functioned at levels 1 and 2 of the IALS quantitative literacy scale. This means that these adults have not acquired the "walking around skills we would expect of almost any citizen" (Dossey 1997). Another 40 percent of the population functioned on a medium level and only about 20 percent on the higher levels of 4 and 5. These results show clearly that quantitative literacy is of *international* concern (OECD 1997; Dossey 1997; Houtkoop 1999).

With the increasing international awareness of the importance of numeracy, the concept of quantitative literacy also has expanded. In particular, *Mathematics and Democracy: The Case for Quantitative Literacy* (Steen 2001) pioneers an effort to broaden the perspective of quantitative literacy by showing its role and influence in the changing world and its place in education. In addition, the Forum background essay "Data, Shapes, Symbols: Achieving Balance in School Mathematics" (Steen, see pp. 53–74) develops a strong link between mathematical literacy, quantitative literacy, and numeracy. Hence the three labels— quantitative literacy, numeracy, and mathematical literacy—now can be used more or less interchangeably, at least in English-speaking countries. My personal preference, however, is to use the word numeracy as a parallel to the concept of literacy.

Numeracy Assessment in the ALL Study

It is the opinion of the ALL team that numeracy itself cannot be tested; rather, "numerate behavior" can be observed. With this in mind and to create items for the numeracy assessment, the team operationalized the definition in a working form, emphasizing five facets: "Numerate behavior involves *managing* a situation or solving a problem in a real context by *responding* to mathematical *information* that is *represented* in a range of ways and requires the *activation* of a range of enabling processes and behaviors" (Gal et al. 1999).

These five facets offer the possibility to link recognizable mathematical information in real-life situations with expected required mathematical actions. This is shown in Figure 1, adapted from Gal et al. (1999). (See also Manly, Tout, van Groenestijn, and Clermont 2001; Manly and Tout 2001.)

By choosing one element from each of these five facets, we can develop a definition for specific situations, for example:

> Numerate behavior involves managing a situation or solving a problem *in everyday life* by *making an estimation with money* (*acting upon*) using information concerning *quantity and number* that is represented by *pictures and numbers in an advertisement in a door-to-door leaflet* and requires the activation of *computational and estimation skills*.

These facets make the definition applicable to almost all situations in which people have to manage a mathematical problem.

Figure 1: Numerate Behavior

Numerate behavior involves

— *managing a situation or solving a problem in a real context*
    everyday life
    work
    societal
    further learning

— *by responding*
    identifying or locating
    acting on (order/sort, count, estimate, compute, measure, model)
    interpreting
    communicating

— *to information about mathematical ideas*
    quantity and number
    dimension and shape
    pattern and relationships
    data and chance
    change

— *that is represented in a range of ways*
    objects and pictures
    numbers and symbols
    formulas
    diagrams and maps
    graphs and tables
    texts

— *and requires activation of a range of enabling knowledge, behaviors, and processes*
    mathematical knowledge and understanding
    mathematical problem-solving skills
    literacy skills
    beliefs and attitudes

The ALL team also identified five complexity factors:

1. *Problem transparency,* varying from obvious/explicit to embedded/hidden. How difficult is it to identify the mathematical problem and decide what action to take? How much literacy proficiency is required?

2. *Plausibility of distractors,* from no distractors to several distractors. How many other pieces of mathematical information are present? Is all the necessary information there?

3. *Complexity of mathematical information/data,* from concrete simple to abstract complex. How complex is the mathematical information that needs to be manipulated?

4. *Type of operation/skill,* from simple to complex. How complex is the mathematical action that is required?

5. *Expected number of operations,* from one to many. How many steps and types of steps are required?

Based on the five facets and five complexity factors, the ALL team set up a grid and developed a bank of about 120 items on five levels for the numeracy domain of the ALL survey. Each item received an individual identity. The ALL team thought that this way of working also could serve as a framework for the development of mathematical content and actions for numeracy programs in educational settings (van Groenestijn 2002).

Implementation of Numeracy in Education

For the implementation of numeracy in educational programs, however, it is not sufficient only to determine mathematical content and actions. It also is necessary to look for components that help develop numerate *behavior,* for now and in the future. In my own study of numeracy in adult basic education (van Groenestijn 2002) I started from the ALL definition but added a second part to include attention to the future:

> Numeracy encompasses the knowledge and skills required to effectively manage mathematical demands in personal, societal and work situations, in combination with the ability to accommodate and adjust flexibly to new demands in a continuously rapidly changing society that is highly dominated by quantitative information and technology (p.37).

To make this definition operational for the implementation of numeracy in educational settings, four components were identified:

- *Functional mathematical knowledge and skills,* recognizable in real-life situations;

- *Management skills* for managing mathematical situations;

- *Skills for processing new information* in out-of-school situations; and

- *Insight into one's own learning skills* to be able to keep up with new developments in the future and to acquire new mathematical knowledge and skills independently in real-life situations.

As for the first component, we can distinguish a general, basic set of mathematical knowledge and skills that everybody should have acquired and that can be the basis for further learning, in combination with an individual set of knowledge and skills required to function in specific personal, work, and social situations. Content for this mathematical component can be developed with the help of the ALL grid for numeracy items.

With respect to the second component, management skills, we can think of a broad range of skills such as:

- *Generative mathematical understanding and insight* to give meaning to and interpret numbers and to plan appropriate mathematical actions;

- *Literacy skills* to read and understand problems and to reason about them;

- *Communication skills* to be able to share problems with others, discuss information, learn from others how they would solve problems, and work cooperatively;

- *Problem-solving skills* to identify, analyze, and structure problems, plan steps for action, select appropriate actions, actually handle problems, and make decisions; and

- *Reflection skills* to be able to control the situation, check computations, evaluate decisions, and come to contextual judgments.

Such management skills often are assumed to evolve spontaneously in the course of life. We argue that it is necessary to pay explicit attention to teaching these skills in educational settings. Training enables adults to develop appropriate skills for different types of mathematical situations.

The same can be said concerning the third component, developing skills for processing new information in real-life situations. The way students learn in school differs from the way in which adults acquire and process new information in out-of-school situations, independently from teachers. Adults almost always process new information in the course of action (Greeno 1999). For this, people need to learn to:

- Read, watch, or listen to information;

- Identify key points in the information;

- Reflect on what is new (What is new to me?);

- Communicate and discuss with others;

- Reflect on possible implications for their personal life (What does it mean to me?); and

- Reflect on possible implications for society or work.

Concerning the fourth component, developing insight into one's own learning skills, we argue that in a rapidly changing and developing society, people need to have developed skills and strategies for lifelong learning to be able to accommodate and adjust flexibly to new situations in the course of life. To be able to do so, people need to have acquired insight into their own learning skills: in what way do they process information best? Where and how can they find more specific information needed for certain purposes? How can one learn from others? In everyday life situations, adults play different roles. They can be spontaneous learners, their own teachers, or teachers of others. Such learning often happens by means of learning by doing and learning in the course of action.

People need to be aware of situations in which learning takes place. In such situations, they must reflect on their own actions. To develop skills for lifelong learning, students need to have opportunities in school settings to discover their own best ways of learning. From this perspective, we identified the following points for attention:

- A general awareness of the need for lifelong learning;

- More emphasis on self-directed, autonomous, teacher-free, cooperative learning;

- More emphasis on problem-based learning environments and learning in contexts;

- Creating opportunities for learning in action;

- Creating facilities for lifelong learning and helping students learn how to benefit from them; and

- Encouraging creativity and curiosity.

For the development of numerate behavior, we argue that it is not sufficient to focus only on what mathematical knowledge and skills are necessary and should be taught in a numeracy program. We also must pay attention to the way in which they are taught. In fact, the emphasis should be on the way in which they are *learned*. Developing numerate behavior is a matter of acquiring and constructing functional knowledge and skills by solving real problems in the course of action in authentic real-life situations and learning how to reflect on this learning. The art of teaching is to create and facilitate learning environments in which such learning is possible and to guide learners in their learning activities. For life-long learning, people need to take the responsibility for their own learning in their own hands.

Conclusion

Becoming numerate is as essential as becoming literate for all citizens in all nations. The case for quantitative literacy, or numeracy, or mathematical literacy, by whatever name, therefore must be an important item on national and international policy agendas.

Achieving numeracy is a matter of learning how to *use* mathematics in real life and how to *manage* mathematical situations. "Citizens need a predisposition to look at the world through mathematical eyes" (Steen 2001, 2). This predisposition can best be acquired in real-life situations in which mathematics is functionally apparent. Hence, numeracy courses embedded in school programs must focus on problem-solving activities in which students can apply their acquired mathematical insights and skills and learn how to manage such situations. The role of teachers is mainly to encourage and reflect students' actions. Learning mathematics and becoming numerate go hand in hand and must start, in fact, in kindergarten.

Notes

1. The Young Adult Literacy Skills (YALS) study was conducted in 1986. The National Adult Literacy Survey (NALS) followed that study in 1992. The International Adult Literacy Study (IALS) in 1996, was a follow-up of the NALS. In the first phase of the IALS (1994, 1996), adults from 14 countries were tested based on methodology that combined household survey research and educational testing. A second cohort of 10 countries conducted surveys in 1998 and 1999 (the Second International Adult Literary Survey, or SIALS). In 1994 and 1996, participating countries were Canada, France, Germany, Ireland, the Netherlands, Sweden, Switzerland, and the United States; in 1996, Australia, the Flemish community in Belgium, Great Britain, New Zealand, and Northern Ireland participated. The second full round of data collection in 1998 and 1999 (SIALS) included Chile, the Czech Republic, Denmark, Finland, Hungary, Italy, Malaysia, Norway, Slovenia, and Switzerland.

2. The OECD Programme for International Student Assessment (PISA 2000) was an international assessment of 15-year-olds that looked at how well they were prepared for life beyond school and was fielded in 32 countries. Four types of skills were assessed: skills and knowledge that prepare students for life and lifelong learning, reading literacy, mathematical literacy, and science literacy.

3. The international Adult Literacy and Lifeskills (ALL) survey is the follow-up to the IALS and is planned for the years 2002 and 2003.

4. The ALL study is being organized by the National Center for Education Statistics (NCES) and Statistics Canada. Participating countries in the ALL pilot study are Argentina, Belgium, Bermuda, Bolivia, Brazil, Canada, Costa Rica, Italy, Luxembourg, Mexico, the Netherlands, Norway, Spain, Switzerland, the United States, and Venezuela.

5. The international ALL numeracy team is comprised of Yvan Clermont, Statistics Canada, Montreal, project manager; Iddo Gal, University of Haifa, Israel; Mieke van Groenestijn, Utrecht University of Professional Education, Utrecht; Myrna Manly, enjoying her retire-

ment; Mary Jane Schmitt, TERC, Cambridge, Massachusetts; and Dave Tout, Language Australia, Melbourne, Australia.

References

Cockcroft, Wilfred H. 1982. *Mathematics Counts.* London: Her Majesty's Stationery Office.

Dossey, John A. 1997. "National Indicators of Quantitative Literacy." In *Why Numbers Count: Quantitative Literacy for Tomorrow's America,* edited by Lynn Arthur Steen, 45–59. New York, NY: College Entrance Examination Board.

Gal, Iddo, Mieke van Groenestijn, Myrna Manly, Mary Jane Schmitt, and Dave Tout. 1999. *Numeracy Framework for the International Adult Literacy and Lifeskills Survey (ALL).* Ottawa, Canada: Statistics Canada, 1999. Retrieved January 25, 2002, at http://nces.ed.gov./surveys/all.

Greeno, James G., Penelope Eckert, Susan U. Stucky, Patricia Sachs, and Etienne Wenger. 1999. "Learning in and for Participation in Society." In *How Adults Learn.* Washington, DC: Organization for Economic Cooperation and Development and U.S. Department of Education.

Groenestijn, Mieke van. 2002. *A Gateway to Numeracy. A Study of Numeracy in Adult Basic Education.* Utrecht, Netherlands: CD-Press.

Houtkoop, W. 1999. *Basisvaardigheden in Nederland.* [Basic Skills in the Netherlands.] (Dutch Report of the IALS Survey.) Amsterdam: Max Goote Kenniscentrum.

Manly, Myrna, Dave Tout, Mieke van Groenestijn, and Yvan Clermont. 2001. "What Makes One Numeracy Task More Difficult Than Another?" In *Adults Learning Mathematics: A Conversation between Researchers and Practitioners,* edited by Mary Jane Schmitt and Kathy Safford-Ramus. Proceedings of the 7th International Conference of Adults Learning Mathematics (ALM-7), Medford, MA. Cambridge, MA: NCSAL, Harvard University Graduate School of Education.

Manly, Myrna, and Dave Tout. 2001. "Numeracy in the Adult Literacy and Lifeskills Project." In *Adult and Lifelong Education in Mathematics,* edited by Gail FitzSimons, John O'Donoghue, and Diana Coben. Melbourne, Australia: Language Australia.

Organization for Economic Cooperation and Development (OECD). 1997. *Literacy Skills for the Knowledge Society: Further Results from the International Adult Literacy Survey.* Ottowa, Canada: Statistics Canada.

Organization for Economic Cooperation and Development (OECD). 1999. *Measuring Student Knowledge and Skills: A New Framework for Assessment.* Programme for International Student Assessment (PISA). Retrieved January 25, 2002, at http://www.pisa.oecd.org/pisa/.

Steen, Lynn Arthur, ed. 2001. *Mathematics and Democracy: The Case for Quantitative Literacy.* Princeton, NJ: National Council on Education and Disciplines.

The Role of Mathematics in Building a Democratic Society

UBIRATAN D'AMBROSIO

Political issues deal with government, economics, relations among nations and social classes, people's welfare, and the preservation of natural and cultural resources. Mathematics is deeply involved with these issues and mathematicians and mathematics educators cannot ignore them.

The possibility of the final extinction of civilization on earth is real, and not only through nuclear war, which was a major threat during the Cold War, and which, in 1955, prompted two eminent mathematicians, Albert Einstein and Bertrand Russell, to invite other Nobel laureates to subscribe to a moving document, which became known as *The Russell-Einstein Manifesto*, and which gave origin to the Pugwash Conferences on Science and World Affairs (Pugwash, retrieved 2002).

We are witnessing an environmental crisis, disruption of the economic system, institutional erosion, mounting social crises in just about every country and, above all, the recurring threat of war. And now, after the attacks in New York and Washington on September 11, 2001, the uncertainties are a real threat to our mental and emotional equilibrium. We are anxious about the next minute and we look with fear and suspicion at our neighbor. A scenario similar to the disruption of the Roman Empire is before us, with the aggravation that the means of disruption are, nowadays, practically impossible to control. Survival of mankind, with dignity for all, is a most urgent and universal problem.

It is clear that mathematics is well integrated into the technological, industrial, military, economic, and political systems and that mathematics has been relying on these systems for the material bases of its continuing progress. It is important to look into the role of mathematicians and mathematics educators in the evolution of mankind, especially because mathematics is recognized as the most universal mode of thought.

Thus it is appropriate to ask what the most universal mode of thought—mathematics—has to do with the most universal problem—survival with dignity (D'Ambrosio 2001). I believe that the need to find the relation between these two universals is an inescapable result of the claim of the universality of mathematics. Consequently, as mathematicians and mathematics educators, we have to reflect about our personal role in reversing the current world situation.

Mathematics, Education, and Curriculum

The nature of mathematical behavior is not yet clearly understood. Although in classical philosophy we notice a concern with the nature of mathematics, only recently have the advances of the cognitive sciences probed into the generation of mathematical knowledge: How is mathematics created? How different is mathematical creativity from other forms of creativity?

Ubiratan D'Ambrosio is Emeritus Professor of Mathematics at the State University of Campinas/UNICAMP in Sao Paulo, Brazil, where he served as Pro-Rector for University Development from 1982 to 1990. D'Ambrosio has served as President of the Inter-American Committee of Mathematics Education (IACME), Vice-President of the International Commission on Mathematics Instruction (ICMI), and as a Member of the Council of the Pugwash Conferences on Science and World Affairs (the organization that was awarded the Nobel Peace Prize in 1995).

From the historical viewpoint, there is need of a complete and structured view of the role of mathematics in building our civilization. For this we have to look into the history and geography of human behavior and find new paths to advance the search. History is global in time and space. It is misleading to see history only as a chronological narrative of events, focused on the narrow geographic limits of a few civilizations that have been successful in a short span of time. The course of the history of mankind, which cannot be separated from the natural history of the planet, reveals an increasing interdependence, which crosses space and time, of cultures, civilizations, and generations.

Education is a strategy created by societies to promote creativity and citizenship. To promote creativity implies helping people to fulfill their potentials to the maximum of their capability. To promote citizenship implies showing people their rights and responsibilities in society. Educational systems throughout history and in every civilization have been focused on two issues: to transmit values from the past and to promote the future.

In other words, education aims equally at the new (*creativity*) and the old (*societal values*). Not irresponsible creativity (we do not want our students to become bright scientists creating new weaponry) nor docile reproduction (we do not want our students to accept rules and codes that violate human dignity). This is our challenge as educators, particularly as mathematics educators.

The strategy of education systems to pursue these goals is the curriculum. Curriculum is usually organized in three strands: objectives, contents, and methods. This Cartesian organization implies accepting the social aims of education systems, then identifying contents that may help to reach the goals and developing methods to transmit those contents.

The Political Dimension of Mathematics Education

To agree on objectives is regarded as the political dimension of education, but very rarely has mathematics content and methodology been examined with respect to this dimension. Indeed, some educators and mathematicians claim that content and methods in mathematics have nothing to do with the political dimension of education.

Even more disturbing is the possibility of offering our children a world convulsed by wars. Because mathematics conveys the imprint of western thought, it is naïve not to look into a possible role of mathematics in framing a state of mind that tolerates war. Our responsibility as mathematicians and mathematics educators is to offer venues of peace (D'Ambrosio 1998).

There is an expectation about our role, as mathematicians and mathematics educators, in the pursuit of peace. Anthony Judge, the director of communications and research of the Union of International Associations, expressed how we, mathematicians, are seen by others:

> Mathematicians, having lent the full support of their discipline to the weapons industry supplying the missile delivery systems, would claim that their subtlest thinking is way beyond the comprehension of those seated around a negotiating table. They have however failed to tackle the challenge of the packing and unpacking of complexity to render it comprehensible without loss of relationships vital to more complex patterns. As with the protagonists in any conflict, they would deny all responsibility for such failures and the manner in which these have reinforced unsustainably simplistic solutions leading to further massacres. (Judge 2000)

I see my role as an educator and my discipline, mathematics, as complementary instruments to fulfill commitments to mankind. To make good use of these instruments, I must master them, but I also need to have a critical view of their potentialities and of the risk involved in misusing them. This is my professional commitment.

It is difficult to deny that mathematics provides an important instrument for social analyses. Western civilization entirely relies on data control and management. "The world of the twenty-first century is a world awash in numbers" (Steen 2001, 1). Social critics will find it difficult to argue without an understanding of basic quantitative mathematics.

Since the emergence of modern science, enormous emphasis has been placed on the rational dimension of man. Recently, multiple intelligences, emotional intelligence, spiritual intelligence, and numerous approaches to cognition, including new developments in artificial intelligence, challenge this. In mathematics education, this challenge is seen in the exclusive emphasis given to skill and drilling, as defended in some circles of mathematicians and mathematics educators.

In this paper I argue that the emphasis on the quantitative cannot be detrimental to the equally important emphasis on the qualitative. My proposal of *literacy, matheracy,* and *technoracy,* discussed below, is an answer to my criticism of the lack of equilibrium. *Literacy* is a communicative instrument and, as such, includes what has been called quantitative literacy or numeracy. This is very much in line with the mathematics learned from the Egyptians and Babylonians, but not central in Greco-Roman civilization nor in the High Middle Ages. It was incorporated into European thought in the Lower Middle Ages and it was essential for mercantilism and for the development of modern science. Indeed, it became the imprint of the modern world. In contrast, *matheracy* is an analytical instrument, as proposed by classical Greek mathematicians (for example, in Plato's *Republic*). I will return to this subsequently.

It is an undeniable right of every human being to share in all the cultural and natural goods needed for material survival and intellectual enhancement. This is the essence of the United Nations' *Universal Declaration of Human Rights* (UN 1948) to which every nation is committed. The educational strand of this important profession on the rights of mankind is the *World Declaration on Education for All* (UNESCO 1990) to which 155 countries are committed. Of course, there are many difficulties in implementing United Nations resolutions and mechanisms. But as yet this is the best instrument available that may lead to a planetary civilization, with peace and dignity for all mankind. Regrettably, mathematics educators are generally unfamiliar with these documents.

The Ethical Dimension of Mathematics Education

It is not possible to relinquish our duty to cooperate, with respect and solidarity, with all human beings who have the same rights for the preservation of good. The essence of the ethics of diversity is respect for, solidarity with, and cooperation with the other (the different). This leads to quality of life and dignity for all.

It is impossible to accept the exclusion of large sectors of the population of the world, both in developed and undeveloped nations. An explanation for this perverse concept of civilization asks for a deep reflection on colonialism. This is not to place blame on one or another, not an attempt to redo the past. Rather, to understand the past is a first step to move into the future. To accept inequity, arrogance, and bigotry is irrational and may lead to disaster. Mathematics has everything to do with this state of the world. A new world order is urgently needed. Our hopes for the future depend on learning—critically—the lessons of the past.

We have to look into history and epistemology with a broader view. The denial and exclusion of the cultures of the periphery, so common in the colonial process, still prevails in modern society. The denial of knowledge that affects populations is of the same nature as the denial of knowledge to individuals, particularly children. To propose directions to counteract ingrained practices is the major challenge of educators, particularly mathematics educators. Large sectors of the population do not have access to full citizenship. Some do not have access to the basic needs for survival. This is the situation in most of the world and occurs even in the most developed and richest nations.

To build a civilization that rejects inequity, arrogance, and bigotry, education must give special attention to the redemption of peoples that have been for a long time subordinated and must give priority to the empowerment of the excluded sectors of societies.

The program *Ethnomathematics* contributes to restoring cultural dignity and offers the intellectual tools for the exercise of citizenship. It enhances creativity, reinforces cultural self-respect, and offers a broad view of mankind. In everyday life, it is a system of knowledge that offers the possibility of a more favorable and harmonious relation between humans and between humans and nature (D'Ambrosio 1999a).

A consequence of this program for a new curriculum is synthesized in my proposal of three strands in curricular organization: literacy, matheracy, and technoracy (D'Ambrosio 1999b). The three provide, in a critical way, the communicative, analytical, and technological instruments necessary for life in the twenty-first century. Let me discuss each one.

Literacy is the capability of processing information, such as the use of written and spoken language, of signs and gestures, of codes and numbers. Clearly, reading has a new meaning today. We have to read a movie or a TV program. It is common to listen to a concert with a new reading of Chopin. Also, socially, the concept of literacy has gone through many changes. Nowadays, reading includes also the competency of numeracy, the interpretation of graphs and tables, and other ways of informing the individual. Reading even includes understanding the condensed language of codes. These competencies have much more to do with screens and buttons than with pencil and paper. There is no way to reverse this trend, just as there has been no successful censorship to prevent people from having access to books in the past 500 years. Getting information through the new media supersedes the use of pencil and paper and numeracy is achieved with calculators. But, if dealing with numbers is part of modern literacy, where has mathematics gone?

Matheracy is the capability of inferring, proposing hypotheses, and drawing conclusions from data. It is a first step toward an intellectual posture, which is almost completely absent in our school systems. Regrettably, even conceding that problem solving, modeling, and projects can be seen in some mathematics classrooms, the main importance is usually given to numeracy, or the manipulation of numbers and operations. Matheracy is closer to the way mathematics was present both in classical Greece and in indigenous cultures. The concern was not with counting and measuring but with divination and philosophy. Matheracy, this deeper reflection about man and society, should not be restricted to the elite, as it has been in the past.

Technoracy is the critical familiarity with technology. Of course, the operative aspects of it are, in most cases, inaccessible to the lay individual. But the basic ideas behind technological devices, their possibilities and dangers, the morality supporting the use of technology, are essential issues to be raised among children at a very early age. History show us that ethics and values are intimately related to technological progress.

The three together constitute what is essential for citizenship in a world moving swiftly toward a planetary civilization.

References

D'Ambrosio, Ubiratan. 1998. "Mathematics and Peace: Our Responsibilities." *Zentralblatt für Didaktik der Mathematik/ZDM*, 30(3): 67–73.

D'Ambrosio, Ubiratan. 1999a. "Ethnomathematics and its First International Congress." *Zentralblatt für Didaktik der Mathematik, ZDM.* 31(2): 50–53.

D'Ambrosio, Ubiratan. 1999b. "Literacy, Matheracy, and Technoracy: A Trivium for Today." *Mathematical Thinking and Learning,* 1(2): 131–53.

D'Ambrosio, Ubiratan. 2001. "Mathematics and Peace: A Reflection on the Basis of Western Civilization." *Leonardo*, 34(4): 327–32.

Judge, Anthony. 2000. "And When the Bombing Stops: Territorial Conflict as a Challenge to Mathematicians." *Union of International Associations.* Retrieved January 25, 2002, at http://www.uia.org/uiadocs/mathbom.htm.

Pugwash Conferences on Science and World Affairs. 2002. Retrieved January 25, 2002, at http://www.pugwash.org/.

Steen, Lynn Arthur, ed. 2001. *Mathematics and Democracy: The Case for Quantitative Literacy.* Princeton, NJ: National Council on Education and the Disciplines.

United Nations. 1948. *Universal Declaration of Human Rights.* Retrieved January 25, 2002, at http://www.un.org/Overview/rights.html.

UNESCO. 1990. *World Declaration on Education for All.* Retrieved January 25, 2002, at http://www.unesco.org/education/efa/ed_for_all/background/jomtien_declaration.shtml.

Why Are We Here?

JEANNE L. NARUM

What [President] Wilson meant by the wholly awakened person who should be the ideal product of American higher education is a person awakened through the power of the imagination to a consciousness of possibilities. . . . James Bryant Conant assures us that scientific discovery begins not in the finding of the laboratory but in the glimpses of the imagination . . . that the true scientist takes off, as the true poet does, not from the notes on his desk, but from a hunch, a feeling in the bones, an intimation. If that is true, Mr. Wilson's whole person will make the better scientist, as he or she will be the better citizen of a free nation.

These words of Harvard scientist and educator James Conant are quoted by Archibald MacLeish in a *festschrift* in memory of President Woodrow Wilson, *Education in the Nation's Service* (MacLeish 1960). For me, the words are a first step in answering the question I was asked to address: "Why are we here?" For me, they suggest one purpose of our coming together to think about issues relating to quantitative literacy—to consider how our educational programs can be shaped to prepare twenty-first century students to be better citizens of a free nation.

I am here because of my work with Project Kaleidoscope (PKAL), an informal national alliance working to strengthen undergraduate programs in mathematics, technology, and the various fields of science and engineering. I have some further answers to that "why . . ." question based on my PKAL experience, assuming that today is the beginning of bringing attention to quantitative literacy at the national level.

Some background: In early 1991, PKAL held its inaugural event in these very halls. None of those early leaders had a vision of the PKAL work that has continued for more than a decade. Yet, even though we had no explicit plan to continue, those who shaped the report presented at that first meeting did not want it to become one of the rank of reports brought to life with great enthusiasm but quickly forgotten. The "Why are we here?" question needs to be asked at this early stage because we are committed to building a sustainable quantitative literacy (QL) movement.

From the PKAL experience, I am convinced that to mobilize an informed community to action it is important to:

- Identify and explore the right questions and take time doing this;

- Have the right people at the table, those who bring a diversity of experiences and responsibilities to the process of identifying, exploring, and implementing;

- Take the kaleidoscopic perspective, recognizing that the work is to change the system, not tinker at the edges;

- Focus on getting something done, moving in a timely and expeditious fashion from discussing to doing;

Jeanne L. Narum is Director of the Independent Colleges Office and the founding Director of Project Kaleidoscope (PKAL), an informal national alliance working to strengthen undergraduate programs in mathematics, engineering, and science. Educated as a musician, Narum's prior experience includes administrative positions at Augsburg College (Vice President for Advancement), Dickinson College (Director of Development), and St. Olaf College (Director of Government and Foundation Relations).

- Talk about what works, not about what does not work. There is not enough time to do both and opportunities will be lost if attention is not given to solutions;

- Connect to everyone whose work will have an impact on or relate to yours, whose work can enhance yours;

- Keep your antennae active: the context will change as systems change, and thus your work must change as you consider timing and context;

- Be ready for the long haul; and

- Have a brisk and memorable vision by which the community will be informed, mobilized, and inspired.

If my first answer to the central question comes from the words of Conant, the second comes from the experiences of PKAL. If we are serious about our work, we are here to set in motion a plan to accomplish the above nine steps. Let me speak to a few of these points, beginning with the need to have a brisk and memorable vision.

In the early days of PKAL, reports were being issued regularly about the dismal quality of undergraduate programs in science and mathematics (there was Science, Technology, Engineering, and Mathematics—STEM—then), reports in large part accurate. Here and there, however, in all parts of the education system but particularly in the liberal arts community that was the initial core of PKAL, reforms in undergraduate STEM were emerging that were making a difference, a positive difference, in student learning. Some of those pioneers in the first PKAL leadership groups worked with us over 18 months to explore questions and identify characteristics of strong undergraduate programs. At one three-day meeting, after much heated discussion involving presidents, deans, and faculty from all STEM disciplines, we arrived at a visionary statement about *what works*. This vision has been the lynchpin of our efforts since 1989, the vision that an effective learning environment is one in which:

- Learning is experiential, hands-on, and steeped in investigation from the very first courses for all students through capstone courses for science and mathematics majors.

- Learning is personally meaningful to students and faculty, makes connections to other fields of inquiry, is embedded in the context of its own history and rationale, and suggests practical applications related to the experience of students.

- Learning takes place in a community in which faculty are committed equally to undergraduate teaching and to their own intellectual vitality, faculty see students as partners in

learning, students collaborate with one another and gain confidence that they can succeed, and institutions support such communities of learners.

Programs organized around these principles motivate students and give them the skills and confidence to succeed. Thus empowered, students learn science and mathematics (PKAL 1991).

My first suggestion to leaders of the anticipated QL movement is that we begin by drafting a similar brisk statement. This QL statement need not present new ideas to the community but it must be a driving vision that inspires others to join the cause because they understand precisely what we are about. We need such a vision as a touchstone for our work in the coming months and years. If we accomplish nothing else at this Forum, preparing such a mission statement would be a significant first step.

In doing so, the words of Conant can be a model and a reminder that our concerns and passions parallel those of past generations and that in becoming involved with QL we pick up the baton of others who have sought to ensure that democracy is well served. Those words also are instructive because of their power and elegance. They make the sense of mission compelling in a way that more pedestrian language could not.

One recommendation made in the pre-Forum essays is to make quantitative literacy visible to the public. Up to this time, it seems we have been addressing our remarks and arguments only to the academy. We probably do not have to convince the public about the connections between disciplines that matter to academics, or about the politics of change, but the public does need to be convinced that the QL movement has an opportunity to make a distinctive contribution to the greater good. A brisk mission statement will help here. It also will help build critical collaborations with other efforts that have similar goals.

Back to PKAL history: Once begun, we put conversations about *what works* on the table in as many venues as possible. We were inspired by Robert Hutchins' idea that *a community needs a common stock of ideas around which to debate;* we took it as our charge to see that our vision of what works became part of that common stock of ideas. We were aiming for the same level of sharing and communicating, of building on and adapting ideas within the community of educational reformers as within the community of researchers. To make this happen, we needed all the voices to help shape the vision.

Our vision statement would not have been as compelling without Spelman College mathematician Etta Falconer urging us toward an expectation that all students can learn; without Jim Gentile from Hope College pressing the case for a research-rich learning environment; or without presidents and deans keeping the institutional implications tightly woven into our discussion. As we think about the future of the QL movement, there is an even greater need to have a diversity of expertise, experience, and responsibility at the table, probably a more representative group than we are today. Success will require the commitment and abilities of politicians, education officials, parents, teachers at all academic levels, textbook publishers, and software developers. Another answer to the "why . . ." question is that we must start now to identify those who will be invited to the QL table when next we meet.

Why is this critical? At the 1991 PKAL National Colloquium, California Congressman George E. Brown ending our meeting with the charge: "We must collaborate. The task is too great and the time too short to do otherwise."

We can all think of potential collaborators. I have in mind faculty and institutions that take quantitative literacy seriously. Some of these participated in a 1998 PKAL workshop on "Building the Quantitative Skills of Non-majors and Majors in Earth and Planetary Science Courses." This workshop was oversubscribed, attracting teams from 30 colleges and universities. A trend was clear even then, four years ago, for colleges and universities to establish new graduation requirements in quantitative literacy or to consider developing new, lower-level QL courses that would serve all students.

Some of the questions posed in applications for the PKAL workshop might help shape the QL vision:

- How can we help geology majors at liberal arts colleges become more "math literate" without increasing the total number of mathematics courses we require them to take?

- In a large, heterogeneous class, how do we include appropriate quantitative content that will not intimidate the "math-phobic" student but will challenge and not patronize the "math-able" student?

- How can we design an introductory or intermediate earth science course that also will fulfill our institution's undergraduate quantitative literacy requirement?

- What quantitative skills are appropriate for an introductory, non-major audience and what techniques can be used to teach these skills in a large class?

- How can we motivate our students to think quantitatively and analytically? How can we show them that their mathematical skills can be usefully applied to interesting and socially significant questions? (Our students are capable of quantitative thinking but they need to be convinced of its importance.)

- Are there gender-based differences in the effectiveness of different approaches to teaching quantitative reasoning?

Such questions illustrate the importance of encouraging people to identify and articulate key issues related to their particular context and circumstance; the questions also reveal that many people are deeply involved in wrestling with the QL issue. It is our responsibility to identify and connect those people to our work.

Beyond the right people, there is another critical potential resource relevant to our work. We should be giving serious consideration to how QL fits into the emerging National Science Digital Library (NSDL). This is an effort receiving priority from the National Science Foundation (NSF) and campuses across the country. As QL materials are developed, we should pay attention to if and how they become part of the NSDL and are made available to (as well as prepared by) schools, colleges, and universities across the country.

If our vision is clear and we have identified collaborators, how do we proceed? Our PKAL experience suggests the development of volunteer networks. No funding agency will support an effort as large as QL potentially can be; no funding agency will support a movement that does not have the visible commitment of those benefiting from it. So we have to think about the kind of networks needed within the QL community. Based on PKAL's experience, I suggest that successful, sustainable networks must have:

- A common goal, one arrived at through consensus, long-term engagement, and communication within a potential group of collaborators;

- People with a passion to make a difference who will put this engagement at the top of their list of priorities for expending time and energy;

- Regular and persistent avenues for communication, both face to face and electronic;

- Visible involvement of persons with a stake in the success of the network, including college presidents, deans, and others who have leadership responsibilities on a campus or within a professional society;

- One or two people who take responsibility to be the connectors, people with credibility in the communities of stakeholders and potential collaborators;

- An understanding that working together is more effective than working in isolation; and

- An affective component, so that people come to enjoy participating and have a sense of belonging.

There is an urgency to this task. In testimony to a congressional committee in 2000, Federal Reserve Board Chairman Alan Greenspan said:

> Expanding the number of individuals prepared to use a greater proportion of their intellectual capacity means, among other things, that our elementary and secondary students must broaden their skills in mathematics and related sciences. In my experience, competency in mathematics—both in numerical manipulation and in understanding its conceptual foundations— enhances a person's ability to handle the more ambiguous and qualitative relationships that dominate our day-to-day decision-making (Greenspan 2000).

My own story as an Iowa farm girl illustrates the urgency from another perspective. My grandparents had no indoor plumbing and used horses for much of the work on the farm, a self-contained, self-sufficient unit of life and work. I suppose they had a telephone, but certainly not the ease of connections to the larger world that we take for granted today. My brothers, still in the family business, today sell tractors that are more technologically sophisticated than most college computer laboratories—and the farmers who buy them are equally sophisticated in their ability to use this equipment.

The world has changed dramatically in a single lifetime. The skills needed to keep a family fed, housed, and clothed in the early twentieth century probably were not too different from those needed in the early nineteenth century but they are certainly very different from those needed in the twenty-first century.

I recognize that the relation between educational accomplishment and economic success is only one among several considerations that educators must address. As we look for allies to build connections and networks beyond the core of those committed to QL, however, it is important to consider the complete range of ways in which QL is a tool for life.

We now come back full circle to the Conant text. I close with an excerpt from an April 2000 report issued by the White House Office of Scientific and Technology Policy (2000), *Ensuring a Strong U.S. Scientific, Technical, and Engineering Workforce in the 21st Century*. It is a wonderful statistical analysis (lots of charts and graphs) of present and future workforce needs based on demographics, school and college enrollments, and workplace opportunities. The report calls for greater nationwide attention to ensuring a strong workforce, but the most compelling line also best describes why we are here, "*. . . . it is the fundamental responsibility of a modern nation to develop the talent of all its citizens.*"

References

Greenspan, Alan. 2000. Testimony before Congressional Committee.

MacLeish, Archibald. 1960. "Mr. Wilson and the Nation's Need." In *Education in the Nation's Service: A Series of Essays on American Education Today*. New York: Woodrow Wilson Foundation.

Office of Scientific and Technology Policy. 2000. *Ensuring a Strong U.S. Scientific, Technical, and Engineering Workforce in the 21st Century*. Washington, DC: U.S. Government Printing Office.

Project Kaleidoscope. 1991. *What Works Building Natural Science Communities, Volume I*. Washington, DC: Project Kaleidoscope.

Quantitative Literacy Goals: Are We Making Progress?

RITA COLWELL

I am very pleased to have the opportunity to address the question of whether we are making progress toward our goals for quantitative literacy. Let me answer by paraphrasing a comment made by the late Congressman George Brown of California. He was the best friend and most constructive critic of science in the U.S. Congress and we all miss his wisdom. He would say that if you don't know where you're headed, any route will be the right one.

What has this to do with making progress toward our quantitative literacy goals? I would answer, everything. We do not really know if we are making progress. We do not have genuine benchmarks for what constitutes quantitative literacy.

I do not mean to be coy. Quantitative literacy for college- and graduate school-bound students is necessarily going to be more important than for those who stop with a high school diploma, followed by technical certification, in competing for the growing number of highly technical jobs generated by society today.

As our society is driven increasingly by science and technology, the need to establish levels of quantitative literacy becomes ever more important. We must remember that levels are not ceilings, but floors. If no child is to be left behind, he or she should have the best opportunity to reach as high as possible.

But, we must be pragmatic. Not everyone will be in the top level, nor can be. We live in, and are enriched by, our highly heterogeneous population—an enviable strength of our nation. Several studies, such as the National Adult Literacy Survey and the Third International Mathematics and Science Study, have revealed that we need to be both active and vigilant. A significant number of our citizens lack basic knowledge in many areas of science and mathematics.

Lack of understanding of basic science has even become the fodder for jokes on "The Tonight Show." Jay Leno can generate humor just by asking people on the street simple questions about science or mathematics. Common knowledge is not always as common as we would hope; the extremes can be rather surprising. If instead of being about science the questions were about Michael Jordan's field goal percentage, or statistics from this year's World Series, or how many ounces there are in a Big Gulp, would the results be different? If any of us had been approached on the street by Jay Leno and asked questions about economics, or civic planning, or even nutrition, how would we have fared?

Literacy is a complicated issue. Despite indicators showing that a lot of work needs to be done, we should not be discouraged. Foremost, educators should be recognized for their efforts, not frustrated with limited resources or branded by public perceptions of their shortcomings.

Rita Colwell is Director of the National Science Foundation. Previously, Colwell was President of the University of Maryland Biotechnology Institute. A member of the National Academy of Sciences, Colwell has served as President of the American Association for the Advancement of Science (AAAS), of the American Society for Microbiology, of Sigma Xi, and of the International Union of Microbiological Societies. Colwell is also a former member of the Mathematical Sciences Education Board (MSEB).

Our efforts should be positive. Our highest priority should be to encourage a favorable impression of mathematics, not just through efforts in the schools but also in the everyday lives of all Americans. We need to accomplish two goals.

First, we need to bring all Americans to a level of literacy appropriate to their daily activities and their future aspirations. Second, we need to communicate that mathematics is everywhere, that in addition to practical value it can be exciting and even artistic and aesthetic.

The need for quantitative literacy can vary from understanding the rise and fall of the stock market, to balancing a checkbook, to understanding risk. The latter, risk, is a greater concern in recent months. In his book *Against the Gods: The Remarkable Story of Risk,* economic consultant Peter L. Bernstein relates the following story, encapsulating how risk perception can change in stressful situations:

> One winter night during one of the many German air raids on Moscow in World War II, a distinguished Soviet professor of statistics showed up in his local air raid shelter. He had never appeared there before. "There are seven million people in Moscow," he used to say. "Why should I expect [the German bombs] to hit me?" His friends were astonished to see him and asked what had happened to change his mind. "Look," he explained, "there are seven million people in Moscow and one elephant. Last night they got the elephant." (Bernstein 1996, 116)

As the statistician knew, the probability was still low that he would be a target. Yet, low probability was shallow comfort when the outcome could be death. That particular case brought home the fact that even low probability events happen. When we have little direct control over our fate, a firm understanding of probability can alleviate some of the stress.

As the recent anthrax crisis demonstrated, the public and the authorities would have benefited from a better understanding of such concepts as diffusion of aerosols, epidemiology, and germ theory. The nation would have benefited from knowing the very small probability of a tainted letter arriving at anyone's doorstep, or from understanding how infection differs from exposure. Fundamentally, the public would have benefited from a solid mix of scientific and quantitative literacy.

But what level of quantitative knowledge does each American need to function effectively under daily conditions? How much interest in quantitative knowledge should we realistically expect when no crisis is imminent?

Quantitative literacy, just like English literacy or historical literacy, exists in degrees. If you asked historians what information they would ideally want each American to know, they probably would suggest topics critical to our nation's future but not relevant to our daily lives: the Whiskey Rebellion,[1] Seward's Folly,[2] the Jethro Tull[3] of circa 1701 Britain, as opposed to the Jethro Tull[4] of circa 1971. And historians would want us to know more than the necessary facts; they would say that we should know the historical context and the insight the events shed on the nature of human experience.

When asked what information all Americans *must* know, however, historians would probably bring up subjects such as the Constitutional Convention, or Standard Oil, or *Brown v. Board of Education*—issues that are critical to understanding our present society.

Ours would be a more effective, and perhaps more rational, society if all Americans felt the same fascination for the magic of numbers and the elegance of graphic representations that we, as scientists, do. The public, however, is most concerned with issues affecting them daily, and it is the role of quantitative literacy in our daily lives that must be understood. People are comfortable using numbers in daily activities with which they are familiar—shopping, tracking sports statistics, even day-trading.

In schools, we likely can make daily quantitative activities a bridge to higher levels of understanding. More may choose to elevate their literacy, coming to appreciate what that master of quantitative representation, Edward Tufte, called "the clear portrayal of complexity. Not the complication of the simple; rather . . . the revelation of the complex" (Tufte 1983, epilogue).

So what are our standards for literacy in the United States? In 1988, Congress passed the Adult Education Amendments, mandating the U.S. Department of Education to define literacy and measure the extent of literacy among Americans. The definition eventually accepted by Congress characterizes literacy as "an individual's ability to read, write, and speak in English and compute and solve problems at levels of proficiency necessary to function on the job and in society, to achieve one's goals, and to develop one's knowledge and potential."

The Department of Education's first National Adult Literacy Survey was conducted in 1992. It questioned 26,000 Americans ages 16 and older and measured not just quantitative literacy but also prose and document literacy. As we would expect, individuals with less formal education dominated the lower levels. Of great concern, minorities tended to have less formal education and were overrepresented in the lower literacy levels.

Similar trends were observed in the Third International Mathematics and Science Study—Repeat (TIMSS-R) and the recent National Assessment of Educational Progress reports on mathematics and science. In the TIMSS-R evaluation of the mathematics and science skills of eighth graders from around the world, the United States ranked only about average in both mathematics and science; however, students from disadvantaged minorities ranked below average. Students from higher-income school districts ranked on a par with their highest-ranking international counterparts.

Americans who are given access to excellent resources are, for the most part, receiving an excellent education. In our country, literacy is most frequently linked to socioeconomic factors. Not all of U.S. education is in crisis, but the unequal distribution of resources is a cause for great concern. For several years, the National Science Foundation (NSF) has funded systemic reform initiatives in both urban and rural school districts to improve overall science and mathematics education. The results have been very encouraging.

Comprehensive and constructive assistance always works better than berating education systems as a whole. Teachers are not the root cause of all problems. We must recognize that there *are* great educators out there for our young people. The problems that exist are complex and the solutions are complex as well. Unequal distribution of resources and poor attitudes about mathematics stretch across all age groups. Innovation in teaching should be recognized and rewarded. Successful efforts to reach out to and motivate students must be recognized and supported.

We all know that bringing quantitative literacy to our schools is only one facet of a complex solution. We also must bring a recognition and, more important, an appreciation, of quantitative knowledge to our daily lives. This is important particularly for adults. People will seek out knowledge that directly affects them. As proof, they are already gravitating to science topics on prime-time TV. Shows produced by National Geographic, Discovery, the Learning Channel, and others draw devoted audiences. NSF is proud to support dynamic children's shows such as "The Magic School Bus," "Bill Nye the Science Guy," and "Find Out Why," a series coproduced with Walt Disney Television Animation for broadcast between Saturday morning cartoons.

All these efforts recognize that everybody confronting a topic for the first time has difficulty. As Ralph Waldo Emerson said, "The secret of education lies in respecting the pupil." Many audiences come to the table with misconceptions and preconceptions, some of which can be shocking—but they need to be respected if we are ever to reach them.

Our efforts should focus on greatly expanding the number of Americans motivated to pursue quantitatively vigorous careers while also abolishing the general mathematics phobia that is pervasive in our society. If we present mathematics in a comfortable way, and even with humor, there is no reason we cannot reverse the present trend.

We can look at numeracy through the metaphor of an analog clock. Some people only need to know how to read the face to accomplish their daily goals. Some need to know that beneath the front a complex system of gears tracks the progression of time. Others need to be able to take the existing clock and innovate, to build the next generation of timekeeping devices. But who needs which information? And is knowledge of gear ratios necessary to appreciate the beauty and simplicity of the clock's face?

I would argue that some of us may be interested in knowing the deepest intricacies of timekeeping, yet we should not spend exhaustive resources teaching every intricate detail to every single person. The more critical lesson is on the clock's face, the thought process, the discovery process. Everyone needs to know how to tell time.

We must set flexible goals for literacy based on standards that are appropriate for every audience. We must recognize that most Americans are unaware of how mathematics permeates their lives. We must find ways of bringing their daily quantitative activities into focus. And most important, we must understand that literacy has levels.

And so we come full circle to the question, are we making progress? Recognition of the problem was the obvious first step. NSF's systemic initiatives mark significant progress. This conference and your hard work are testament to progress. Industry's concern and support is a mark of progress, and so are many other efforts.

Will we ever be able to say we have reached the finish line? Absolutely not. The finish line is a moving target and we must perpetually pursue it if we are to stay out front as individuals and as a nation. Who knows what the quantitative literacy needs of society will be in 2050 or the year 3000?

Notes

1. Angered by a 1791 federal excise tax on whiskey, farmers in the western counties of Pennsylvania began attacking tax agents. On August 7, 1794, President George Washington issued a proclamation, calling out the militias to respond. Thirteen thousand troops led by Washington and General Harry Lee, Robert E. Lee's father, quelled the uprising. This was the first use of the Militia Law of 1792, setting a precedent for the use of the militia to "execute the laws of the union,

[and] suppress insurrections," and asserting the right of the national government to enforce order in one state with troops raised in other states. Even more important, it was the first test of power of the new federal government, establishing its primacy in disputes with individual states. [Adapted from August 11, 1794, *Claypoole's Daily Advertiser*.]

2. On March 30, 1867, Secretary of State William H. Seward agreed to purchase relatively unexplored Alaska from Russia for $7 million. At the time, critics thought Seward was crazy and called the deal "Seward's folly." Major discoveries of gold were made there in the 1880s and 1890s. These discoveries brought attention and people to Alaska. Today, petroleum transported across the state through a pipeline is Alaska's richest mineral resource. [AmericasLibrary.gov, Library of Congress.]

3. Jethro Tull (farmer, 1674–1741) designed a machine (a seed drill) to plant seed more efficiently, minimizing the number of workers needed to sow a field. His system was a major influence on the agricultural revolution. [From BBC history.]

4. *Jethro Tull* (band, 1968–present), famous for flute-heavy tunes and such hits as "Aqualung" and "Living in the Past."

References

Bernstein, Peter L. 1996. *Against the Gods: The Remarkable Story of Risk*. New York, NY: John Wiley.

Tufte, Edward R. 1983. *The Visual Display of Quantitative Information*. Cheshire, CT: Graphics Press.

What Have We Learned, ... and Have Yet to Learn?

HYMAN BASS

This remarkable Forum more than achieved its aim of stimulating a continuing national conversation on quantitative literacy. (Without expressing a preference, I shall for convenience use this term, abbreviated as QL, for what was variously referred to during this Forum as quantitative literacy, mathematical literacy, and numeracy.) I shall try to summarize some of the diverse messages that I heard here, as best I could understand them, and add some personal reflections.

Defining QL

Although we have no precise definition of QL, the case statement in *Mathematics and Democracy: The Case for Quantitative Literacy* and the background essays contributed to this Forum give us a rich, and not always consistent, set of characterizations and expressions of it. A common characterization seems to be this: QL is about knowledge and skills in *use*, so it is a kind of *applied knowledge* that is typically illustrated in particular *contexts*. But these contexts are extremely diverse, and many of them, if treated in more than a caricature fashion, are quite complex. This presents a challenge to the design of curricula for QL. What is its focus? What is its disciplinary locus?

Voices at this Forum offered a very broad perspective. In our collective minds, QL appears to be some sort of constellation of knowledge, skills, habits of mind, and dispositions that provide the resources and capacity to deal with the quantitative aspects of understanding, making sense of, participating in, and solving problems in the worlds that we inhabit, for example, the workplace, the demands of responsible citizenship in a democracy, personal concerns, and cultural enrichment.

Urgency for QL arises primarily from the effects of technology, which exposes us to vastly more quantitative information and data. Therefore, the tools of data analysis, statistics, and probabilistic reasoning (in risk assessment, for example) are becoming increasingly important. Yet there is broad agreement, with some evidence cited, that most adult Americans are substantially deficient in QL, however it may be defined. This is viewed as a serious societal problem in several respects—economic (capacity of the workforce), political (functioning of a modern industrial democracy), cultural (appreciation of the heritage and beauty of mathematics), and personal (capacity for a responsible and productive life).

I agree with the views expressed that it is neither urgent, nor even necessarily productive, to attempt to achieve a precise consensus definition of QL. At the same time, this is not an entirely benign consideration. To illustrate, one speaker proposed that university mathematicians send a collective letter to the College Board requesting more QL on the SAT and other examinations. Such a recommendation, if implemented, is not immediately actionable by the College Board without an operational interpretation of what QL should mean in that context, and that interpretation is open

---

Hyman Bass is the Roger Lyndon Collegiate Professor of Mathematics and Professor of Mathematics Education at the University of Michigan. His mathematical research interests cover broad areas of algebra. A member of the National Academy of Sciences, Bass is president of the American Mathematical Society and of the International Commission on Mathematics Instruction (ICMI). A former chair of the Mathematical Sciences Education Board, Bass is currently helping investigate the mathematical requirements involved in teaching mathematics at the elementary level.

to considerable license. What the College Board could end up offering in response, if it chose to respond, might not please all signers of such a letter.

Absent a definition, there is little basis for reconciling views. On the other hand, it might be an important and fruitful step not only for the College Board but also for the higher education mathematics community to conduct a negotiation of what a credible list of illustrative test items that could claim to represent a proper and balanced sampling of QL knowledge might look like, to which the professional community could subscribe. Putting such a list in a letter to the College Board would be a very different, knowledge-based gesture.

Similar cautions apply to any attempt to translate our sentiments about QL into far-reaching policy positions. Our knowledge base about QL is not sufficient to rush toward major transformations of the school curriculum, not to mention the necessary capacity-building among teachers to support such change.

Educating for QL

Remedies to the problem of QL are generally assumed to be primarily the responsibility of the education system, principally in grades 10 to 14. In fact, QL must be taught starting in the earliest grades if we are to make any headway on this problem. Nonetheless, most of the discussion at this Forum centered on ideas about QL in later grades. I note three recurrent themes:

1. The curriculum should include much more statistics and other alternatives to the calculus trajectory that are focused more on data analysis, modeling, etc.

This recommendation often has been accompanied by disparagement of the teaching of traditional mathematics topics. This reminds me of some of the debates about the teaching of computational algorithms. At root the objections were not to the skills and concepts being taught but rather to the pedagogy, to the oppressive or obscure ways in which these topics have often been taught, which the debaters could not see as distinct from the subject matter. Although a full exposure to calculus may not be appropriate for a majority of students, algebra and geometry remain fundamental to all developed uses of mathematics.

2. Mathematics instruction should be contextualized and avoid the abstraction associated with the traditional curriculum.

This common refrain of current reforms is more complex than most of its advocates appreciate. One argument, which goes back to John Dewey and others, is that learning best starts with experience, to provide both meaning and motivation for the more

general and structured ideas that will follow. Dewey's notion differs in two respects from the above recommendation. First, it does not eschew abstraction. Second, it speaks of the experience of the learner, not of the eventual context of the application of the ideas, which may be highly specialized and occur much later in adult experience.

Another argument is that mathematics is best learned in the complex contexts in which it is most significantly used. This idea has a certain appeal, provided that it is kept in balance. Authentic contexts are complex and idiosyncratic. Which contexts should we choose for a curriculum? Their very complexity often buries the mathematical ideas in other features so that, although the mathematical effects might be appreciated, there is limited opportunity to learn the underlying mathematical principles.

The main danger here, therefore, is the impulse to convert a major part of the curriculum to this form of instruction. The resulting failure to learn general (abstract) principles then may, if neglected, deprive the learner of the foundation necessary for recognizing how the same mathematics witnessed in one context in fact applies to many others.

Finally, contextualization is seen as providing early experience with the very important process of mathematical modeling. This is a laudable goal but it is often treated naïvely, in ways that violate its own purpose. Serious modeling must treat both the context and the mathematics with respect and integrity. Yet much contextualized curricular mathematics presents artificial caricatures of contexts that beg credibility. Either many of their particular features, their ambiguities, and the need for interpretation are ignored in setting up the intended mathematics, which defeats the point of the context, or else many of these features are attended to and they obscure the mathematical objectives of the lesson. Good contextualizing of mathematics is a high skill well beyond that of many of its current practitioners.

3. Quantitative knowledge and skills for QL should have a much more cross-disciplinary agenda, rather than one situated primarily in mathematics curricula.

I am generally sympathetic to this recommendation. Because mathematics is a foundational and enabling discipline for so many others, it is natural that mathematics learning in general, not just for QL, should evolve from an ongoing conversation and sometimes collaboration with client disciplines. At the same time, the historical reasons for situating the learning of QL skills in mathematics study have not lost their relevance. And I am speaking of more than the learning of basic arithmetic and measurement.

Take, for example, the learning of deductive reasoning, which most of us would count as an important component of QL. Although applicable in all contexts in which mathematical ideas and methods are used, this is a practice that can most naturally be cultivated in core mathematical domains, beginning in the earliest grades. For example, it is both reasonable and educationally productive to have third graders *explain* why some algorithm for subtraction, or the multiplication of whole numbers, actually works. Or, for example, they could be asked to *prove* that they have all the possible solutions to a problem with finitely many solutions. The basic mathematics curriculum, including the primary grades, naturally affords a context for the development of the skills of disciplined mathematical reasoning, although this seems rarely to be done today. Other subject areas do not provide similar opportunities to learn this kind of deductive reasoning.

Lynn Arthur Steen recounted to me some conversations with Harvard mathematician Andrew Gleason in the early years of the Mathematical Sciences Education Board, in which Gleason argued energetically that mathematics is the only subject in which primary-grade children can gain an internal sense of truth independent of adult authority. By the power of their own minds they can, in principle, know for certain that some things are right (or wrong) even if they are different from what their teacher may say. They really cannot do this in any other area. Of course, as Steen notes, probably relatively few children have the psychological strength to adhere to their own logic in the face of contrary adult authority.

Some have argued that rigorous mathematical study develops analytical skills and qualities of mind that are of intellectual and cultural value well beyond mathematics. Although this is a fond belief of mathematicians, such broad transfer has not been established, and the public discourse of many mathematicians in non-mathematical domains, involving different evidentiary norms and warrants, calls it seriously into doubt.

Moving Forward

Where do we go from here? Has this Forum accomplished its goals? Many speakers have argued that, given the alarmingly low rates of quantitative literacy among American adults and the already lengthy discussions of this problem, we should move quickly to programs of dramatic action to improve the situation, with a strongly articulated vision of what we want to accomplish.

Although I do not want to rain on your parade, I suggest that our knowledge base about quantitative literacy is not yet adequate for designing major interventions in the school curriculum. The comprehensive agenda of providing QL to all students is one measured in decades, not years, but it is work that can productively begin in incremental ways right now.

This Forum has taken an important step. The case statement in *Mathematics and Democracy* and the collection of very interesting and provocative background essays prepared for this Forum provide a rich articulation of questions and concerns regarding QL, many analyses of the problems we face, and many stimulating but somewhat divergent suggestions for what to do about them. Together, these provide a rich resource for an ongoing, disciplined, and coordinated national (or even international) conversation about these issues.

References

Steen, Lynn Arthur, ed. 2001. *Mathematics and Democracy: The Case for Quantitative Literacy.* Princeton, NJ: National Council on Education and the Disciplines.

Reflections

A selection of brief observations by participants at the national Forum, "Quantitative Literacy: Why Numeracy Matters for Schools and Colleges," offering different perspectives on issues covered at the Forum.

To advance quantitative literacy, improve college algebra — Don Small

Look for QL in major organizing questions, not in techniques — Robert Cole

Ensure quality in the way subjects are taught — Russell Edgerton

Teach and assess for QL in all curriculum areas — Charlotte Frank

The changing role of numbers in everyday life — Edward Tenner

Teaching quantitative literacy across the curriculum — William G. Steenken

Not content, but pedagogy and assessment — Peter Ewell

Confronting external impediments to QL — Jo Ann Lutz

Learning mathematics by using mathematics — Gene Bottoms

Do not focus on the distinctions between mathematics and quantitative literacy — William Haver

QL is the sophisticated use of elementary mathematics — Andrea Leskes

Do not underestimate arithmetic — Philip Mahler

Support faculty, develop examples, and fix admissions tests — Stephen B. Maurer

Numeracy from cradle to grave — Mary Jane Schmitt

To advance quantitative literacy, improve college algebra

For many reasons, the most effective way to advance quantitative literacy (QL) is to improve the traditional college algebra course to serve as a foundation course for QL. The improved course should focus on elementary data analysis, functions, and modeling. It also should emphasize developing communication skills, the use of appropriate technology, and small-group projects. The goal of the course should be to enable students to gain confidence in their ability to approach quantitative problems in other disciplines, in society, and in the workplace. This goal underscores the importance of interdisciplinary cooperation both in the development and in the ongoing assessment of the course. This cooperation would establish links to other disciplines that can provide problem-solving experiences for students based on their college algebra course. In this manner, college algebra can merge with quantitative literacy to form problem-solving programs that extend throughout students' academic careers. The interdisciplinary component is essential to realize the potential of a symbiotic relationship between improved college algebra and quantitative literacy.

There are several advantages in improving the traditional college algebra course over establishing a new course to serve quantitative literacy. For example, college algebra is well entrenched in the college curriculum, it serves more students than any other credit-bearing mathematics course, and it is a college gateway for a large percentage of students. Moreover, traditional college algebra is generally recognized as a course that *does not work*. It is characterized by high FDW (fail, drop, withdraw) rates, few students advancing to calculus, and content not applicable to student interests. Thus many mathematics departments may be receptive to changing both the focus and the content of the traditional course.

Improving college algebra to serve as a foundation course for quantitative literacy allows us to avoid both the political problem of finding a home for a competing course and the practical problems of attracting students and developing faculty support. Avoiding these unnecessary challenges allows us to focus on the more important issues of building interdisciplinary collaboration and developing appropriate curricula. The growing parallel movements to improve college algebra and to develop quantitative literacy programs can and should reinforce each other.

—**Don Small,** Department of Mathematics,
United States Military Academy

Look for QL in major organizing questions, not in techniques

Despite learning a great deal from the QL Forum, I was repeatedly reminded of the narrowness of many people's disciplinary thinking, of how difficult it is for some to imagine teaching outside their own discipline or to make meaningful cross-curricular connections. I worry about the constricted vision many folks have of curriculum development. For many, QL was simply another potpourri of (mathematics) techniques to be sandwiched into some kind of course that had to be fit (somehow) into the existing sequence of departmental offerings. Although many at the Forum recognized the need for "applications," few saw the applications as anything other than a delivery vehicle for the QL or mathematical techniques, the latter being the real meat. If QL goes down this road—a smorgasbord of techniques squeezed into a general education course—I think we run the danger of not addressing the real need outlined in the case statement in *Mathematics and Democracy: The Case for Quantitative Literacy,* namely, the need of citizens to find a use for mathematics that connects with their perception of the real world.

Although several people I spoke with seemed interested in developing curricula around organizing questions and themes rather than disciplinary content, they were, initially, uneasy with the idea. Because their mind was still on a set of content to be covered, it took a while for them to begin to see how this could be done. The notion of designing curricula around important questions was, at first, quite a stretch. One person said that it was a great idea but that it would never fit into the departments he knew. I took that to be a measure of how ingrown and isolated higher education has become from the society that supports it.

One way of exposing how banal curriculum design questions have become at most universities would be to do a QL analysis of departmental and curricular structures. By analyzing the currencies we use to justify our academic enterprise (numbers of majors, time to graduation, course sequencing, needs of majors, graduate school preparation, hiring priorities, etc.), we might gain some insight into what really drives curricular design. My hunch is that such an analysis would not engage the important questions facing homo sapiens on this planet at this time in history. Little wonder that students often find our courses disconnected from the real world.

The twenty-first century will be a "crunch" time for our species. We currently are engaging in wholesale destruction of the ecosystem and far too many of us are chasing far too few natural resources. To the degree that the academic curriculum does not organize itself to confront these important questions, it will continue a decline into irrelevance. Designing QL to address some of these crucial questions will go a long way toward connecting with students' perception of the real world.

—**Robert Cole,** Evergreen State College

Ensure quality in the way subjects are taught

I came to this Forum with a general interest in how the academy can take more responsibility for ensuring that undergraduates acquire core abilities (or literacies) that require persistent work across a variety of courses. I came away with a heightened awareness of the importance of clarifying whether students acquire an outcome such as quantitative literacy as a result of the subjects they experience (the curriculum) or of the way these subjects are taught (the pedagogy).

The answer is obviously both. But the more that the answer lies with the pedagogical practices students experience (for example, the nature of the assignments students are given), the wider the possibilities are that many courses across the curriculum can contribute to the desired objective. In the case of quantitative literacy, it seems that many elements (such as statistical competence and data analysis) could be acquired through a wide range of courses.

It is encouraging that so many faculty and so many courses can contribute to the acquisition of quantitative literacy, as well as to other literacies such as writing. But it is also discouraging because our internal mechanisms for quality assurance (for example, curriculum review committees) are overwhelmingly focused on what subjects are taught, not on whether subjects are taught in ways that help students acquire core abilities. So I also left with the conviction that we have to invent mechanisms of quality assurance that look at how courses are being taught as well as simply at whether the content of the courses seems right.

—**Russell Edgerton,** Director, Pew Forum on Undergraduate Learning

Teach and assess for QL in all curriculum areas

After spending a weekend discussing quantitative literacy, it became clear that QL competencies include skills that all students should have before they graduate from high school as well as skills they should have on an even more sophisticated level as college graduates. Young students acquire QL skills at a very basic level when learning about saving money in a bank or writing a check, as well as when talking together about what to order for a class party

and then preparing a chart listing how many different kinds of drinks, sandwiches, or pizzas are needed. QL is clearly very important. It should be infused in all curriculum areas and then assessed in these areas to provide teachers with guidance in determining appropriate next steps. The QL skills of interpreting and discussing data and then presenting information in a coherent manner are absolutely essential if our young people are going to be successful as responsible citizens in this new world of technology.

—**Charlotte Frank,** Vice President, McGraw-Hill and New York State Regent

The changing role of numbers in everyday life

My primary impression from the Forum is of an emerging QL vanguard at a range of institutions that is eager to change the courses in and goals of the mathematics curriculum in the interest of practical competence. Some envision a campus wide campaign potentially extending across every discipline; others favor special courses or programs; and still others believe that new courses within mathematics and statistics departments, or reorientation of existing courses, can work equally well. There also is a substantial minority of QL skeptics, not opponents of the goal but realists who emphasize the cost of professional development for college faculty and (especially in two-year colleges) the burdens of remediation. They seem to favor much longer-term measures, seeing the movement as a gradual reorientation.

Both groups appear ready to eliminate or place less emphasis on certain aspects of the mathematics curriculum to highlight QL. Both also feel helpless to fight against the accountability movement—oddly to me, because the rationale for accountability is precisely the development of QL skills. Perhaps they are right that public opinion will accept only one idea at a time, but if so it is sad. (Of course, if voters lack QL, how can anybody hope to get them to change their minds by presenting them with the data? Then again, as a number of participants observed, the meeting itself revolved more around values than numbers.)

The Forum also reflected a movement against mathematics as pure gatekeeping for medicine and other professions. One mathematician acknowledged the priority he and his colleagues give to prospective majors: "We want to clone ourselves." There well may be a certain conflict between identifying and nurturing of future mathematician-teachers, especially the "naturals" who might otherwise choose subjects such as computer science and economics, and developing the practical skills of average students.

From the papers and discussions, I would conclude that the most promising approach at the college level might be to acknowledge that only a minority of the mathematics, science, and social science faculty are potentially strong QL teachers. I would favor identifying and working with this motivated group rather than trying to bring everybody on board at once. For QL to succeed, it must be perceived as an intellectual challenge by the faculty, not just as a remedial activity. I can easily imagine that an economist or sociologist might feel that teaching QL skills just delays developing the substance of their own courses.

An inspiring example for QL might be the late Edward Purcell, whom I got to know when I was in the Society of Fellows at Harvard. He had a Nobel Prize in physics, but he equally loved simple and elegant explanations—for example, how to tell if a set of numbers might have been tampered with, or why quantum theory is necessary for the world as we know it. For many years he wrote a wonderful column for the *American Journal of Physics* that consisted largely of Fermi problems—back-of-the-envelope calculations mixing common sense with sensible estimates—proving that QL can be a high art in its own right.

At least one Forum participant mentioned a paradox that also occurred to me. Some people with very limited formal mathematics instruction, such as market traders in developing countries, are proficient in handling numbers, while many westerners growing up with advanced calculators are not. This suggests that we should pay more attention not just to the pedagogical side of quantitative literacy but also to the changing role of numbers in everyday and professional life.

Two aspects of this changing role have especially interested me. The first is the rhetorical side of numbers, the fact that people use tables and graphs to prove points in which they have emotional or financial stakes. There is surely a message in the failure of organizations such as Long Term Capital and Enron that were packed with quantitatively sophisticated people yet succumbed to self-deception. The second, and the main subject of my own investigations, is the tenuous nature of many vital measurements. Cost-of-living indexes measure shifting breadbaskets of goods, including changing tastes and spending patterns. Television ratings measure a self-selected sample of the population, and the presence of monitoring technology also may change viewer behavior. I think of these problems not so much as obstacles but as opportunities to help students and adults achieve a deeper understanding of measurement and its uses.

—**Edward Tenner,** Department of English, Princeton University

Teaching quantitative literacy across the curriculum

Although no clear consensus evolved from the Forum on what it means to be quantitatively literate, it is clear that a citizen should have skills, facility, and understanding in some or all of the areas of arithmetic, data, computers, modeling, statistics, chance, and reasoning that are elaborated in *Mathematics and Democracy*:

- *Arithmetic:* Having facility with simple mental arithmetic; estimating arithmetic calculations; reasoning with proportions; counting by indirection (combinatorics).

- *Data:* Using information conveyed as data, graphs, and charts; drawing inferences from data; recognizing disaggregation as a factor in interpreting data.

- *Computers:* Using spreadsheets, recording data, performing calculations, creating graphic displays, extrapolating, fitting lines or curves to data.

- *Modeling:* Formulating problems, seeking patterns, and drawing conclusions; recognizing interactions in complex systems; understanding linear, exponential, multivariate, and simulation models; understanding the impact of different rates of growth.

- *Statistics:* Understanding the importance of variability; recognizing the differences between correlation and causation, between randomized experiments and observational studies, between finding no effect and finding no statistically significant effect (especially with small samples), and between statistical significance and practical importance (especially with large samples).

- *Chance:* Recognizing that seemingly improbable coincidences are not uncommon; evaluating risks from available evidence; understanding the value of random samples.

- *Reasoning:* Using logical thinking; recognizing levels of rigor in methods of inference; checking hypotheses; exercising caution in making generalizations.

Because these skills defining quantitative literacy have their foundations in mathematics, most participants believed that the primary responsibility for introducing concepts associated with the tools of quantitative literacy lies with mathematics departments; however, most also thought that developing special courses in quantitative literacy would be the wrong approach.

What is needed, instead, is emphasis on QL in many courses and many subjects. There should be no special courses in quantitative literacy. The National Council of Teachers of Mathematics (NCTM) standards should be used, embellished, and built on to ensure that the concepts of quantitative literacy flow throughout the mathematics curriculum in an appropriate manner at all grade levels, thus ensuring that quantitative literacy is neither something new nor a "fad du jour." In addition, the skills of quantitative literacy must be used throughout all subject areas including the language arts, history, geography, and social studies—not only in mathematics and the sciences.

To make this happen, numeracy skills should be taught and modeled in all courses in all content areas that are part of a teacher's degree program. Only in this way will students be exposed to numeracy in both primary and secondary schools in a way that helps them become quantitatively literate across all subject areas. This approach also will help alleviate the fear that is often associated with mathematics-based concepts.

—**William G. Steenken,** General Electric Aircraft Engines (Retired)

Not content, but pedagogy and assessment

Despite the presence of a cross-section of interested and interesting people, the Forum was still, in large part, a mathematics meeting. Granted, the discussion was chiefly on point with regard to quantitative literacy, but to me the unspoken subtext and the dominant culture of the gathering was unmistakably mathematical. The most vivid example I can think of was Daniel Goroff's presentation about a phenomenon of misunderstanding that I used to encounter frequently in political science, a phenomenon that—as I now recognize—I tried to address in QL rather than mathematical terms: getting students to read contingency tables both down and across to make educated guesses about missing data and to draw different policy and personal conclusions. Goroff's use of conditional probability and Bayesian reasoning was far more subtle and sophisticated than anything I used to do, but I am not sure my students ever would have gotten beyond the fearsome notation of conditional probabilities. This kind of disjuncture occurred frequently at the Forum as people talked about QL but did so in the language of mathematics. We may need a new language, more than a new set of concepts, that allows everybody to participate more fully in the conversation.

There was clear consensus on the problem but a lot of trouble pinning it down in terms of definitions. I fully agree with the many comments that a further search for definition is not profit-

able. What we need are many concrete examples—of failures to understand and their consequences and of real and effective programs that can increase competence. For external audiences, for instance, we need a strong, short statement that contains concrete (quantitative) evidence of the failure to master QL and what it may be costing us as a society. For disciplinary audiences, we need very concrete identification of the latent (and perhaps even unrecognized) QL content in their subject areas. Everybody can easily agree on the "it" in terms of examples, but going much farther at the conceptual level just leaves people confused.

Different audiences need very different messages. The policy community needs a very short statement concerning what QL is (defined by example), why it is important (demonstrated in terms of concrete evidence of shortfalls and their consequences in lost productivity and quality of life), and what might be done about it (a concerted policy effort aimed, probably, at points of transition between high school and college and between education and the world of work). The K–12 mathematics community needs a different message—already in part delivered by the NCTM standards—but probably more focused on pedagogy. The postsecondary nonmathematics community needs a message that identifies common QL threads in what it is doing, together with an urge to make common cause in working together and working with mathematics. Finally, the postsecondary mathematics community needs a message that affirms that QL is not an attack on mathematics per se but a discussion about the ways mathematics is taught and applied. (There were, for instance, too many needless arguments for and against algebra.)

In many ways, the real Forum conversation was more about pedagogy and assessment than about content. This is important first because much QL writing leads with content, which inevitably leads in turn to unproductive fights about what content is "in" and what is "out." I find myself more and more persuaded that one barrier to achieving quantitative literacy is, as Alan Schoenfeld noted in *Mathematics and Democracy,* the way mathematics is taught in the early school grades, especially how abstractions are introduced and contextually anchored. Second, as Grant Wiggins argued in one of the Forum's background essays, fixing assignments and tests may be far more important than fixing syllabi (Wiggins, see pp. 121–143).

Finally, I found myself more convinced than ever that the dynamics—and therefore the levers—for change are quite different in K–12 and higher education. Top-down methods, largely led by the mathematics community, will work in K–12—employing organizations such as NCTM and the Mathematical Association of America (MAA). Other teachers and disciplines can help, but in K–12 the movement needs to be led by the mathematics community. This in part is because, as a number of Forum speakers pointed out, many K–12 teachers outside mathematics are not themselves quantitatively literate.

I am not at all convinced that the same is true for higher education. Here, I think the movement has to be led largely from outside mathematics—relying on practitioners in client disciplines who really understand and practice QL to make common cause. Of course, needs will be different in the sciences and engineering (algebra/calculus-based disciplines) and the social sciences and business (statistics and applied numeracy-based disciplines). I never thought I would say this, but one approach in higher education might be to empower client disciplines to teach their own quantitative courses in greater numbers (which, of course, already happens in statistics), leaving mathematics departments to the business of educating the few who want to take the traditional path.

—**Peter Ewell,** Partner, National Center for Higher Education Management Systems

Confronting external impediments to QL

The task of improving the quantitative literacy of all students seems daunting. The more we talked at the Forum, the more the task grew. Thinking about the work that needs to be done in the early grades, in high school, and then in college made it clear that a coordinated effort is needed. Students at every level, and their teachers, need to recognize that quantitative literacy is important and that it is valued. Students learn what they are taught; therefore, faculty at every level must teach the QL practices we claim to value.

Because it is what I know best, I think most about the tasks facing high school teachers. High school curricula are determined to a great extent by outside forces. College admissions processes that place the greatest value on the highest-level mathematics course (e.g., Advanced Placement) do not always help teachers teach what would be best for their students. College placement tests and procedures that value very traditional mathematics hurt students who have been taught a mathematics curriculum that has a strong emphasis on quantitative literacy, and therefore discourage teachers from moving toward a quantitative literacy focus in their teaching. The NCTM standards-based course of study, which supports quantitative literacy, does not always seem to be valued by college faculty. Therefore, students prepared in a standards-based mathematics program may be hurt in the transition to college courses. Parents' views of what is important and administrators' responses both to parents and to colleges also have an effect

on what teachers are allowed to do. Until a quantitative literacy-based curriculum is valued by these outside forces, high school teachers will not be able to do what is best for all students.

—**Jo Ann Lutz,** North Carolina School of Mathematics and Science, and College Board Trustee

Learning mathematics by using mathematics

Clearly, our first priority must be to improve the quality of mathematics instruction. Evidence from the High Schools That Work (HSTW) network shows a dramatic change in mathematics courses taken by career-oriented students over the past 12 years. In 1988, only 25 percent of these students took three mathematics credits (including two or more of Algebra I, Algebra II, and Geometry), while in 2000, 85 percent had reached this standard, with 80 percent completing geometry and nearly 70 percent completing Algebra II. During this time the average mathematics scores of these students increased from the low 280s on a NAEP-based examination to over 300. In 2000, only 4 percent had a mathematics score below 250.

Interestingly, female students take more, and more advanced, mathematics courses than male students, while young men still have slightly higher mathematics test scores. (The achievement gap is diminishing.) Although male students take fewer and easier mathematics courses than females, males tend to be enrolled in vocational programs in which they make greater use of mathematics to complete authentic assignments and are much more likely to be given joint assignments from their mathematics and vocational teachers. Extensive classroom visits show that much of the instruction in mathematics classrooms is designed to teach students how to follow procedures. In too many classrooms, teachers simply skip the reading problems in their texts, some of which are actually rather decent problems. Students need to take courses in other areas to see mathematics used, and when they do it is noticeable in their test scores.

Thus the first priority: to support mathematics teachers in assigning real-world problems that will help students understand mathematical concepts and engage in mathematical reasoning. Such support is crucial politically as well as pedagogically, because if we do not see the expected improvement in achievement as students are required to take more mathematics courses, mathematics teachers will come under increasing criticism. We need a major initiative to help mathematics teachers teach in ways that engage students in using mathematics to do real things in various contexts.

A second priority, clearly articulated at the Forum, is to emphasize quantitative literacy across the curriculum. This may mean developing individuals in both the middle grades and high schools to become "QL coaches" to devise learning experiences within non-mathematical disciplines that are quantitative in nature and that improve students' understanding of those disciplines. A QL coach would help integrate quantitative analysis throughout the curriculum. The focus of coaching has to be on empowering teachers to use quantitative literacy—not to teach mathematics but to advance students' learning and understanding in their own disciplines. If teachers interpret QL to mean that they are now to teach mathematics in addition to their own disciplines, they will simply turn off.

We have known for a long time at HSTW sites that science, vocational, and technical arts teachers who devise learning experiences that require students to draw on mathematical knowledge produce students with consistently higher mathematics achievement and much better performance on problem-solving items on a NAEP-based examination. Yet too many high school students study science or technical courses devoid of mathematics. Only about one-third are in classes in which they frequently have to use mathematics to complete authentic tasks. In too many cases, only the best students do mathematics while the rest simply do what they are told. Science, vocational, and technical arts teachers need special help devising learning experiences with a mathematical base, using instructional strategies through which they hold all students accountable for doing quantitative analysis, and developing assessments to determine whether students are able to apply essential mathematical concepts to typical problems they will encounter in diverse careers. Physical education, social studies, and art teachers also can use quantitative literacy to enhance student learning in those disciplines. Most of these teachers could benefit from a QL coach.

Third, if we want to change how mathematics is taught, we must change the nature of the questions that are asked on various examinations. Most state and end-of-course examinations and even the ACT and SAT mathematics examinations have very few questions that focus on the ability of students to reason and think with mathematics to solve authentic real-world problems. In too many instances, mathematics examinations encourage teachers to teach the wrong way. They encourage teachers to cover the material, teach students the procedures, and hope that students will remember them long enough to pass the examination. The emphasis of the examinations, and thus of teaching, is not on deep understanding of mathematical concepts or on advancing students' reasoning skills. Moreover, there are no consequences for failure to show improvement over time.

Fourth, changes need to be made in mathematics texts to include more real-world problems that can be used to teach quantitative literacy. Moreover, textbook publishers should provide more coordination between mathematics and science textbooks to align mathematics concepts and the quantitative literacy potential of science. In visiting hundreds of schools and high school classrooms over the past 15 years, it has been my observation that more than any other teachers in high school, mathematics teachers depend on textbooks. Therefore, without quality text materials to give students opportunities to use mathematics in a variety of challenging contexts, QL simply will not happen.

Finally, one of the points made by many Forum participants was that if quantitative literacy is not viewed as something for all students, it will lead to further tracking in mathematics, which these participants saw as undesirable. This is certainly a valid point, but I fear that by stressing this distinction the quantitative literacy movement runs the risk of being interpreted as saying that what we are now doing is not working. We cannot simply overthrow one system and substitute another. We must develop mathematics course sequences that are appropriate for all students and that offer a suitable balance between the more procedural emphases that now are taught to too many students and a QL-like emphasis that engages students in using mathematics to do real things in contexts that have meaning for them.

—**Gene Bottoms,** Director, High Schools That Work, Southern Regional Education Board (SREB)

Do not focus on the distinctions between mathematics and quantitative literacy

Advocates for the skills, abilities, knowledge, and mind-set embodied in quantitative literacy, particularly those advocates outside the mathematics community, can have a strong influence on improving mathematics instruction and student learning. Many within the mathematics community are taking big steps toward revising the mathematics curriculum in the directions called for under the QL banner. Reports from mathematics professional organizations—the NCTM at the school level and the MAA and the American Statistical Association (ASA) at the college level—call for such changes. The mathematics curriculum projects at the elementary, middle, and high school levels supported by the National Science Foundation infuse quantitative literacy into the K–12 mathematics curriculum. Changes at the college level are taking place under banners such as "calculus reform," "alternatives to college algebra," or, in many mathematics departments, "quantitative literacy."

Those of us committed to this work at our own institutions very much need the help of advocates outside the mathematics community:

- We need to know that what we are doing matters in a broader world; anything that catches the eye of administrators would be very useful.

- We need assistance and encouragement in urging disciplines outside mathematics to work together with us in promoting quantitative literacy.

- Perhaps most critically, we need support to include quantitative literacy on high-stakes tests, particularly on the mathematics portions of the tests many states are requiring for high school graduation and the new grade-level tests now being mandated at the national level.

All of this said, I think it is a big mistake to focus on the distinctions between mathematics and quantitative literacy, as was sometimes the case at the Forum and in *Mathematics and Democracy*. Such artificial distinctions let mathematicians and the broader mathematics community off the hook. In my opinion, the abilities and mind-set described as quantitative literacy are central to mathematics (definitely including research mathematics) as well as to effective teaching and learning of mathematics. Many in positions of influence, however, would prefer to keep all students focused on technical manipulation skills in the elementary algebra, formal geometry, intermediate algebra, college algebra, and pre-calculus courses that are studied by masses of students today, students who have no intention of entering fields that require calculus.

If we make distinctions that can be translated as "quantitative literacy is not mathematics," we run the risk of giving ammunition to those who oppose reforming the mathematics curriculum and instruction in ways encouraged by quantitative literacy advocates. The chance that leadership in implementing quantitative literacy programs will come from anywhere but the mathematics community is slight to nonexistent. States require testing of mathematics, language arts, and often social science and science. The chances of adding a fifth test on quantitative literacy are nonexistent. The federal government now requires states to test mathematics at every grade level between three and eight. There is no possibility of adding an additional test on quantitative literacy. Mathematics is taught to all students from kindergarten through at least grade 10. An additional "quantitative literacy" subject will not be added to the curriculum. Large numbers of colleges and universities require mathematics course work of all their students. Some may replace a mathematics requirement by a quantitative literacy requirement, but very few would add a quantitative literacy requirement on top of a mathematics requirement. Finally, colleges and

universities provide support to departments of mathematics; they will not support or fund new departments of quantitative literacy.

In short, leadership for quantitative literacy needs to come from mathematical sciences departments (mathematics and statistics) at both the school and college levels and mathematicians must take the lead if wide-scale change is to occur. Support from outside the mathematics community would be very useful; however, if quantitative literacy is viewed as not a central part of mathematics, it will be much more difficult to direct the energy and resources of mathematicians and mathematical sciences departments toward this important effort.

—**William Haver,** Mathematics Department,
Virginia Commonwealth University

QL is the sophisticated use of elementary mathematics

I was struck most at the Forum by the need to continue educating faculty about the concept of quantitative literacy. Even among the group of people who were interested enough to spend a weekend discussing QL, there was no common understanding of the term. Conversations kept slipping between QL and mathematics as if they were one and the same, and the mathematicians seemed to be the ones most often conflating the concepts. In addition to assuming that QL was the same as mathematics (without even a nod in the direction of context or applicability), very often concepts that should be learning outcomes or capacities were immediately turned into mathematics courses.

I found the suggestion that quantitative literacy involves the sophisticated use of relatively elementary mathematics to be illuminating and useful. With this interpretation, it becomes clearer how teaching elementary mathematical concepts could be part of the high school curriculum (to make sure students have a solid foundation in the concepts applied in an introductory manner), while the responsibility for ensuring their sophisticated use would devolve to the colleges. (A possible parallel in writing—which may not hold up to greater scrutiny — is to master basic grammar and organization by the end of secondary school through writing about relevant, albeit elementary issues, and then employ these skills to write well about complex issues from many fields in college.)

Should a commitment to quantitative literacy replace, supplement, or transform the mathematics curriculum? This seemed to be one of the basic questions asked at the Forum, one that, I believe, is best addressed by clarifying the goals for learning. Do we want students to have "experienced" algebra, geometry, probability, and statistics (is the experience the goal?), or to be able to "use" the tools of these fields in a variety of ways, both in formal college study and in life?

A second basic question concerned the home of QL: in the mathematics department (preferably one that commits to teaching the practical nature of mathematics), in the social sciences (as many suggested), or in an interdisciplinary unit? If the college contribution to QL is, indeed, increasingly sophisticated use of elementary concepts, a "through the disciplines" approach seems entirely appropriate.

A third basic question concerned expected level of ability. At the elementary end, we heard about people who could not understand orders of magnitude or appropriate precision; then we moved through the intermediate level of finding patterns in numerical data to the higher end of appropriately using quantitative concepts in science and other fields. Clearly the first is a societal problem, but the solution probably lies in grades 6 to 9. I did not sense agreement as to whether the higher levels also were cause for major concern about QL, although the corporate sector seemed to suggest that they were.

—**Andrea Leskes,** Association of American Colleges and Universities

Do not underestimate arithmetic

QL is as much an attitude as a set of skills. We know that one thing that makes a person who is good at mathematics different from one who is not is the belief that tackling a problem that involves mathematics is worth the effort and that eventually, somehow, an answer will be obtained. QL is about sharing computational and analytical skills for social purposes.

QL must include a recognition that numeric computation is not a trivial precursor to algebra but a difficult skill on its own. Even when supported by technology, computation is not easy. Two-thirds of our population has never really mastered computational skills. Arithmetic is hard and data analysis is even harder.

QL needs a different title. Anything with computation, mathematics, or statistics is problematic. QL will not thrive when viewed as a part of mathematics or statistics. It must be viewed as a pursuit in its own right. Perhaps we need a larger concept that might be called Full Literacy, or Whole Literacy, or 3M Literacy (literacy for the third millennium)—something to suggest, inclu-

sively, reading, writing, document literacy, data analysis, and computational literacy.

QL needs to recognize that there are different levels of literacy. A passive literacy is one target. An active literacy is another, more ambitious one. Many argue that literacy is by nature more passive than an active use of skills. Active use may be—dare we say it—what distinguishes mathematics and statistics from quantitative literacy.

—**Philip Mahler,** Middlesex Community College; President, American Mathematical Association of Two-Year Colleges

Support faculty, develop examples, and fix admissions tests

A year or two ago, I thought I had a reasonable understanding of quantitative literacy based on general knowledge and discussions at my college; however, this Forum made me aware that there is much more to it than I had at first suspected. First, there is a lot more mathematics to it than just good number sense. I really like Lynn Steen's phrase "sophisticated use of elementary mathematics." Second, as an educational and societal problem, it is much more urgent than I realized.

The Forum added both clarity and passion to our understanding of QL. Some railed against the usual suspects—many of which we have all heard before. We listened to impassioned pleading ranging from "let's stop talking and do something" to "it's too early to do anything because we haven't defined what we are talking about." In an important way, I found the Forum discouraging because it showed that the problem is even harder than I thought and because we ourselves do not seem to have QL in focus.

At the precollege level, it is not clear how much QL differs from various aspects of the NCTM Standards, but it is clear that there is a lot of overlap. Probably the best way to make progress on getting QL into the schools is to make progress on serious and broad implementation of those Standards. (Reaching out to other subjects such as natural and social science will help, but these courses cannot carry the primary load.) In college, the best way to learn QL is to have it show up in regular courses in the various disciplines. Enticing faculty to put more QL into their courses by offering them course development and revision grants is one good approach. (It is much less clear what to do at the college level for the great majority of institutions that must teach a lot of precollege mathematics.) In any event, it seems clear that QL, like writing, is something we can never finish learning, so it needs to be emphasized at all levels of the curriculum.

Most important, it does not do colleges and universities much good to provide QL reinforcement at the higher levels if schools do not get the message that we are expecting students to have basic QL at entrance. I am not sure statements by colleges about admissions expectations have much effect, but I am sure that standardized admissions tests do have an influence. These must change. Those calling for improved education (e.g., business groups) must be made aware of what these improvements need to be. State governments and education administrators at all levels have to understand the issue and get behind it. This is a long haul.

Do we have to agree on a definition of QL? No. But without some agreement it is too easy to slip into thinking that QL means to everyone else just what we think it is. We should assume that everyone we speak to in hopes of alerting them to the QL problem also has an idea about QL but that their idea is probably different from ours. Thus we have our work cut out just to ensure that others really hear us.

In pure mathematics, definitions make more sense with concrete examples; so much more so with an amorphous topic such as QL. What I would really like to see are several carefully laid out examples of QL problem tasks (or classroom activities) at various educational levels—especially examples that are different from what already is being done under the banner of the NCTM standards, or reformed calculus, or introductory statistics, or discrete mathematics. I then will have a clearer idea of what I have to change and what I have to try to sell (if I still want to sell it) to my colleagues and my community.

Even without full clarity on a definition or ready examples of QL problems, there is much that I can do on my own campus:

- I can seek internal money for grants to faculty to develop QL components in their courses.

- I can talk to my department to make sure that people who teach pre-calculus have some appreciation of the QL issues and urge them to put more QL aspects into this course.

- I can talk to teachers and the curriculum specialists in our local school district (where I have sometimes been a mathematics consultant) to see how aware they are of QL issues.

- I can do some more reading and Web exploring to deepen my personal insights into QL.

> —**Stephen B. Maurer,** Associate Provost for Information Technology and Professor of Mathematics, Swarthmore College

Numeracy from cradle to grave

As the quantitative literacy movement grows, it is critical that it be inclusive of populations as well as of contexts. Who are we thinking about when we say people need to be quantitatively literate? And when and where will folks need to learn and use quantitative reasoning?

What struck me at the Forum is that both of these dimensions expanded considerably as the discussions proceeded. We started out with an explicit focus on adolescents in grades 11 to 14, but by the end of the Forum there seemed to be tacit agreement that we were really talking about "pre-K through gray." Moreover, although the focus primarily remained on topics from statistics and data analysis, it soon became apparent that quantitative reasoning matters in almost every discipline and in every adult role: worker, citizen, and family member.

In other words, in the two days of the Forum we went from:

	School Mathematics	Other Disciplines
High school		
College		

to

	School Mathematics	Other Disciplines	At Work	In the Community
Pre-K–5				
Middle school				
High school				
College				
Adult workforce and citizenry				

This expansion requires many groups to shoulder the responsibility for helping to create a more quantitatively literate populace. The usual suspects—high school and four-year college mathematics educators—are joined by faculty from other disciplines as well as by elementary educators on one side and, on the other, by community college and adult basic education teachers as well as a host of informal education venues for adults such as the media, the workplace, and the community. All of which bring my crowd into the QL loop.

We teach adults returning to study. Each year over four million adults enroll in adult basic education, literacy, GED, or high school equivalency programs. (One of every seven high school diplomas awarded each year is a GED.) It is essential that the content and pedagogy of courses for adults be critically reviewed so that they reflect what is most important for adults in their roles at work, in the community, and at home, as well as for further learning. At present, these courses generally put more stress on traditional arithmetic (decontextualized computation and one-step word problems) than on reasoning and decision making using real data and focusing on real-life issues. On behalf of adult educators, I hope the continuing discussions about quantitative literacy will include us and the populations we teach because it keeps us focused on what is really important for adults.

As a member of the Adult Literacy and Lifeskills (ALL) survey numeracy team, my colleagues and I have spent three years thinking hard about just what it means when we say we are looking at the distribution of numeracy skills in the adult population within and across countries. What is the range of skills to be assessed and what are the most critical concepts? The issues raised at the QL Forum resonated with the ALL team discussions and will help us in our work.

—**Mary Jane Schmitt,** TERC, Cambridge, MA